Contents

1	Introduction	5
2	Climate now: the Earth's climate system	10
2.1	Introduction	10
2.2	The global energy balance	10
2.3	A wider look at the climate system	26
2.4	Linking the climate system together	43
	Summary of Chapter 2	45
3	Causes of climatic change	47
3.1	Past changes in climate	47
3.2	Lithospheric plate movements	51
3.3	Variations in the Earth's orbit	52
3.4	Variations in the solar constant	63
3.5	Volcanic activity	67
3.6	Atmospheric composition	71
	Summary of Chapter 3	74
4	The changing atmosphere	76
4.1	Introduction	76
4.2	Carbon dioxide and the global carbon cycle	79
4.3	Other greenhouse gases: natural and unnatural	94
4.4	Drawing the threads together: what of the future?	104
	Summary of Chapter 4	106
5	Simulating climatic change	109
5.1	Introduction	109
5.2	The 'radiative forcing' of climate	109
5.3	Modelling the climate system	114
5.4	Model validation	121
5.5	Equilibrium climatic change scenarios	124
5.6	Assessing the pace of climatic change	128
	Summary of Chapter 5	134
6	The 'detection issue'	136
6.1	The issue	136
6.2	Global warming trends: the instrumental record	138
6.3	The question of attribution	141

6.4   The 'climate debate' of the late 1980s   153
Summary of Chapter 6   161

7   *Future climates: projections and scenarios*   162
7.1   Emission scenarios   162
7.2   What might a 'Business as Usual' future be like?   176
7.3   What about surprises?   180
Summary of Chapter 7   188

8   *Potential impacts of climatic change*   191
8.1   Introduction   191
8.2   Changes in sea-level   192
8.3   Effects on living organisms   202
8.4   Impacts on natural communities and agriculture   212
8.5   Economic and political impacts   221

9   *Responding to the challenge*   224
9.1   Response strategies   224
9.2   The Framework Convention on Climate Change   227
9.3   Science and the international review process   230
9.4   Negotiating limits   236
Summary of Chapter 9   240

Further Reading   242

Skills   244

Answers to questions   245

Answers to activities   250

Acknowledgements   271

Index   275

1 Introduction

Perhaps the most poignant image of our time is that of Earth as seen by the space voyagers: a blue sphere, shimmering with life and light, alone and unique in the cold vastness of the cosmos. From this perspective, the maps of geopolitics vanish, and the underlying interconnectedness of all the components of this extraordinary living system — animal, plant, water, land, and atmosphere — becomes strikingly evident.

(R. E. Benedick, 1991, Ozone Diplomacy)

The Earth's climate changes. On a geological time-scale, steamy swamplands have come and gone; vast ice-sheets have spread down from the poles and receded again. In the more recent past, historical and other records convey an increasingly rich and detailed picture of the vagaries of climate and their impact on the environment and on human affairs. They tell us, for example, of more genial climes in medieval Europe and North America — followed by several centuries of a generally colder regime than now, known as the 'Little Ice Age' (see Plate 1.1).

Natural variations in climate — and the forces that drive them — form an important backdrop to the discussion in this book. However, its central concern is one of the more potent and hotly debated issues of recent times: the prospect of climatic changes of a sort unprecedented within historic time, due to human interference with the composition of the atmosphere. As Roger Revelle and Hans Suess (two scientists then at the Scripps Institution of Oceanography in the USA) put it as long ago as 1957: by disturbing the atmospheric balance, 'human beings are now carrying out a large-scale geophysical experiment of a kind that could not have happened in the past'.

Over the years since then, data collected at monitoring stations around the world have confirmed the concern behind this warning: a steady accumulation in the atmosphere of carbon dioxide and other so-called 'greenhouse gases', such as methane and the chlorofluorocarbons (CFCs, better known for their role in damaging the ozone layer). That much is clear. The problem is unravelling the climatic consequences of changing the atmospheric composition in this way. The idea that it might lead to global warming is not new. On the contrary, it has deep historical roots, traceable back to the work of such 19th century luminaries of science as Jean-Baptiste Fourier, John Tyndall and Svante Arrhenius. But the modern era of climatic change research only really got under way in the 1960s, with the development of the tools — mathematical models, now run on the world's largest and fastest supercomputers — needed for a serious scientific assessment of the problem.

From the mid-1970s onwards, the visions of the future generated by these models have fuelled a growing concern about the wide-ranging and potentially serious consequences of continuing with the 'experiment' going on in the real world. In the late 1980s, that concern hit the headlines (see Figure 1.1): visions of the coming apocalypse were rife. In reality, however, the images conjured up by the climatologists' 'crystal balls' are decidedly murky. Understanding of the processes of climatic change is still somewhat sketchy. Existing models are flawed, oversimplified and incomplete. Their projections of what the future might be like are beset with uncertainties.

These uncertainties have long been the source of contention in debates about the prospect of global warming — and the urgency of adopting policies to confront that

Figure 1.1   A montage of headlines, from the period of 1988–1990.

prospect. Uncertainties undoubtedly remain. Yet, at the Second World Climate Conference, held in Geneva in November 1990, government representatives from 137 countries formally agreed that the risk of global warming was sufficiently well established scientifically to warrant an urgent international response to the problem. The Ministerial Declaration at the end of the conference stated:

> *We agree that the ultimate global objective should be to stabilise greenhouse gas concentrations at a level that would prevent dangerous anthropogenic inter-ference with climate … We stress, as a first step, the need to stabilise, while ensuring sustainable development of the world economy, emissions of green-house gases.*

Negotiations to crystallize that intent in a formal 'climate convention' began the following February. The aim was to have an agreement ready for signing at the Earth Summit — officially the United Nations Conference on Environment and Develop-ment (UNCED) — which was held in Rio de Janeiro in June 1992.

Thus, the beginning of the 1990s saw the global warming problem move into the mainstream of international politics. A major aim of this book is to explore the scien-tific case behind that move. Some of the elements we shall weave into the story are mentioned in the extracts from (carefully written) articles of this period reproduced in Figure 1.2: lessons from the (at times, equally contentious) debate about damage to the ozone layer, the significance (or otherwise) of the record warmth of the 1980s, and other unusual weather events. But the main emphasis will be on the unusually power-ful scientific consensus that the prospect of global warming is a 'legitimate cause for concern' — entailing long-term risks that are no less real, and possibly serious, for being uncertain.

In 1990, that consensus was embodied in the report from the scientific working group of the **Intergovernmental Panel on Climate Change (IPCC)** — referred to in one of the extracts in Figure 1.2. In fact, the IPCC report was just the most recent in a succession of authoritative assessments of the 'current state of knowledge' about climatic change. However, it was undoubtedly the most determined effort to put together a broad — and internationally based — consensus view among scientists working in the field, and the most politically influential. The final report is a weighty document — over 300 closely printed pages of technical detail about the various facets of the problem. We shall draw on its conclusions throughout this book — examining the basis for estimates like the ones reported in Figure 1.2, highlighting the key areas of uncertainty that remain and some of the research programmes that are planned or underway to address those uncertainties.

The Earth Summit in 1992 saw the threat of climatic change firmly established on the world's agendas. However, the process of formulating guidelines for an international response to that threat has only just begun. As you will see, the buildup of greenhouse gases in the atmosphere is, in effect, an inadvertent by-product of human population growth and economic development. The many contributing factors are bound up with basic activities in contemporary society. Efforts to restrain the further accumulation of greenhouse gases have far-reaching policy implications, involving socially and economically painful choices, and an unprecedented level of international cooperation. There are complex issues here, touched on in one of the extracts in Figure 1.2. In this book, we can only hint at some of the factors involved.

However, that perspective is important. As the process of formulating response strategies continues through the 1990s and beyond, the social and economic consequences of various courses of action will be increasingly to the fore. Science will continue to inform and interact with the policy-making process — not least, through updated assessments of the risks of simply carrying on with 'business-as-usual'. The overall aim of this book is to give you a firm basis from which to follow future developments in an informed and *critical* way, and to judge for yourself the import of new research findings as these are reported in the media and in popular scientific articles.

But we also hope that you will take something else from our unfolding story — a growing sense of the 'interconnectedness' of the 'total Earth system', the perspective captured with poetic force in our opening quote. As research continues, the extraordinary web of interrelated processes — physical, chemical and biological — that binds this complex system together becomes ever more apparent. Gaining a better understanding of how the planet functions as an *integrated* whole — and hence of its likely responses to being perturbed by human actions — is a formidable, and inherently *interdisciplinary*, task. Cutting across traditional boundaries, it requires the expertise and collaboration of scientists from every discipline — and increasingly, of social scientists as well.

The corollary is that to develop this sense of 'interconnectedness', you will sometimes have to deal with areas of science that you might prefer to avoid. One general piece of advice: try not to get bogged down in the details. Often, these are collected in boxes which you can either study and get to grips with (if you are interested), or simply read through (if you are not). The key points are spelt out in the summary at the end of each chapter. Further, much of the material introduced in Chapters 2–5 is reinforced and drawn together later on. If you find a particular section in these early chapters difficult first time round, move on, and then refer back if need be — taking your cue about the basic level of understanding required from the later material. The activities in Chapters 6 and 7 should be especially helpful in this respect.

As Earth stands on the brink of a global temperature increase unprecedented in the history of human civilization, the international scientific and policy communities are mobilizing to minimize the effects of a greenhouse warming. Scientists' views of the future are as murky as ever, but there is a new sense of urgency, fuelled in part by disquieting surprises in the stratosphere.

The U.S. droughts and the century-long global warming culminating in the 1980s (*Science*, 5 February, p. 559, and 13 May, p. 883) are catching the public's attention, despite scientists' refusal to link any one climate extreme to the greenhouse. Even the claim by a lone expert that the greenhouse has arrived has failed to gain support from other scientists. Instead, it is basic scientific understanding, the dearth of time for effective action, and a growing uneasiness about man's fiddling with the atmosphere that is driving a new international organizing process. This movement is akin to the one that recently produced agreement on how to deal with destruction of stratospheric ozone.

Science, 1 July 1988

In the 11 years since the first World Climate Conference met in Geneva, climatology has developed into the stuff of international diplomacy. Few in the circus of officials, scientists and world leaders in Geneva for the second conference, now doubt the possibility of unprecedented man-made climate warming within a generation ...

How different things were in February 1979. The idea of a buildup of carbon dioxide in the atmosphere, leading quickly to a warming, was only one of several theories at the time. Mild cooling, due to sunspots, was another, with the possibility of another Ice Age, a favourite idea. Since then, after five of the hottest years on record, science has swung overwhelmingly behind the warmers ...

The IPCC's report predicts that there will be a global temperature rise of around 1.1 °C by 2030 with a 20 cm rise in sea levels but 'business as usual', and a 4 °C rise by the end of the century. As a result, low-lying areas would be at risk of flooding, and poor agricultural areas in Africa, southeast Asia, and eastern Brazil could lose their fertility. Some countries might gain, but in the face of mass migrations and ecological and agricultural shifts, any winners from climate change could be invaded by losers from elsewhere.

Daily Telegraph, 7 November 1990

The world is warming. Climatic zones are shifting. Glaciers are melting. Sea level is rising. These are not hypothetical events from a science-fiction movie; these changes and others are already taking place, and we expect them to accelerate over the years as the amounts of carbon dioxide, methane and other trace gases accumulating in the atmosphere through human activities increase.

There may be controversy over whether the data are adequate and whether the warming is caused by changes in the atmosphere. Yet there is an unusually powerful consensus among climatologists that the dominant influence on global climate over the next centuries will be a warming driven by the accumulation of heat-trapping gases. The consequences are threatening enough so that many scientists, citizens and even political leaders are urging immediate action to halt the warming.

Scientific American, April 1989

The Earth's surface was, on the average, warmer in 1990 than in any year since records began in the mid-nineteenth century. The 1990 value for global mean surface temperature, released last week by the UK Meteorological Office and the University of East Anglia (UEA)'s Climatic Research Unit, exceeded the previous record, in 1988, by 0.05 °C. But it is still too early to say with certainty whether the recent warmth is due to the buildup of greenhouse gases in the atmosphere.

Six of the seven warmest years on record have occurred since 1980, making the past decade the warmest ever recorded ...

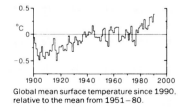

Global mean surface temperature since 1990, relative to the mean from 1951–80.

The Meteorological Office/UEA value is the most reliable calculation of the global mean surface temperature, based on data from land- and sea-based monitoring stations. A similar value produced by the NASA Goddard Institute for Space Studies is calculated from land-based data alone.

Nature, 17 January 1991

The theory that the Earth is warming because of an enhanced greenhouse effect now commands wide support among scientists. Important debates remain: notably, there are cogent arguments regarding the stringency and urgency of greenhouse policies — if any — which are needed. But the threat of global warming may warrant policy action long before fundamental uncertainties are answered. Indeed, much of the present debate over climate policy acknowledges that the political schedule to slow warming may have to proceed more rapidly than the advance in scientific understanding.

Because of the extremely complex nature of the climate issue, many students of international affairs are pessimistic about the near-term prospects for an agreement to control climate change. Global policy action to control the climate will confront the classic problem of managing the commons, with the costs and benefits of collective action to slow global warming widely dispersed across political boundaries. Concentrated interests aligned against the diffuse beneficiaries of climate control will further block action.

Although it may be in the collective interest of the community of nations to slow global warming to some degree, it will be difficult to foster collective action. Cooperation will be easier if there is a leader, but the largest contributors to global warming (the Soviet Union and the United States, which account for 38 per cent of annual fossil fuel carbon dioxide emissions) are moving slowly.

… the 1992 UN conference on the environment and development (UNCED) may help link global environmental policy to a long-standing interest in realigning North–South inequity. States from the South — historically not the largest contributors to global warming but probably large emitters of greenhouse gases in the future (and already the largest sources of carbon dioxide from deforestation) — may have strong additional incentives to cooperate with international greenhouse policy.

Nature, 7 February 1991

Figure 1.2 Extracts from articles about the threat of global warming, from the period of 1988–1991.

2 Climate now: the Earth's climate system

2.1 Introduction

The simplest definition of climate is the 'average weather' of a given place or region. Actually, it's a bit more than that. A full description of climate incorporates not just the average weather conditions — average values of temperature, rainfall, wind speed, and so on, and the way these change with the seasons — but also some measure of the year-by-year variability. Indeed, the extreme events to which a given region may be prey, albeit infrequently, are often as important as the more typical conditions. The disasters wrought by floods, droughts and violent storms come immediately to mind.

For now, the important general point is that the Earth does not have a single uniform climate. On the contrary, it varies widely around the world — from the heat and rain that prevails in tropical regions near the Equator, to the cold, snow-bound wastes at the highest latitudes. In between, there are hot, dry deserts; regions with a 'mediterranean' type of climate; mild, rainy 'temperate' regimes like that in Britain; and so on. Some regions — the tropics, for example — experience much the same temperature all year round. Elsewhere, in the continental interiors of the Northern Hemisphere, for instance, temperature varies markedly with the seasons. Equally, some regions can have rain in any month; others, such as northwest India, have well-defined wet seasons.

Climatic conditions — especially temperature and precipitation and their seasonal variations — are the main influence over the kinds of 'natural vegetation' found in different parts of the world. Thus, the geographical distribution of major vegetation types — or **biomes** — is largely determined by, and hence reflects, the pattern of regional climates around the globe (see Figure 2.1). One of the aims of this chapter is to explore the interrelated forces that govern this rich variety of climatic regimes. That will begin our story of the 'interconnectedness' of the planetary system.

Before embarking on that, however, we shall first take a simpler, 'globally-averaged' view of the Earth's climate. From this perspective, conditions at the Earth's surface *can* be characterized by a single parameter — the '**global-mean surface temperature**' or 'average surface temperature', or even just 'global-mean temperature', for short. But what determines this global-mean surface temperature? In particular, how does the composition of the atmosphere come into that equation? Answers to these questions are a vital prelude to our study of the problem outlined in Chapter 1: the threat of an increase in the global-mean surface temperature — global warming — induced by a buildup of certain trace constituents (greenhouse gases) in the atmosphere.

2.2 The global energy balance

To address these questions, we shall proceed in stages. The first step will be to analyse the overall energy balance on a planet heated by absorbing radiation from the Sun. The planet in question does not exist; it is a hypothetical world that resembles the Earth in all important respects save one — it has no atmosphere. Analysing the situation on this 'airless' world tells us what the Earth's global-mean temperature would be if the atmosphere were stripped away. This serves to highlight the crucial

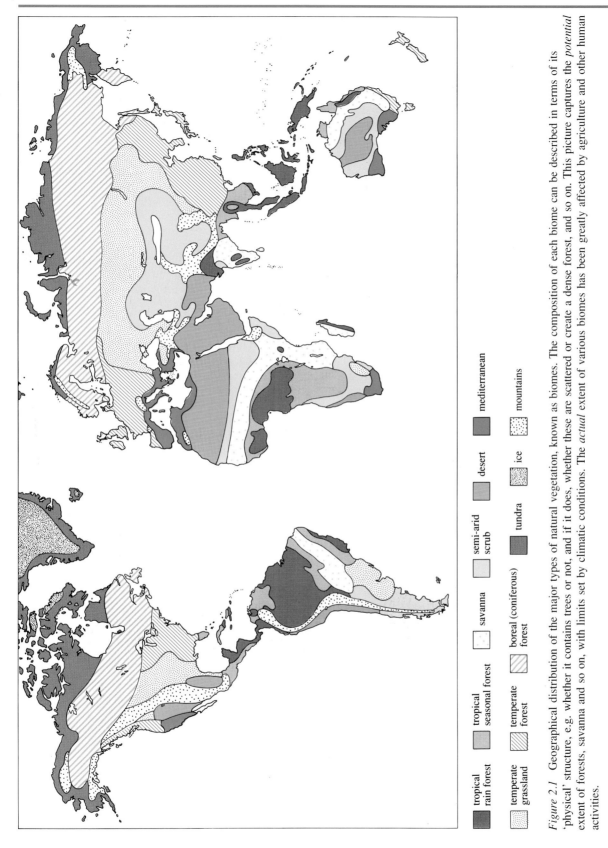

Figure 2.1 Geographical distribution of the major types of natural vegetation, known as biomes. The composition of each biome can be described in terms of its 'physical' structure, e.g. whether it contains trees or not, and if it does, whether these are scattered or create a dense forest, and so on. This picture captures the *potential* extent of forests, savanna and so on, with limits set by climatic conditions. The *actual* extent of various biomes has been greatly affected by agriculture and other human activities.

tropical rain forest

tropical seasonal forest

savanna

semi-arid scrub

desert

mediterranean

temperate grassland

temperate forest

boreal (coniferous) forest

tundra

ice

mountains

importance of the *natural* 'greenhouse effect' in maintaining temperatures suitable for life on Earth. Having examined the greenhouse effect, we then draw in some of the other processes that help to determine the Earth's global-mean temperature — not just at the surface, but also at different levels within the atmosphere.

2.2.1 A simple model of planetary heating and cooling: the overall radiation balance

For the purpose of this exercise, we assume that our hypothetical planet follows the Earth's orbit around the Sun. Like the Earth, it intercepts a certain amount of the energy radiated out by the Sun, but it does not actually absorb *all* of this. Seen from space, the Earth 'shines with light' because it *reflects* back some of the incoming solar radiation — a percentage known as the planetary **albedo** (call it x% for now). Assuming that our airless world behaves likewise, the remaining $(100 - x)$% is absorbed by materials at the planet's surface.

By itself, this would be expected to warm the planet, with its surface getting progressively hotter and hotter. But there is a compensating *cooling* effect. Like the Sun, *all* hot, or indeed warm objects (you and I included!) emit electromagnetic radiation. Further, the rate at which an object radiates energy away from itself depends on its temperature: the hotter the object, the greater the rate of radiation. For our planet, this in turn suggests that a *constant* global-mean surface temperature is maintained by a *dynamic* balance: the rate at which energy comes in from the Sun must balance the rate at which it is radiated out to space by the planet. If the two rates fail to match, the planet will either cool down or heat up until a balance is restored. To pursue this idea, we need to quantify these energy flows.

Consider, first, the planetary output. The link with its temperature can be quantified if we make an important assumption — that the planet behaves as a 'perfect emitter', known to physicists as a **black body**. For now the key point about a black body (a glowing lump of coal is a good example) is that it radiates energy at the maximum possible rate for its temperature. That rate is described by a well-established law of physics, known as the **Stefan–Boltzmann Law**. It states that:

$$\text{energy flux} = \sigma T^4 \tag{2.1}$$

Here, the **energy flux** is *the energy per unit time per unit area* radiated away from the surface of a black body of temperature T, measured on the kelvin scale. (Remember that a kelvin (K) is equivalent to a degree Celsius (°C), but the starting point for the two scales is different, with 0 °C defined as 273 K, so that 20 °C is 293 K, and so on.) In Equation 2.1, σ is called the Stefan–Boltzmann constant; in SI units it has the value, $\sigma = 5.67 \times 10^{-8}\,\text{W}\,\text{m}^{-2}\,\text{K}^{-4}$.

▷ Does the expression in Equation 2.1 produce something with the units of an 'energy flux', as defined above?

▶ Yes. Multiplying σ (in $\text{W}\,\text{m}^{-2}\,\text{K}^{-4}$) by the fourth power of a temperature (K^4) produces a quantity with the units $\text{W}\,\text{m}^{-2}$. Since a watt is defined as a joule per second, this is an energy flux.

Figure 2.2a captures an image of our black-body planet radiating to space *in all directions*, where we have used the symbol T_s to represent its global-mean surface temperature. To carry out the desired balancing act, we now need a figure for the incoming solar energy flux (Figure 2.2b), or **solar flux** for short. This is generally characterized by a quantity known as the **solar constant**, or sometimes the '**solar irradiance**', at the

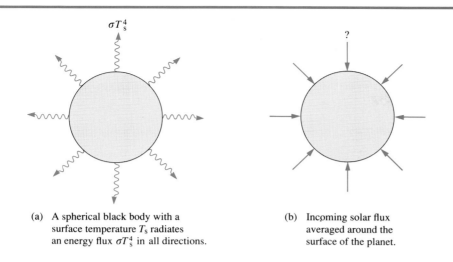

(a) A spherical black body with a surface temperature T_s radiates an energy flux σT_s^4 in all directions.

(b) Incoming solar flux averaged around the surface of the planet.

Figure 2.2 The outflow (a) and inflow (b) of energy to a hypothetical planet with no atmosphere. Here, wiggly arrows are outgoing planetary radiation, straight ones are incoming solar radiation. To maintain a constant planetary temperature, the outgoing energy flux (a) must balance the incoming solar flux, *averaged around the globe* (b).

planet. It is a measure of the energy flux incident on a surface, at the planet's average distance from the Sun — *provided the surface is at right angles to the Sun's rays.*

Recent satellite measurements give the solar constant for a planet at the Earth's average distance from the Sun (some 150×10^6 km) a value of approximately $1\,368$ W m^{-2}. But the proviso emphasized above means this is not quite the required figure. Assuming the planet to be a rotating, spherical body (as is the Earth, more or less), then at any given instant just one location will be 'lined up' perpendicular to the incoming solar beam (where the sun is directly overhead, Figure 2.3), and so intercepting the 'full' $1\,368$ watts per square metre. Everywhere else on the sunlit hemisphere, the Sun's rays strike at a more glancing angle, so the incident radiation is effectively 'spread' over a wider area. Meanwhile, the incoming solar flux is zero everywhere on the dark side of the planet. A few hours later, the pattern of light and dark will have shifted around the globe — to different longitudes, that is — and so on, through a full 24-hour rotation.

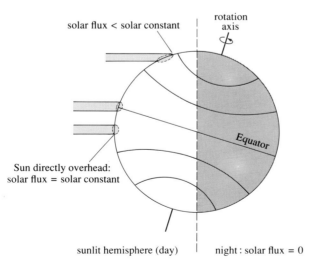

Figure 2.3 The solar flux incident on the surface is equal to the solar constant only where the Sun is directly overhead. (As indicated here, the Earth's rotation axis is tilted at an angle to the plane of its orbit around the Sun. The consequences that has for regional climates, etc. are taken up in Section 2.3.)

The difficulty in estimating the global energy balance depicted in Figure 2.2 is that it requires a figure for the solar input averaged over the *whole* surface of the planet. That demands a little mental gymnastics. Concentrate on Figure 2.4. This invites you to imagine a flat, circular disk, with the same radius (r) as the planet, placed in the path of the incoming solar radiation. Now think of the Sun's rays marking dots on the imaginary disk (of surface area πr^2) as they cross it — and then stretch the disk around the whole planet (of surface area $4\pi r^2$).

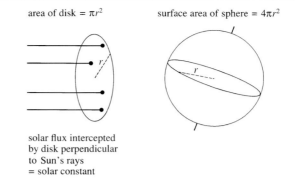

Figure 2.4 The relation between the solar constant and the solar flux averaged over all latitudes and longitudes, as described in the text.

area of disk = πr^2 surface area of sphere = $4\pi r^2$

solar flux intercepted by disk perpendicular to Sun's rays = solar constant

▷   Can you now see why the incoming solar flux averaged over all latitudes and longitudes is a *quarter* of the solar constant?

▶   The clue is in the ratio $4\pi r^2/\pi r^2$ of the surface area of a sphere to that of a circle with the same radius. When the disk is stretched, the imaginary dots end up being one-fourth as densely packed on average — so the incident radiation *per unit area* comes down by a factor of four.

At this stage, it helps to summarize the key points of our analysis in diagrammatic form. Thus, for a planet with no atmosphere, the overall **radiation balance** at the planetary surface can be represented schematically, as shown in Figure 2.5. Here, the 'units' refer to percentages of the globally-averaged solar flux incident on the planet.

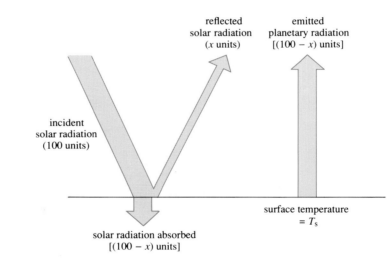

Figure 2.5 Schematic representation of the globally-averaged radiation balance for a hypothetical planet with no atmosphere. One hundred units of incoming solar radiation are incident on the planet, and $[x + (100 - x)]$, i.e. 100, units escape back out to space from the planet's surface, by a combination of reflection (x units of solar radiation) and emission ($(100 - x)$ units of planetary radiation).

reflected solar radiation (x units)

emitted planetary radiation [$(100 - x)$ units]

incident solar radiation (100 units)

solar radiation absorbed [$(100 - x)$ units]

surface temperature = T_s

Activity 2.1

To get an estimate of what the Earth's global-mean surface temperature might be like *without* an atmosphere, you need to feed 'real Earth' data into the energy balances depicted in Figure 2.5. In particular, take 100 units to be equivalent to a quarter of the solar constant at Earth, i.e. $(1\,368/4)\,W\,m^{-2}$, and assume a planetary albedo of 30% (roughly the Earth's overall albedo at present: more on this later in the chapter).

(a)   Given these figures, what is the globally-averaged solar flux actually absorbed by the planet?

(b)   By equating the outgoing flux with the expression in Equation 2.1, calculate the global-mean surface temperature, T_s. Quote your answer in kelvin and in °C.

2.2.2 Radiation 'trapping' by the atmosphere: the 'natural' greenhouse effect

All but one of the key assumptions embedded in the analysis above hold — or are good approximations, at least — for the real Earth. Indeed, the temperature you calculated in Activity 2.1 — around −18 °C (255 K) — is known as the **'effective radiating temperature'** of Earth. Yet the global-mean *surface* temperature of our planet is a vital 33 °C warmer than this — the figure commonly quoted being 15 °C (288 K). The crucial distinction is that Earth *does* have an atmosphere. The effect that has on the energy balance *at the planetary surface* is bound up with an aspect of black body radiation not brought up in the previous section: the radiating temperature determines not only the total radiation flux, but also the distribution of wavelengths emitted. Here everyday experience is a good guide.

Activity 2.2

Figure 2.6 shows part of the **electromagnetic spectrum**. Remember that the energy (E) of a 'packet' or 'photon' of electromagnetic radiation is related to its frequency (f) or wavelength (λ) through the expression:

$$E = hf = \frac{hc}{\lambda} \tag{2.2}$$

where h is Planck's constant, and c is the speed of light. Thus, high-energy photons correspond to short wavelengths, and vice versa.

Heated in an ordinary fire, a poker glows 'red-hot'; if heated to a higher temperature — in an oxy-acetylene flame, say — it would glow 'white-hot'. Generalizing from this example, does the average wavelength of emitted radiation increase or decrease as the temperature of the emitting body rises? Try to rationalize your conclusion in terms of the temperature dependence of the *total* energy flux emitted by a black body, as given by Equation 2.1.

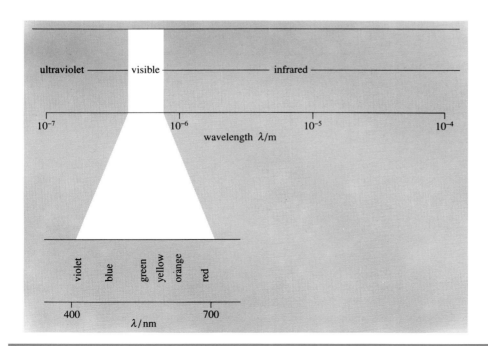

Figure 2.6 A portion of the electromagnetic spectrum. The expanded section shows the visible band, with wavelengths in nanometres; $1 \, nm = 10^{-9} \, m$, so for example $400 \, nm = 4 \times 10^{-7} \, m$.

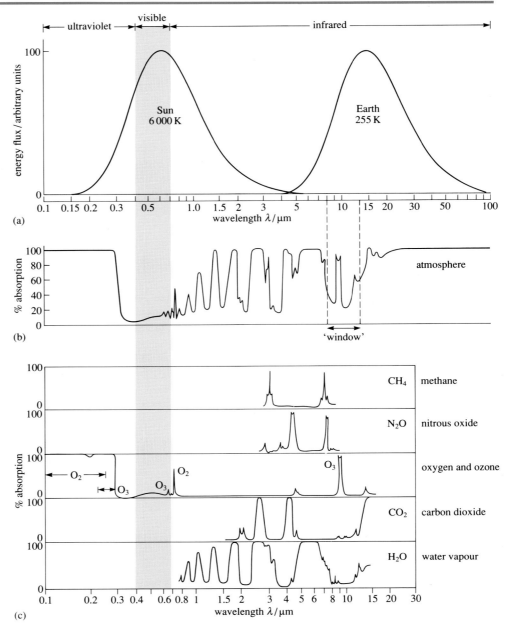

Figure 2.7 (a) Spectral distribution* of radiation emitted by black bodies at 6 000 K and 255 K, corresponding to the effective radiating temperatures of the Sun and the Earth, respectively. Notice that wavelengths are recorded in micrometres (µm), where 1 µm = 10^{-6} m. (b) The percentage of atmospheric absorption for radiation passing through the atmosphere, as a function of wavelength. (c) The percentage of the absorption in (b) that is attributable to various atmospheric gases occurring in their natural proportions (see Table 2.1).

The trend you have just identified is evident in Figure 2.7a. (Ignore the rest of this figure for the moment.) Here, each curve records the distribution, or *spectrum*, of wavelengths emitted by black bodies at the effective radiating temperatures of the Sun (some 6 000 K) and the Earth (255 K). The plots are schematic, in the sense that the vertical scale is not defined, but each shows how the total energy flux is apportioned among the range of wavelengths emitted.

Notice that the two curves barely overlap. The Sun's emission peaks in the visible band — although there are contributions at both shorter wavelengths (in the

---

* The spectral distribution of black-body radiation has a seminal place in the history of physics. Max Planck's efforts to explain the observed spectra led him to postulate that radiant energy is emitted in 'packets'—or quanta, as he called them. So quantum theory was born! Planck's analysis produced a general law which allows curves like the ones in our figure to be calculated for any given temperature.

ultraviolet, (**uv**) region) and longer wavelengths (in a region often called the 'near' infrared). By contrast, radiation emitted at cooler terrestrial temperatures — and the spectral distribution at 288 K differs little from the one shown — lies entirely at longer **infrared** (**ir**) wavelengths.

This pattern — with incoming 'shortwave' radiation and outgoing 'longwave' radiation — is important because molecules of some of the gases that make up the atmosphere (Table 2.1) themselves absorb radiation. However, they do so *selectively*: different gases absorb different wavelengths in either the solar or terrestrial range — or both. Parts (b) and (c) of Figure 2.7 illustrate the point: note that each peak in the 'composite' diagram (Figure 2.7b) represents absorption of a range of wavelengths by one or more gases — the individual contributions being those depicted in Figure 2.7c. These diagrams look complicated, but take heart. We shall neither dwell on, nor seek to interpret, the detail recorded here. For now, the main point to register about the composite diagram in Figure 2.7b is a striking contrast:

o The 'wings' of the solar spectrum apart (of which more later), the atmosphere is more or less transparent to the bulk of the *incoming* radiation — that in the visible band: most of this reaches the Earth's surface.

o On the other hand, trace constituents or 'trace gases' (Table 2.1) in the atmosphere — water vapour, carbon dioxide, methane, ozone and nitrous oxide — absorb wavelengths throughout most of the range emitted from the underlying Earth's surface. Especially striking are the strong absorptions by water vapour and carbon dioxide (Figure 2.7c). Indeed, there is only one region, known as the '**atmospheric window**' — between about 8 and 12 μm — where absorption by these two gases is weak. Even this is partially 'closed' by the ozone peak near 9.6 μm. With this exception, wavelengths in the window region can escape *directly* to space: other wavelengths in the outgoing terrestrial radiation cannot.

The energy that these atmospheric gases acquire by absorbing infrared radiation makes their molecules *vibrate* (see Box 2.1 for a little more on that if you are interested). Once 'excited' in this way, molecules can lose energy again, *either* by re-emitting radiation *or* by converting it to kinetic energy — energy of motion, that is — by bumping into other molecules. The net effect of the latter process is to increase the total 'energy content' of the gas — strictly its 'internal' energy — manifest as an increase in temperature.

Table 2.1 A selection of the gases naturally present in Earth's atmosphere, and the current concentration (fractional abundance) of each.

Gas	Concentration*
Major constituents	
nitrogen (N_2)	0.781 (78.1%)
oxygen (O_2)	0.209 (20.9%)
Minor constituents	
water vapour (H_2O)	$\sim 3\,000 \times 10^{-6} = 3\,000$ p.p.m.
carbon dioxide (CO_2)	$353 \times 10^{-6} = 353$ p.p.m.
ozone (O_3)	$\sim 0.01–0.1 \times 10^{-6} = 0.01–0.1$ p.p.m.
methane (CH_4)	$1.72 \times 10^{-6} = 1.72$ p.p.m.
nitrous oxide (N_2O)	$0.31 \times 10^{-6} = 0.31$ p.p.m.

* The values recorded here are a measure of the *fraction* of the total number of molecules in the atmosphere contributed by each constituent. Clearly, the overwhelming majority (99%) are N_2 and O_2. There are other minor constituents as well (notably argon), but the ones listed are those that influence the Earth's natural radiation balance. Present in trace amounts, their concentrations are commonly recorded as *parts per million* (p.p.m.) as shown.

2.1

Box 2.1   Molecular vibrations

All molecules vibrate. Take a water (H_2O) molecule, for example — and think of the bonds holding it together as tiny springs, Figure 2.8a; Figure 2.8b depicts a vibration of this particular molecule.

Molecular vibrations like this always have a *characteristic* frequency. If a vibrating molecule absorbs radiation of a matching frequency (Equation 2.2), the vibration becomes more 'energetic' — or to be a bit more precise, the extent or amplitude of the vibration increases (Figure 2.8c, for example). Equally, the 'excited' molecule can lose vibrational energy by re-emitting radiation — *again of the characteristic frequency* — so returning to its original state.

In practice, most triatomic and more complex molecules (H_2O included) can vibrate in several ways — each with its own characteristic frequency. But whatever the molecule, the frequencies involved invariably correspond to wavelengths (Equation 2.2 again) in the infrared part of the spectrum. So most so-called 'infrared-active' molecules can absorb a range of wavelengths in the infrared.

One final point. There are reasons why infrared radiation cannot 'lay hands', as it were, on the vibrations of *symmetric* diatomic molecules — the pertinent examples here being the *major* atmospheric constituents, N_2 and O_2 — but we shall not pursue the matter. ■

Figure 2.8 (a) A representation of the H_2O molecule, and (b) of a characteristic vibration. (c) If the molecule absorbs a photon with the same frequency as its vibration, the energy it gains increases the amplitude of the vibration.

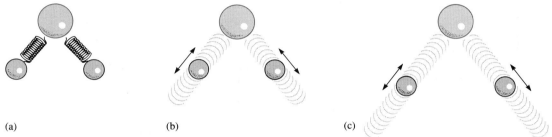

(a)   (b)   (c)

For our purposes, the important general point is that the presence of an absorbing atmosphere changes the simple picture you worked with in Activity 2.1 (Figure 2.5) substantially. Its central consequence is summarized schematically in Figure 2.9. Details apart, the crucial difference is that now much of the longwave radiation emitted by the Earth's surface does *not* escape directly to space. Rather, it effectively 'cycles' within the atmosphere — being repeatedly absorbed and *re-emitted* in all directions by the minor atmospheric constituents noted in Table 2.1. This warms the atmosphere. Some of the re-emitted radiation ultimately goes out to space: the overall Earth–atmosphere system still has to be in a state of balance as far as incoming and outgoing radiation is concerned, as indicated in Figure 2.9. But the key point to note is that re-emitted longwave radiation also goes back downwards, thereby *increasing* the energy input to the underlying surface.

The details of radiation transfer in the real Earth's atmosphere are a good deal more complicated than the simple picture in Figure 2.9 might suggest. But the basic principle is the same — with longwave radiation absorbed by the atmosphere being partially re-emitted back to the planetary surface. As a result, the Earth's global-mean *surface* temperature is substantially higher than the effective radiating temperature you calculated earlier. This phenomenon, which keeps the Earth warmer than it would otherwise be, is known as the **greenhouse effect**.* So, not surprisingly, atmospheric constituents that absorb in the infrared — and hence contribute to this surface warming — are known as **greenhouse gases**.

---

* The supposed analogy—with radiation trapping by the panes of glass in a greenhouse—is a misleading one. In reality, a greenhouse owes its effectiveness more to the fact that it limits air circulation, so that warm air is trapped inside it, and not constantly replaced by cooler air. Climatic greenhouse warming is a purely radiative effect.

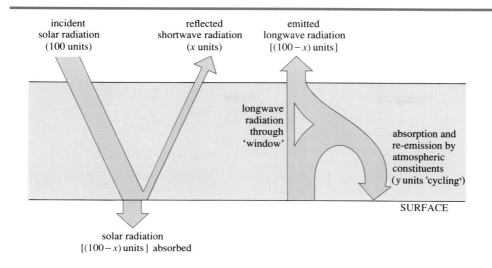

Figure 2.9 Schematic representation of the globally-averaged radiation balance for a planet with an atmosphere (grey tone) that absorbs and re-emits (both downward and upward) longwave radiation from the surface. As in Figure 2.5, the 100 units of incident solar radiation are again balanced by a total of 100 units of radiation escaping back to space from the top of the atmosphere. However, y units of longwave radiation also cycle within the atmosphere.

The contribution each of the greenhouse gases makes to the total effect varies, depending on two main factors: the wavelengths it actually absorbs (Figure 2.7c), and its atmospheric concentration (Table 2.1). The combined influence of these two factors produces the strong absorptions by water vapour and carbon dioxide recorded in Figure 2.7c. This, in turn, ensures that 'radiation trapping' by these two gases dominates the Earth's *natural* greenhouse effect (the surface warming of about 33 °C mentioned earlier); together H_2O and CO_2 account for some 85% of the total. The other three gases included in Figure 2.7c have much lower atmospheric concentrations. Nevertheless, the fact that they absorb strongly at wavelengths within the window region (ozone) or close to it (methane and nitrous oxide) means that they too make a significant — if much smaller — contribution. This is important. It points to the impact trace amounts of *other* infrared-absorbing gases can have if they happen to further 'contaminate' the atmospheric window. That, *and* the on-going increase in the atmospheric burden of the '*natural*' greenhouse gases considered here, are issues central to the *anthropogenic* or '*enhanced*' greenhouse effect — our major concern from Chapter 4 through to the end of this book. For now, we shall explore some of the shortcomings of the simple picture in Figure 2.9.

2.2.3 The Earth's temperature 'profile'

In reality, the Earth's atmosphere is not a simple, uniform slab of absorbing material. On the contrary, it gets progressively 'thinner' or less dense with increasing altitude, i.e. the *total* number of molecules in a given volume is lower, and so is the pressure (Figure 2.10). In practice, the bulk of the atmosphere is relatively close to the surface — 50% of its total mass is within some 5.5 km of the surface, and 99% lies below 30 km.

For our present purposes, the important corollary is that the key greenhouse gas molecules (H_2O and CO_2) are also more abundant close to ground level, and increasingly scarce at higher altitudes. So a better picture of radiation trapping in the real atmosphere is to imagine it happening in a series of stages. Radiation of the pertinent wavelengths is repeatedly absorbed and re-emitted by different molecules of each greenhouse gas as it 'works up' through the atmosphere. It is re-radiated to space only from levels high enough (i.e. 'thin' enough) for absorption to have become weak. Without elaborating this picture any further, it seems intuitively obvious that this would tend to produce the highest temperatures at the bottom of the atmosphere — close to the source of the outgoing radiation, and where the absorbing molecules are more abundant.

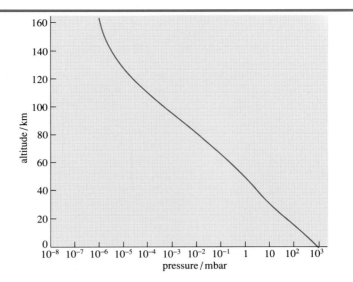

Figure 2.10 Pressure as a function of altitude in the Earth's atmosphere. Atmospheric scientists in general, and meteorologists in particular, have not yet adopted the SI unit of pressure, which is the Pascal, Pa. Instead, the millibar (mbar) — familiar from weather forecasts — is almost universally used: 1 mbar = 10^2 Pa.

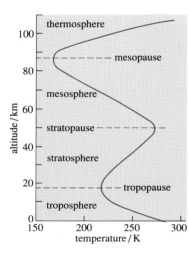

Figure 2.11 The vertical 'structure' of the atmosphere is defined by the way in which temperature varies with altitude. In each successive 'sphere' or zone, the temperature gradient is reversed.

Figure 2.11 reveals the extent to which this expectation is borne out in practice. The outer, more rarefied, reaches of the atmosphere (the mesosphere and thermosphere) are included for completeness, but it is generally believed that events there have relatively little impact on the Earth's surface climate: we shall not consider them further. Thus, focusing solely on the two lower zones (the stratosphere and the troposphere), the profile in Figure 2.11 indicates that temperature does indeed fall with increasing altitude throughout the lower atmosphere or **troposphere**. However, beyond the upper 'boundary' to this region — known as the **tropopause** — the temperature starts to increase again, and continues to do so throughout the **stratosphere**. This phenomenon is bound up with the workings of the Earth's major 'ozone factory'.

Unlike the other atmospheric constituents listed in Table 2.1, only about 10% of the Earth's ozone is in the lower atmosphere (troposphere): the bulk of it (some 90%) is in the stratosphere. Figure 2.12 depicts the marked altitude dependence of the ozone concentration — the so-called **ozone layer** being the distinctive bulge in this profile, centred at an altitude of around 30 km. This characteristic profile is maintained by a dynamic balance between processes that continually produce and destroy ozone in the stratosphere — the basic raw materials being ordinary molecular oxygen (O_2) and *incoming* solar radiation. The essential features of that ongoing drama are outlined in Box 2.2. As you will see later on, the twin stories of 'damage to the ozone layer' and 'global warming' are interwoven in countless ways, so you may need to refer back to the material in this Box. At this stage, a quick read through will suffice. Do that now.

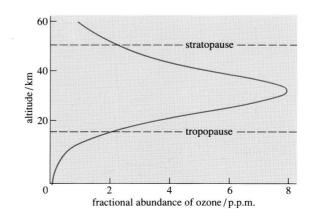

Figure 2.12 The variation with altitude of the atmospheric concentration (strictly fractional abundance, as defined in Table 2.1) of ozone, O_3, expressed in parts per million (p.p.m.).

Box 2.2 *The ozone layer: a balance between creation and destruction*

Have another look at the oxygen and ozone panel in Figure 2.7c. Notice the strong absorption of the shorter uv wavelengths in the incoming solar radiation by both molecular oxygen (O_2) and ozone (O_3). Absorbing outgoing infrared radiation 'excites' molecular vibrations (Box 2.1). Absorbing shorter wavelength (higher energy) uv radiation can have a much more dramatic effect. It can impart sufficient energy to break chemical bonds, thus splitting the molecule into fragments. This process — known as **photolysis** — is central to the ozone budget in the stratosphere.

1   Molecular oxygen absorbs solar uv radiation with wavelengths below about 240 nm (0.24 μm): this provides enough energy to break the O–O bond in O_2. Once released, free oxygen atoms can combine with intact oxygen molecules to form ozone:

$$O + O_2 \rightarrow O_3 \qquad (2.3)$$

2   However, ozone also absorbs strongly in the ultraviolet — mainly in a band between 215 and 295 nm, although wavelengths up to 320 nm are also absorbed to some extent. Because the O–O bonds in O_3 are significantly weaker than the bond in O_2, the critical threshold for photolysis is at a lower energy, i.e. it now lies at longer wavelengths — about 310 nm. Since the incoming solar radiation is 'richer' in these longer wavelengths (see Figure 2.7a) you might (rightly) expect ozone to have a somewhat fleeting existence in the stratosphere. Concentrations build up if there is enough O_2 around to provide numerous opportunities for the interaction in Equation 2.3 to take place. Ozone is then effectively 'pushed' through the cycle of reactions captured in the centre of Figure 2.13; it absorbs uv, breaking into its constituent parts, only to be formed again. After many trips around this cycle, the end comes when an O_3 molecule encounters a free O atom, and is converted back into ordinary oxygen:

$$O_3 + O \rightarrow O_2 + O_2 \qquad (2.4)$$

3   The reactions collected in Figure 2.13 comprise what is called a 'chemical mechanism'. In the present context, it is a description of the individual steps, both chemical and **photochemical**, believed to contribute to the stratospheric burden of O_3, and its vertical distribution. This chemical mechanism was first proposed in 1930, but the enormous burst of research in recent years has revealed that matters are actually a good deal more complicated than this. Nevertheless, this simple scheme does capture the essence of the ozone budget: it will suffice for our present purposes.

The crucial point to grasp is that ozone is constantly being created and destroyed in the stratosphere. However, *given constant conditions* a dynamic **steady state** is set up; the concentration of ozone stays the same because the *rate* at which it is formed (via Equation 2.3) is balanced by the rate of loss (through Equation 2.4). A useful analogy here is with a bucket of water: think of it being filled from a tap at a steady rate, but also drained through a hole in the bottom of the bucket at the *same* rate. The level of water in the bucket (analogous to the steady-state concentration of ozone) does not change.

▷   Except for the outer reaches of the atmosphere (above about 100 km), the major atmospheric constituents (N_2 and O_2) are present at a constant *fractional* abundance. In broad terms, how does the scheme in Figure 2.13 also account for the characteristic bulge in the steady-state ozone profile (Figure 2.12)?

▶   The formation of ozone is driven by the interaction between O_2 molecules and *incoming* uv radiation (with $\lambda < 240$ nm), so you might expect the rate at which it is made to depend both on the number of O_2 molecules around, and the 'amount' or intensity of this radiation. However, these change with altitude in exactly opposite ways. The fractional abundance

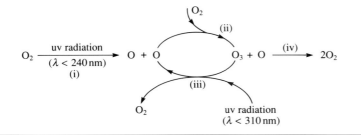

$$O_2 \xrightarrow[\substack{(\lambda < 240\,nm) \\ (i)}]{\text{uv radiation}} O + O \qquad O_3 + O \xrightarrow{(iv)} 2O_2$$

Figure 2.13 Ozone is created when short wavelength uv radiation breaks up an O_2 molecule (i), freeing its atoms to combine with other O_2 molecules (ii). The ozone so formed is repeatedly broken up (iii) and reformed (ii), until it is destroyed by collision with an oxygen atom (iv).

of O_2 is constant, but since the total number of molecules falls with increasing altitude, so too does the number of O_2 molecules (whence the dangers of altitude sickness). Too high in the atmosphere, there are insufficient O_2 molecules to absorb much uv radiation and to associate with O atoms to make O_3: too low, most of the radiation with $\lambda < 240\,\text{nm}$ has already been 'filtered' out, i.e. there are insufficient short-wavelength photons left to dissociate much O_2. This trade-off ensures that the steady-state concentration of ozone (the result of a balance, remember, between its creation and destruction) peaks somewhere in between.

4   Stratospheric ozone plays two vital roles. First, it protects living things from the full intensity of the Sun's uv radiation — the role most often cited as the cause for con-

cern about human activities which are disturbing the natural balance, and progressively eroding the ozone layer (more on that in later chapters). In brief, proteins and nucleic acids are damaged by uv radiation with wavelengths less than about 290 nm. Up to 240 nm, absorption by O_2 (in and above the stratosphere) provides an effective filter. But O_3 is the *only* atmospheric constituent able to absorb in the 240–290 nm range (recall Figure 2.7c).

Second, and more pertinent here, the two purely chemical steps in our reaction scheme (Equations 2.3 and 2.4) are strongly *exothermic* — that is, they release heat. As ozone cycles through its round of creation and destruction, the incoming *solar* energy absorbed by both O_2 and O_3 is ultimately released as heat — an extra *in situ* heating effect in the stratosphere that is not related to the absorption of outgoing longwave radiation. ■

How does the information in Box 2.2 affect our evolving picture of radiation transfer in the real atmosphere? A key point to note is that solar radiation absorbed in the stratosphere heats that zone directly — *and so represents an energy flux that never reaches the planetary surface.* For example, as a global annual average, stratospheric ozone absorbs about $12\,\text{W m}^{-2}$ of the incoming solar flux. It *also* absorbs about $8\,\text{W m}^{-2}$ of the 9–10 μm longwave radiation coming up from below. Roughly half of this longwave radiation is re-emitted — some $2.5\,\text{W m}^{-2}$ out to space (from altitudes above about 30 km), and about $1.5\,\text{W m}^{-2}$ (from the lower stratosphere) back down to the troposphere: the remainder contributes to the net heating of the stratosphere. It is this heating that causes the temperature *inversion* shown in Figure 2.11, which defines the stratosphere. *Indeed, without the ozone layer there would be no stratosphere.*

2.2.4 *Energy balances* within *the Earth–atmosphere system: a first look*

The names of the two lower regions of the atmosphere reflect an important aspect of their physical behaviour — 'tropos' is Greek for 'turning', and 'stratos' is Latin for 'layered'. 'Warm air rises' is a familiar observation. Actually, the situation in the real atmosphere is a bit more complicated than this simple dictum might suggest, but we shall not pursue the matter here. Suffice it to say that the troposphere is warmed from *below*, with temperature then falling with increasing altitude (Figure 2.11). Much as it does when you heat a saucepan of water on the stove, this situation sets the scene for the onset of **convection** — large scale, and often rapid, vertical motions within the lower atmosphere.

By contrast, with warmer air lying above cooler air, the stratosphere is inherently stable to convection. Indeed, it is sometimes said that the temperature inversion at the tropopause acts like a lid — separating the turbulent zone in which we live from the calm, stable stratosphere above. True, vertical transport up through the stratosphere is slow — with a time-scale of the order of years, rather than the days (at most) typical of the troposphere — and the mechanisms involved are more complex. In reality, however, the 'lid' is decidedly leaky. For example, rapidly rising air can 'overshoot' the tropopause, carrying its constituents into the stratosphere. And there are return routes as well; more on this in Chapter 4.

For our immediate purposes, the important point is that convection in the lower atmosphere is intimately bound up with two other mechanisms — *quite apart from radiation*, that is — whereby the energy absorbed by the Earth's surface is transferred to the atmosphere. The first is by *conduction*, which heats air in immediate contact with a warmer, underlying surface. By itself, this mechanism would have little effect because air is a poor conductor of heat, so the temperature difference needed to drive the energy transfer across the surface–air boundary could not be maintained. But convection currents sweep the warmed air away, allowing more cool air to come into contact with the surface (just as conduction and convection together heat a saucepan of water on the stove). Atmospheric scientists refer to the resulting transfer of energy across the surface–air boundary as **sensible heat** (i.e. heat that gives rise to an increase in temperature that can be detected or 'sensed'). The rising and mixing of warmed air distributes sensible heat throughout the troposphere.

The second form of energy transfer is indirect and involves the evaporation of water from the planetary surface. Evaporation requires energy — strictly the *enthalpy* of vaporization, but commonly known in the present context by its older name, the **latent heat** of vaporization. Whenever water evaporates, the surface loses energy; the atmosphere gains an equivalent amount when the water vapour subsequently condenses, releasing its 'latent' heat. It is important to appreciate that air can 'hold' only a certain amount of water vapour — its saturation limit, as it were, which depends mainly on temperature.

Question 2.1 Can you see why convection — or indeed any turbulence in the overlying air — might be expected to enhance the latent heat transfer across the surface–air boundary? (Hint: think about trying to get the washing dry!)

As the estimates included in Figure 2.14 (*overleaf*) reveal, heat lost via these two mechanisms makes a significant contribution to the *actual* energy balance at the planetary surface. Essentially a more detailed version of Figure 2.9, this figure gives a quantitative (if approximate) picture of the globally-averaged energy budget for the whole Earth–atmosphere system, and its component parts. As well as the *non-radiative* energy transfers across the surface–air boundary, Figure 2.14 incorporates the influence of two other additional factors. The first — touched on in Section 2.2.3 — is the *incoming* solar radiation absorbed by atmospheric constituents. The second is the effect of clouds that are formed when water vapour condenses *en masse*.

Activity 2.3 should help you to find your way around Figure 2.14. At the same time, it serves to draw together and reinforce many of the key points developed so far.

Activity 2.3 *You should spend up to 30 minutes on this activity.*

With reference to Figure 2.14:

(a) How many units of the incoming (shortwave) solar radiation are reflected back to space? How is this figure related to the Earth's overall albedo?

(b) How many units of terrestrial (longwave) radiation ultimately escape to space?

(c) What does the sum of your answers to (a) and (b) show about the total radiation budget?

(d) By referring back to Figure 2.7, can you suggest any atmospheric constituents that contribute to the 20 units of *incoming* solar radiation absorbed in the *troposphere*?

(e) Check that the energy fluxes *absorbed* and emitted by the atmosphere as a whole balance.

(f) Why does it appear that we 'accumulate more than we receive', with 115% of the original solar input emitted as longwave radiation by the planetary surface?

(g) If the Earth's surface behaves as a black-body emitter (i.e. according to Equation 2.1), what is its global-mean surface temperature? Give your answer in kelvin.

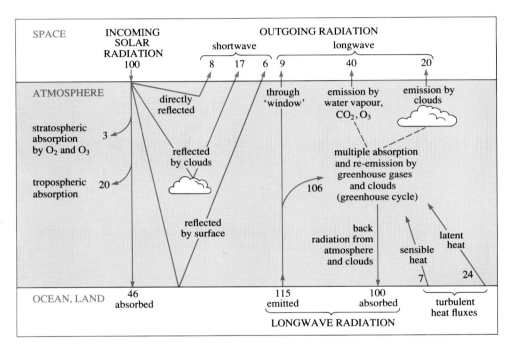

Figure 2.14 Schematic representation of the overall energy budget for the Earth and its atmosphere. Figures are global annual averages, expressed as a percentage of the incoming solar flux, i.e. 100 units (100%) is equivalent to 342 W m^{-2} (recall the answer to part (a) of Activity 2.1). The overall planetary albedo (i.e. reflected solar flux) and total longwave flux escaping to space have been measured by satellite-borne instruments: other data may be derived from model calculations or measurements, so you may find slightly different values quoted elsewhere.

Having reviewed the broad features of Figure 2.14 for yourself, we should stress one more specific point.

▷ What proportion of the overall planetary albedo (31%, from Activity 2.3a) is attributed to solar radiation reflected back to space by clouds?

▶ From Figure 2.14, $(17/31) \times 100$, or about 55% of the total.

This highlights one very important role that clouds play in the overall radiation balance of the whole Earth–atmosphere system. As indicated in Figure 2.14, however, clouds also trap *outgoing* longwave radiation, i.e. they too make a contribution to the Earth's natural greenhouse effect. Because they behave (to a good approximation) like black bodies, they absorb and emit radiation across the full spectrum of terrestrial wavelengths. Radiation re-emitted back towards the surface is caught up in the overall greenhouse cycle, but much of the emission from cloud tops (especially at wavelengths in the window region) goes directly out to space. As the estimates collected in Figure 2.14 suggest, this makes a significant contribution to the radiation balance at the top of the atmosphere. The bulk of the remaining longwave radiation comes from the net emission to space by the major greenhouse gases (CO_2, H_2O and O_3) at altitudes high up in the troposphere and beyond.

Activity 2.4

The black line in Figure 2.15 shows the spectrum of infrared emission from Earth as recorded by a satellite-borne instrument outside the atmosphere. The coloured lines trace the emission spectra expected from a black body at various temperatures. These lines can be used to get a rough idea of the temperature at the *altitude* from which different wavelengths in the Earth's *actual* spectrum are emitted to space. How does this figure provide support for the final sentence above? (Remember that each of the greenhouse gases absorbs *and re-emits* only certain characteristic wavelengths in the outgoing longwave radiation. You will need to refer back to Figures 2.7c and 2.11. Look carefully at these figures, in conjunction with Figure 2.15, and think about the discussion above.)

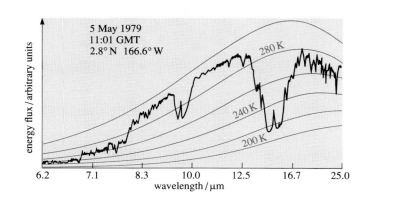

Figure 2.15 Spectrum of the ir radiation emitted to space, as recorded by a satellite-borne instrument through a cloud-free field of view over the eastern Pacific. The coloured lines represent the emission expected from a black body at various temperatures in the range found at different altitudes in the Earth's atmosphere.

2.2.5 Drawing the threads together

At this stage, a pause to take stock is in order. We have come a long way from the simple model of planetary heating and cooling developed in Section 2.2.1. To an observer far out in space, the detailed spectral distribution in Figure 2.15 would be 'averaged out', suggesting a planet with an effective radiating temperature of about −18 °C (255 K). Closer in, the detail provides compelling evidence for the greenhouse effect; some radiation from the Earth's surface is 'trapped' by the greenhouse gases (and clouds) in the atmosphere, and ultimately re-radiated to space from higher, colder levels. Together with the turbulent mixing of the lower atmosphere — and the consequent redistribution of sensible and latent heat — this serves to keep the planetary surface a comfortable 33 °C warmer, on average, than it would otherwise be. Meanwhile, chemical and photochemical events higher up in the atmosphere generate the ozone layer, which helps to modulate the solar (*and* longwave) flux to the troposphere — and without which, there would be no stratosphere.

Figure 2.14 captures the net effect of all these processes. On a global, annual average basis, the energy flows in and out of the whole system, and its component parts — the planetary surface and atmosphere — are balanced. But the full drama of the Earth's weather, and its variety — from the Equator to the poles, and with the passing of the seasons — is driven by energy *im*balances within this overall picture. It is time to take on board the fact that our planet is a spherical rotating body — its surface marked by a particular geographical distribution of land, sea and ice.

2.3 A wider look at the climate system

The last section looked at the energy balance of the Earth–atmosphere system as a whole, but we shall now focus on the *variations* in climate over the Earth's surface and the reasons for them. In Section 2.2, the situation was simplified by taking a single temperature — the global-mean surface temperature — for the Earth. However, as Figure 2.16 shows, the surface temperature varies considerably around the Earth, from values below −40 °C in polar regions in winter to over +35 °C in tropical regions in summer. Temperature varies not only with latitude, but also with the time of year (the differences between Figure 2.16a and 2.16b), and there are less obvious variations as well: why, for example, is the temperature in Iceland in January 0 °C but at the same latitude in Siberia it is 30 °C colder? Also, why is the temperature in Britain in January around 5 °C, but that in Canada, at the same latitude but on the opposite side of the Atlantic Ocean, some 15 °C colder? The main aim of this section is to explore the forces that govern these, and other differences in the climate experienced by various regions.

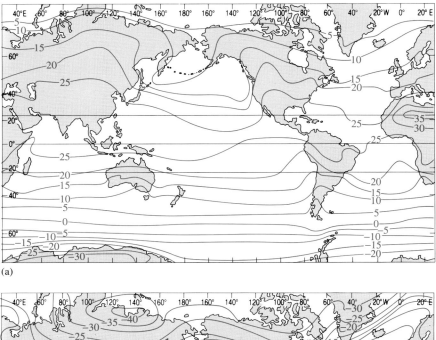

(a)

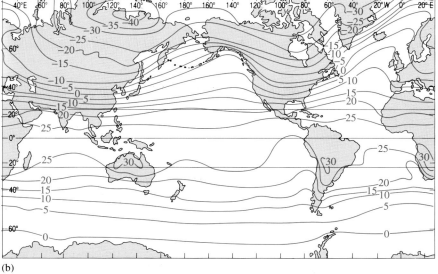

(b)

Figure 2.16 Surface temperatures at sea and on land (at sea-level or corrected to sea-level) (a) in July, (b) in January (monthly averages, in °C).

2.3.1 The global distribution of solar radiation

▷ Have another look at Figure 2.16. What is the main factor controlling the pattern of temperature variation recorded there?

▶ Distance from the Equator, i.e. increasing latitude. The temperature decreases from the Equator to the poles.

The major climatic regions that you are probably familiar with depend strongly on latitude: a tropical climate at low latitudes; a polar climate at high latitudes near the poles; and a temperate climate (like that in Britain) at middle latitudes, and so on.

Why does latitude affect climate? It is because of the relative orientation of the Earth and Sun. At different times of the year the Sun can be directly overhead in the sky at the Equator or in tropical regions, but never at higher latitudes. The amount of incoming solar radiation intercepted by a square metre of the Earth's surface at the Equator would be incident over a greater area at higher latitudes (Figure 2.3). Higher latitudes therefore receive less solar radiation per unit area (a lower solar flux) than lower latitudes, so they are cooler.

▷ What else is a major controlling factor over how temperature varies in a given location?

▶ The time of year, i.e. the seasons.

Temperature varies with the seasons because of the *tilt* of the Earth (Figure 2.17). An Earth that was not tilted would spin around an axis perpendicular to a line drawn from the centre of the Earth to the centre of the Sun. Then, each day everywhere on Earth would have exactly 12 hours of daylight and 12 hours of night, and there would be no seasonal variations. However, the Earth is tilted at 23.5° from the perpendicular (Figure 2.17a), and maintains this orientation as it orbits around the Sun (Figure 2.17b).

Figure 2.17 (a) The Earth's rotational axis is tilted relative to the plane of the Earth's orbit around the Sun. (b) The seasons result from the tilt of the Earth. The hemisphere that is tilted towards the Sun is warmer because the Sun is visible for *more* than 12 hours, and also because it rises higher in the sky so the solar flux is greater. In this hemisphere it is summer and the polar region has sunlight for 24 hours a day. Midsummer day for the Northern Hemisphere occurs on 22 or 23 June each year, and is known as the Northern Hemisphere summer solstice. This is midwinter for the Southern Hemisphere, which has less than 12 hours of sunlight a day, and the sun is lower in the sky. Six months later the situation is reversed, giving the Southern Hemisphere summer and the Northern Hemisphere winter: the winter solstice for the Northern Hemisphere is 22 or 23 December. Spring and autumn correspond to intermediate positions of the Earth around the Sun, marked by the equinoxes, when every part of the Earth has 12 hours of sunlight a day. The solstices and equinoxes on the figure are for the Northern Hemisphere: the Southern Hemisphere has opposite ones.

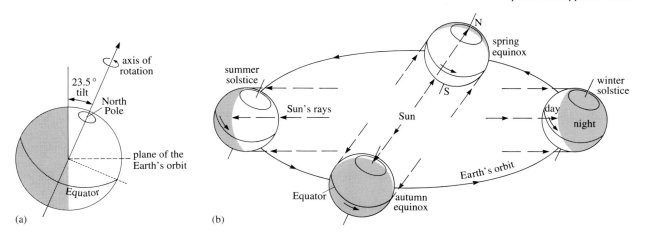

We will now ignore the effect of seasonal changes, and examine the variation, with latitude, of the incoming solar flux — and the proportion of that actually absorbed by the Earth–atmosphere system — *averaged over a year* (Figure 2.18). The top curve in the figure is the solar flux incident at the top of the atmosphere. Of this, part is reflected back to space by clouds and by the Earth's surface (the lower two curves). Part of Figure 2.14 is a globally-averaged version of this figure.

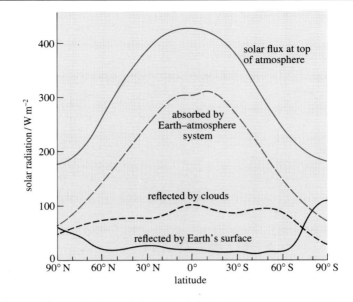

Figure 2.18 The variation with latitude (averaged over all longitudes and over a year) for the incoming solar flux at the top of the atmosphere, the radiation absorbed by the Earth's surface and atmosphere, the radiation reflected by clouds and the radiation reflected by the Earth's surface.

▷ According to Figure 2.14 (and Activity 2.3a), what percentage of the solar flux, *averaged over all longitudes and latitudes*, is reflected back to space?

▶ The average albedo of the Earth is 31%, so as a global average 31% of the solar flux is reflected back to space.

However, the Earth's *local* albedo can vary markedly, from less than 10% to over 90%. This is important. The key factors involved here are collected in Box 2.3.

2.3 | *Box 2.3 Cloud and surface albedos*

Clouds form when water vapour in the air condenses into water droplets, or, at greater heights and lower temperatures, into ice crystals, around tiny solid particles called **cloud condensation nuclei (CCN)**, such as pollen grains, dust or salt from sea-spray. This condensation occurs

particularly when warm, moist air cools, because cool air can hold less moisture than warm air.

As indicated in Figure 2.19, clouds can have many different forms: some typical examples are illustrated by the photographs in Figure 2.20.

Figure 2.19 Types of cloud. Clouds are classified as high clouds (above 6 km), middle clouds, and low clouds (below 2 km). Clouds are named according to their general form as well as height: for example, cirrocumulus clouds are cumuliform clouds (flat bases and bubbly tops) at high levels, whereas altocumulus clouds are cumuliform clouds at middle levels, and so on. Stratiform clouds have a blanket-like layer structure.

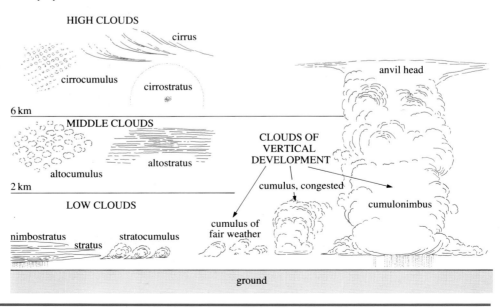

The albedo of clouds depends on the cloud *type*, from less than 20% to 70% (Table 2.2). The solar radiation reflected by clouds depends also on how much of the surface is cloud covered. Cloud cover tends to be greatest in equatorial regions and over parts of continental areas in summer.

(a)

(b)

(c)

Figure 2.20 (a) Cumulonimbus clouds (often called 'thunder-heads'); towering upwards to an anvil-shaped top at heights near the top of the troposphere, these massive clouds are common at low latitudes near the Equator (more on which shortly).
(b) Stratocumulus clouds: these low-level fluffy clouds are usually arranged in roughly parallel lines. They are widespread over the oceans in temperate zones.
(c) Cirrus clouds: occurring at the highest (and coldest) altitudes, these wispy and feather-like clouds are comprised of ice crystals.

Table 2.2 Typical albedos of various surfaces.

Clouds	Ocean	Land
cirrus < 20%	seawater (Sun elevation > 40°) < 5%	cities 12–18%
stratocumulus 50%	sea-ice 80–90%	bare soil 13–18%
cumulonimbus 70%		forest 13–18%
		grassland 25–33%
		desert 35%
		fresh snow 80–90%

▷ From Table 2.2, does the land or sea absorb a greater proportion of solar radiation per unit area?

▶ The sea has a much lower albedo (less than 5% in general) than the land (12–35% in general), and so absorbs more solar radiation.

▷ How does a cover of snow or ice affect the amount of solar radiation absorbed by the land or sea?

▶ Both snow on land and sea-ice have a very high albedo (80–90%) and so will reduce the amount of solar radiation absorbed. ■

Now look back at Figure 2.18. Notice first the latitudinal variation of the solar radiation reflected by clouds — a pattern determined by the geographical distribution of the different types of cloud cover noted in Box 2.3. For example, the maximum near the Equator reflects the extensive coverage of high albedo cumulonimbus clouds that is common at these latitudes.

▷ Why is the amount of radiation reflected by the *surface* (Figure 2.18) a maximum in the polar regions?

▶ The reflection of radiation is high because the polar regions are extensively covered by snow or ice, both of which have a high albedo.

The combined influence of clouds and surface characteristics produces the variation of albedo with latitude shown in Figure 2.21a. The solar radiation that is not reflected back to space is absorbed by the Earth's surface and atmosphere. Not surprisingly, this is highest at low latitudes (around 300 W m^{-2}), dropping to less than 100 W m^{-2} at polar latitudes (Figure 2.21b). The outgoing longwave radiation from the Earth is fairly uniform (at just over 200 W m^{-2}) at latitudes up to 40°, dropping to 150–170 W m^{-2} at the poles.

▷ Between which latitudes is there a net gain of radiant energy by the Earth–atmosphere system, and at which latitudes is there a net loss?

▶ There is a net gain of radiant energy when the amount of absorbed solar radiation is greater than the outgoing longwave radiation, which occurs from the Equator to about 40° latitude. At higher latitudes the absorbed radiation is lower than the outgoing radiation, so there is a net loss of radiant energy.

The areas between the absorbed radiation and outgoing radiation curves, marked 'gain' and 'loss' on Figure 2.21b, represent the amount of radiant energy gained at low latitudes and lost at higher ones. These two areas are approximately equal because the latitude scale of the figure is proportional to area, not to distance from the Equator. In other words, the total amount of radiant energy gained at low latitudes is

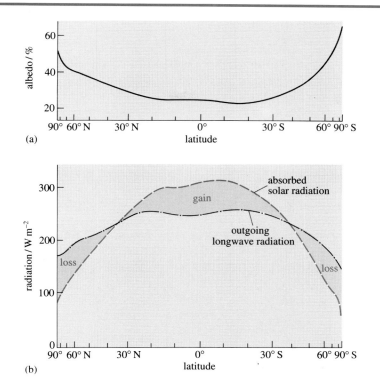

Figure 2.21 (a) The variation with latitude of the albedo of the Earth–atmosphere system. (b) The variation with latitude of the solar radiation absorbed by the Earth–atmosphere system (black), and the outgoing radiation lost to space (blue). The values are averaged over a year, and differ in each hemisphere because of differences in the surface: type and distribution of land, sea or ice. The latitude axis is scaled in proportion to the Earth's surface area (see text) so this figure is not directly comparable with Figure 2.18.

equal to that lost at high latitudes: *there is no overall gain or loss of energy*. This was illustrated for a globally-averaged situation in Figure 2.9: $(100 - x)$ units of radiation were absorbed and $(100 - x)$ units emitted.

It would seem from Figure 2.21b that low latitudes should be getting warmer because of the net gain in energy, and high latitudes should be getting cooler. However, this does not happen, because heat energy is transferred from low latitudes to high latitudes by winds and ocean currents, balancing the gains and losses (Figure 2.22). The amount of heat transferred is enormous: without it, equatorial latitudes would be some 10 °C warmer, on average, and polar regions would be around 20 °C colder.

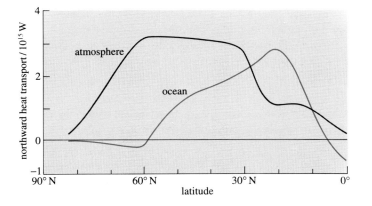

Figure 2.22 The transport of heat towards the pole at different latitudes (averaged at each latitude around the Earth over a year) by winds in the atmosphere and by ocean currents. This is for the Northern Hemisphere (positive values show transport towards the North Pole).

Question 2.2 Use Figure 2.22 to estimate whether the atmosphere or ocean transports more heat towards the pole in the Northern Hemisphere.

In the next sections we will look in more detail at how winds and ocean currents influence climate.

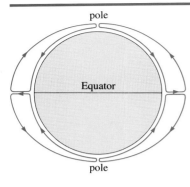

Figure 2.23 Atmospheric circulation for a simplified, non-rotating water-covered Earth. The circulation is not to scale: the height is greatly exaggerated.

2.3.2 Atmospheric circulation

The *differential* heating of the Earth between the Equator and the poles (shown in Figure 2.21b) is the driving force for the large-scale circulation of the atmosphere. Just as we started by considering a planet with no atmosphere in Section 2.2, it is useful here to consider first a simplified water-covered Earth, which has no land and is not rotating. Movement of the atmosphere results from changes in temperature which cause air to expand and become less dense when it is heated. The warmer, less dense air rises, creating high-pressure above so that high-level air moves away sideways from the high pressure. This leaves a low-pressure area near the surface, towards which air moves in a surface wind. More energy is absorbed near the Equator than at the poles (Figure 2.18), so around the Equator heated air rises until it reaches a height in the upper troposphere where its density is the same as the surrounding air, when it begins to move horizontally towards the poles. In principle then, a single 'convection cell' would be set up; air in the upper troposphere would move towards the poles, where there is strong cooling, causing sinking of the air, which would then blow as a surface wind to the low pressure area at the Equator (Figure 2.23). This 'idealized' circulation system is called a **Hadley cell**, named after the 18th century British meteorologist, George Hadley. According to this simple picture, the net effect is for warm air to move from the Equator to the poles in the upper troposphere, and cooler surface air to move towards the Equator.

In practice, the general circulation of the atmosphere on the Earth is a good deal more complicated than this. For a start, winds do not blow directly north or south. In reality, the Earth rotates once in 24 hours, so every point on the Earth's surface completes one rotation in this time. A point on the Equator is travelling very fast, as it has to travel a considerable distance, around the Equator, in 24 hours. However, near the poles a point is travelling more slowly, as it has much less far to go. The Earth is spinning towards the east, so air at the Equator will therefore have a higher velocity in an east–west direction than will air at a higher latitude. If air is blowing towards the pole it will be deflected towards the east, as it is moving eastward faster than it should be at that latitude. Conversely, air blowing towards the Equator will have a lower velocity to the east than expected for the latitude, so will be deflected to the west, relative to the rotating Earth.

Newton's first law of motion tells us that to change the velocity of an object a force must act on it, so it seems to an observer on the rotating Earth that there must be a force acting on the winds; this **Coriolis force** is caused by the Earth's rotation. Its effect is to deflect winds from the direction they would travel on a 'stationary' Earth, i.e. to the east if travelling towards the poles, and to the west if travelling towards the Equator.

In practice, the Hadley cell circulation only exists at low latitudes, less than about 30°. For reasons we cannot go into fully here, a convection cell encompassing each hemisphere, with a much greater horizontal than vertical extent (as depicted in Figure 2.23), is inherently unstable on a rotating Earth. Suffice it to say that the transfer of heat towards the poles takes place by another process at higher latitudes, involving the action of smaller-scale systems, e.g. cyclones, discussed later in this section. Figure 2.24 is a schematic representation of the surface winds on a water-covered, rotating Earth, with the Hadley cells shown near the Equator, and other convection cells near the poles. Near the Equator winds blow from the northeast in the Northern Hemisphere (note the deflection by the Coriolis force). These are fairly consistent prevailing winds, called the **northeast trade winds** (somewhat confusingly, winds are named according to the direction *from* which they are blowing: in this case, these are bringing air from the northeast). The Hadley cell in the Southern Hemisphere forms **southeast trade winds** at the surface.

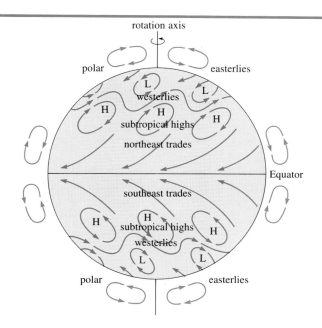

Figure 2.24 A schematic representation of the surface winds on a simplified water-covered, rotating Earth. This is a plan view, except for the convection cells which are vertical cross-sections. Low-pressure areas, with cyclonic circulation, are marked with L, and high-pressure anticyclonic areas are marked with H (see text for an explanation of these terms).

In the polar regions the surface winds, called the **polar easterlies**, actually blow from the northeast, or southeast, not from due east. Between the trade winds and the polar easterlies is the zone of surface **westerlies**, which blow from the southwest in the Northern Hemisphere and northwest in the Southern Hemisphere. It is these westerlies that influence Britain's weather: the prevailing wind is from the southwest, bringing rain with it, but sometimes polar easterlies penetrate as far south as Britain, giving a period of cold, dry weather.

Progressing from this water-covered model of the Earth, the real (but very simplified) wind system on the Earth is shown in Figure 2.25. You do not have to remember details of these complicated figures! They have the major features in common with the expected wind system on a water-covered, rotating Earth (Figure 2.24): for example, the westerlies in the North Pacific, North Atlantic and between 40°S and 60°S are obvious, as are the northern polar easterlies and the trade winds in some locations. But there are also many differences from the schematic representation of Figure 2.24, mainly caused by the effect of land. The distribution of land and ocean significantly affects the atmospheric circulation and alters it from that of the water-covered Earth.

The surface wind systems of the Northern and Southern Hemispheres do not meet exactly at the Equator, but at a region called the **Intertropical Convergence Zone (ITCZ)**. This area was called the doldrums by early mariners because of its calm or light and variable winds, and cumulonimbus clouds. The ITCZ has the highest surface temperature, and its position is also dependent on the distribution of land and ocean. It tends to be further north over land than ocean in the Northern Hemisphere summer (for example, China) and further south over land than ocean in the Southern Hemisphere summer (South America, Afric, Australia, see Figure 2.25).

Over Britain our weather systems often have winds that are blowing in a circular path, around a temporary low- or high-pressure area (Figure 2.26: this may look familiar from weather forecasts). These are instabilities in the general westerly circulation at midlatitudes (Figure 2.24). Air circulation around a low-pressure area is called a **cyclone**. Air circulation around a high-pressure area is called an **anticyclone** and has air moving in the opposite direction to that in cyclones, outwards and clockwise (in the Northern Hemisphere). Both cyclones and anticyclones move heat towards the poles, carried by warm air; this air then returns to the Equator, having lost some of its heat.

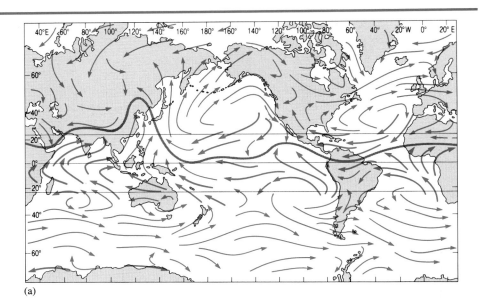

(a)

mean position of ITCZ

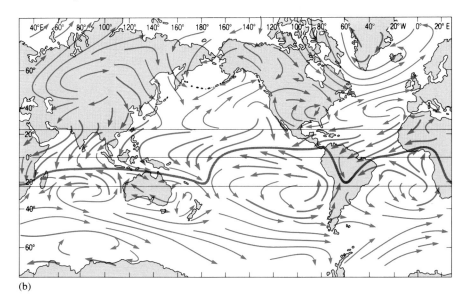

(b)

Figure 2.25 The surface winds on the real Earth, (a) in July, for the Northern Hemisphere summer, (b) in January, for the Southern Hemisphere summer. ITCZ, Intertropical Convergence Zone.

Figure 2.26 A cyclone, developed around a low-pressure area over the North Sea. Wind blows anticlockwise around the centre of a cyclone in the Northern Hemisphere. The black lines are isobars (lines of equal air pressure) with values in millibars. The wind does not blow directly towards the centre of the low-pressure area, but both inwards and anticlockwise around the centre in the Northern Hemisphere, because of the effect of the Coriolis force on the wind. Winds blow clockwise in a Southern Hemisphere cyclone.

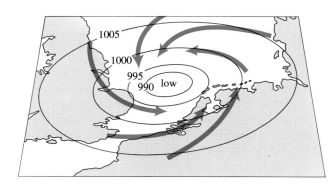

There are also **tropical cyclones**, often referred to as **hurricanes** or **typhoons**. They have a different origin to the mid-latitude cyclones, being related to high seawater temperatures. Tropical cyclones have much lower air pressures at their centre than mid-latitude cyclones, and correspondingly greater wind speeds which often cause great danger to ships and destruction on land. Tropical cyclones are about 300–400 km in diameter, whilst mid-latitude cyclones are usually larger, with diameters of 500–2 000 km.

Question 2.3 How does the temperature of North America, at a latitude of about 50° N, compare with that of the Pacific Ocean at the same latitude, for (a) summer, (b) winter (Figure 2.16)?

Contrasts like those in Question 2.3 reflect the high *heat capacity* of water. Put simply, land masses are more 'sensitive' to seasonal (and indeed, daily) variations in solar radiation than are ocean regions at comparable latitudes: they heat up more quickly in summer, and cool down faster in winter. As a result, the land is generally warmer than the nearby ocean in summer, and vice versa in winter. In summer, the air above land is warmed by the underlying surface, and so expands and rises, creating high pressure above so that high-level air moves away, producing a low-pressure area over the land. Thus, on a local scale at least, surface winds from the ocean often blow towards the land in summer (Figure 2.27a). In winter, the direction is reversed: the air above the cold land is cooled and sinks, producing a high-pressure area over land, and surface winds generally blow from this towards the ocean (Figure 2.27b).

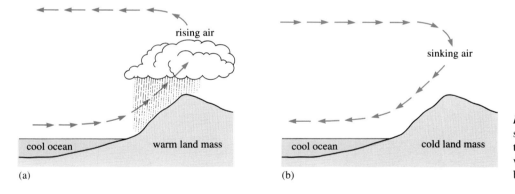

Figure 2.27 (a) In summer, surface winds generally blow from the ocean towards the land. (b) In winter, surface winds generally blow from the land to the ocean.

▷ Do winds blow towards land in summer and towards the ocean in winter on the global scale (Figure 2.25)?

▶ In some cases. Asia provides the most obvious example of prevailing winds changing between winter and summer. However, in other cases there is little or no change: western Europe for example.

Winds that reverse direction between winter and summer are called **monsoons**. The most dramatic effect of monsoon winds occurs in south and east Asia, particularly over the Indian subcontinent (Figure 2.25). In summer, this area has southwesterly winds that have travelled over the warm Indian Ocean, and have collected a lot of water vapour. This water vapour gives clouds, storms and intense rainfall when it rises over the land. In winter, the area has northeasterly winds from central Asia, bringing cold, dry and clear weather.

2.3.3 Oceanic circulation

Part of the atmospheric circulation, the surface wind system, is the main driving force behind the surface currents of the ocean. Like the winds, currents are influenced by the rotation of the Earth, so they do not flow directly downwind, but are deflected by the Coriolis force to the right of the downwind direction in the Northern Hemisphere and the left in the Southern Hemisphere. Winds can cross the boundary between ocean and land, but currents obviously cannot, so their pattern is also influenced by the shapes of the ocean basins. The surface current pattern (Figure 2.28) is generally similar to that of surface winds, with circulating wind and current systems over and in the major ocean basins (the North and South Atlantic, and the North and South Pacific) and a major current, the West wind drift travelling right around the world in the Southern Hemisphere in the zone of westerlies. However, there are many differences on a smaller scale.

▷ How do the directions of the surface winds (Figure 2.25b) and surface currents (Figure 2.28) in January compare for (1) the western Pacific Ocean in the Northern Hemisphere, (2) the equatorial Pacific Ocean, and (3) the North Pacific Ocean?

▶ (1) The western side of the Kuroshio is opposed by the January winds blowing from Asia (but is in the same direction as the July winds).

(2) The North and South Equatorial currents have a more consistently east–west direction than do the winds. There is an easterly-flowing Equatorial counter-current but no wind in this direction.

(3) Generally, currents in the North Pacific do not appear to be related to winds.

Some of the most conspicuous features of Figure 2.28 are the currents that move in a broad circular pattern, called **gyres**, e.g. the North Pacific gyre, which includes the Kuroshio, the North Pacific current, the California current and the North Equatorial current. Currents move large volumes of water, as they are relatively wide, 50–100 km or so for currents on the western side of oceans and even wider for the slower eastern currents, so they can transport a lot of heat.

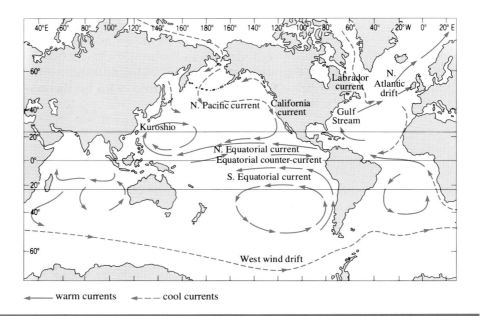

Figure 2.28 The surface currents in the oceans. This is the average January situation: there are seasonal differences in some areas, particularly in the areas affected by monsoon winds. Currents are conventionally named by the direction *towards* which they flow, the opposite to winds.

Currents that carry water from the Equator towards the poles are warm, and transport heat very effectively to higher latitudes (Figure 2.22). The heat supplied by the Gulf Stream and North Atlantic drift system has a great influence on the temperatures in northern Europe (Figure 2.16). Britain has much milder winters than land at the same latitude in eastern Canada (which has a cold current offshore), and Norway is much milder than areas at similar latitudes in Greenland (which has a permanent ice-cap over all but the coastal regions).

There is one major difference in the current systems in the Northern and Southern Hemispheres: that is the presence of a current in the Southern Hemisphere that does not travel in a gyre but circulates around the world — the West wind drift (also called the Antarctic circumpolar current). This occurs because there is no land to deflect the current, which is driven by the westerly winds.

▷ The Arctic region is generally less cold than the Antarctic region. Can you suggest a reason for this, based on Figure 2.28?

▶ A major warm current, the North Atlantic drift, penetrates into the Arctic Ocean, warming the region. There is no similar warm current reaching the Antarctic continent.

So far, we have considered the long-term, average surface circulation of the oceans. We know that the atmospheric circulation has transient weather systems, but does the ocean too? It does, particularly with an equivalent of the cyclonic and anticyclonic weather systems, called **mesoscale eddies** which, like their atmospheric counterparts, can also transfer heat towards the polar regions. Mesoscale eddies are smaller than atmospheric cyclones and anticyclones (50–200 km in diameter) and last longer (a few months or even years instead of a week or so).

We now need to look at what happens below the surface layer of the ocean. The oceans are mainly around 4–5 km deep: are there, for example, deep currents in the ocean? Are there movements of water between the surface and deep parts of the ocean? As we did for the atmosphere in Figure 2.11, we will start by examining a temperature profile in the ocean to see whether it has a layered structure similar to that in the atmosphere. Figure 2.29 is a temperature profile for the ocean at low latitudes. The top part of the ocean is heated by solar radiation and is fairly warm, over 20 °C in low latitudes, 10–15 °C in middle latitudes, but less than 5 °C in polar regions. This **mixed layer** has the same temperature at the surface as at depths down to a hundred metres or so because the water is agitated and mixed by wave action. In middle and high latitudes the mixed layer is deeper in winter, when the surface water is coldest and it is stirred up to a greater depth by storms. Throughout the oceans, the temperature decreases sharply below the mixed layer, in a zone called the **thermocline**. Below about 1 km the temperature decreases only slowly and by a few degrees, and this is independent of latitude: the deep water of the tropics is almost as cold as the deep water of the polar regions.

This three-layer ocean structure is essentially a stable structure because the warmest, and therefore least dense water, is at the top and the coldest, most dense water is at the bottom. In addition, the more saline the water is (i.e. the greater the amount of salts dissolved in it), the denser it is. However, the density changes caused by temperature variations between the mixed and deep layers are usually greater than the density changes caused by salinity variations, so the thermocline generally acts as a barrier to the large-scale mixing of surface and deep water.

Water below the thermocline *can* return to the surface very slowly, by mixing through the thermocline, but it does so more quickly in specific areas of **upwelling**,

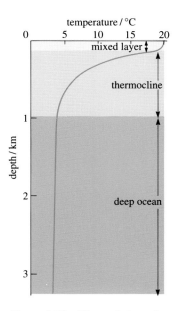

Figure 2.29 The variation of temperature with depth in the ocean for low latitudes.

such as in coastal areas or in some ocean basins. In the open oceans, upwelling is driven by wind systems, which cause surface water to move away (diverge) from an area, thus 'drawing up' sub-surface water. This happens predominantly in parts of the polar regions, for example at around 60° S in the Southern Ocean (to the south of the West wind drift, see Figure 2.28) — a phenomenon known as the **Antarctic Divergence** — and in equatorial regions. Coastal upwelling occurs when winds cause surface water to move away from the land (Figure 2.30), so that the surface water is replaced by colder water, which upwells from below. This happens, for example, along the coast of Ecuador and Peru. **Downwelling** can also occur by the opposite of the conditions causing upwelling, i.e. through surface water coming together (converging) in an area, causing the sinking of surface water. Downwelling occurs, like upwelling, predominantly in polar and equatorial regions, such as in the Antarctic Polar Frontal Zone (within the area of the West wind drift), north of the Antarctic Divergence.

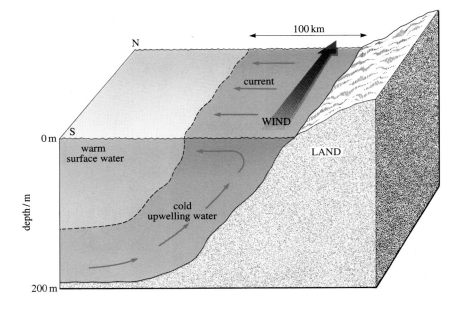

Figure 2.30 Coastal upwelling in the Southern Hemisphere. A southerly wind along a north–south coastline will drive surface water offshore, not alongshore, because of the effect of the Coriolis force, causing upwelling of deeper, colder water.

Now we will turn to the oceanic circulation at high latitudes. The two polar regions of the Earth are dramatically different. The Northern Hemisphere's Arctic polar region is an area of ocean surrounded by land, with only one deep-water connection to the major oceans, into the Atlantic between Greenland and Norway (the link to the Pacific via the Bering Straits is very shallow, about 45 m deep). In contrast, the Southern Hemisphere's Antarctic polar region is a large continent surrounded by ocean. Plate 2.1 shows the extent of the sea-ice cover in the polar regions.

▷ In Plate 2.1, how does the proportion of area covered by sea-ice change in (a) the Arctic, and (b) the Antarctic, between the end of the winter and the end of the summer (March/September)?

▶ (a) About one half of the area covered by sea-ice in the Arctic winter melts in the summer.

(b) Most, about 90%, of the area covered by sea-ice in the Antarctic melts in the summer.

In short, much of the Arctic Ocean has a permanent cover of sea-ice, unlike in the ocean around the Antarctic, where most of the sea-ice melts each summer.

▷ By comparing Plate 2.1 and Figure 2.28, what seems to be the major control over which parts of the Arctic do *not* have a permanent sea-ice cover?

▶ Ocean currents. The North Atlantic part of the Arctic is ice-free all the year. This area is warmed by the North Atlantic drift (Figure 2.28), which brings warm water into the Arctic Ocean, preventing sea-ice from forming.

▷ How does the formation of sea-ice affect the solar radiation absorbed by the ocean?

▶ The albedo of the ice-free ocean is low so it absorbs a high proportion of the solar radiation (Table 2.2). Sea-ice has a high albedo, so once sea-ice has formed the amount of solar radiation absorbed by the ocean is very low and, in the absence of warm currents, sea-ice will tend to persist.

Another — *and crucially important* — way that sea-ice influences the energy balance and heat transport by the ocean is its role in causing surface water to sink. Strong polar winds, blowing from sea-ice or from an ice-cap on land, cool the surface water, which gives up its heat as sensible heat and latent heat to the atmosphere, possibly enough to cause the seawater to freeze (Figure 2.31). Sea-ice forms, leaving most of the salt in the remaining seawater, which thus becomes more saline. This higher salinity, cold seawater is very dense, and sinks to greater depths.

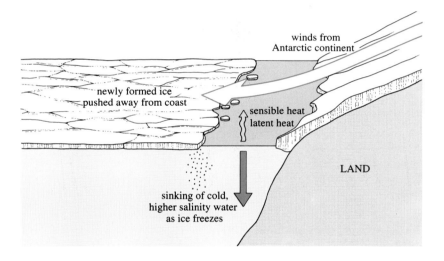

Figure 2.31 The sinking (downwelling) of surface water at high latitudes, which accompanies the formation of sea-ice.

Some of the densest water in the oceans forms in this way near Antarctica, at a temperature of about −2 °C (seawater has a lower freezing point than freshwater). The resulting large, deep mass of water, called the **Antarctic Bottom Water**, flows along the bottom of the ocean around Antarctica and out into the Atlantic, Pacific and Indian Oceans. The other main area where surface water sinks is in the North Atlantic between Greenland and Norway: here, seawater is cooled by cold winds to less than −1 °C and sinks, forming a deep-water mass. This is an important constituent of the **North Atlantic Deep Water**, which flows south along the bottom of the Atlantic Ocean. The reason that the ocean has a low temperature at depth everywhere is because of these cold deep-water masses that are formed in polar regions. Where they meet, the North Atlantic Deep Water is less dense than the Antarctic Bottom Water, so the North Atlantic Deep Water flows over the Antarctic Bottom Water. There is another major subsurface water body in the Atlantic, the Antarctic Intermediate Water, which forms by downwelling at a wind-driven convergence generally between 50 and 60 °S: it is less dense than the other two deep waters, so flows over them. The deep waters flow out from the Atlantic and the Antarctic region along the bottom of the Indian and North Pacific Oceans, where they slowly rise to the surface, to become

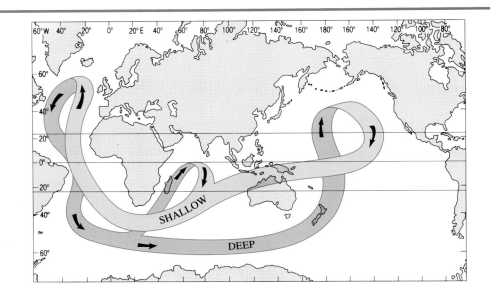

Figure 2.32 The general long-term thermohaline circulation of water throughout the deep ocean. The deep water rises in the Indian and North Pacific Oceans and returns in surface currents to sink in the North Atlantic Ocean.

part of the surface current system. This deep-water circulation of the oceans is called the **thermohaline circulation**, as it is driven by temperature (thermo) and salinity (haline) differences in water masses. In the long term there is a general motion of deep water in the oceans from the North and South Atlantic into the Indian and Pacific Oceans, and a return flow of warm water near the surface (Figure 2.32). This gigantic ocean 'conveyor belt' of deep water is driven by the cold, dense water sinking in the polar regions. The conveyor generally acts to transfer heat from the Indian and North Pacific Oceans into the North Atlantic, and if it stopped, or even reversed in direction, the global climate would be very different.

How long does water take to move around this 'conveyor'? Estimates vary, but between 200 and 1 000 years is generally accepted. This means that, once it has sunk from the surface, deep water is out of contact with the atmosphere for this length of time, regarded as the 'age' of the water. However, not all the deep water travels all the way round the conveyor; instead some of it returns to the surface in the Atlantic, reducing the time it is out of contact with the atmosphere.

This discussion of ocean circulation, especially that of the deep ocean, has been simplified and generalized in many aspects. There is also much that still needs to be discovered about the detailed working of the ocean circulation and its influence on climate: more on this in later chapters.

2.3.4 The hydrological cycle

So far in Section 2.3 we have focused mainly on the differential heating between low and high latitudes on our spherical, rotating planet. You have seen how this powers the system whereby heat is transported towards the poles via the general circulation of the atmosphere, and by surface currents in the world's oceans. Embedded within our outline of how that system operates are important ways in which the atmosphere and the oceans influence one another. These and other 'interconnections' within the Earth's overall climate system are drawn out and underlined in Section 2.4. As a prelude to that, however, there is one, all pervasive, link between the atmosphere and the *whole* planetary surface that warrants special attention.

Have another look at Figure 2.14 (Section 2.2.4). Notice that the bulk of the solar input to the global energy budget is absorbed first by the *surface* of the planet — not the atmosphere. This energy only becomes 'available' to the atmosphere through the transfer of heat across the surface–air boundary.

Question 2.4 What *three* mechanisms are responsible for transferring the solar energy absorbed at the Earth's surface to the atmosphere? According to the globally-averaged estimates in Figure 2.14, which of these is the most important?

In short, over half of the solar energy absorbed by the Earth's surface is used in evaporating water. This not only transfers heat to the atmosphere when the water vapour subsequently condenses (more on which shortly), it also drives the global **hydrological cycle** — the overall movement and storage of water around the world. From this global perspective, each major repository of water — whatever its physical form (vapour, liquid or snow and ice) — can be regarded as a 'compartment' or '**reservoir**' in the overall cycle, as shown schematically in Figure 2.33. The figure incorporates current estimates of the amount of water stored in each reservoir and the annual transfers between them. Not surprisingly, the overwhelming majority of the world's water (some 96%) is in the oceans. Indeed, only around 2% of the total is freshwater — and some 75% of this is locked up in ice-sheets and glaciers. Most of the rest is in groundwater (water in the subsoil and in rocks): only a tiny fraction of *all* freshwater is held on the surface — in lakes and rivers.

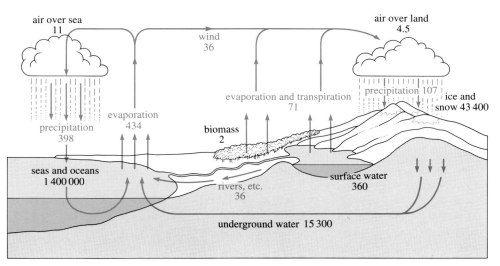

Figure 2.33 The global hydrological cycle, showing global estimates of the volume of water (in 10^3 km^3) stored in each reservoir (in black lettering), and the annual transfers (averaged over several years) between them (in blue lettering), with units of 10^3 km^3 yr^{-1}. *All* of the figures recorded here are subject to large uncertainties.

Most of the transfers depicted in Figure 2.33 are self-evident. However, it does include one, possibly unfamiliar, factor that affects the rate at which moisture enters the air from land — the presence of vegetation, especially trees. Plants lose water from their leaves by a process known as **transpiration**. Figure 2.34 emphasizes the important and *active* role that plants in general — and trees in particular — play in the overall hydrological cycle.

Activity 2.5

(a) Given the estimates collected in Figure 2.33, check that the *total* amounts of water entering and leaving the atmosphere each year balance. What would happen were this not the case?

(b) Does the overall balance in the atmosphere hold *separately* over the oceans and over the land surface? What conclusions can be drawn from your answer?

Figure 2.34 The effect of plants on the hydrological cycle. Plants can intercept rainfall and evaporate some of it directly. Rain that reaches the ground can evaporate, or run off the surface (eventually contributing to river flow), or infiltrate the soil to form groundwater. Some soil moisture is taken up by plant roots and then transpired (i.e. returned to the atmosphere) by the leaves. The amount of transpiration depends on the type of vegetation (a many-leaved tree canopy tops the list), together with factors that also influence the surface energy balance: wind speed, solar radiation, albedo, and the temperature and moisture content of the air. This will be discussed in more detail in Section 2.4.

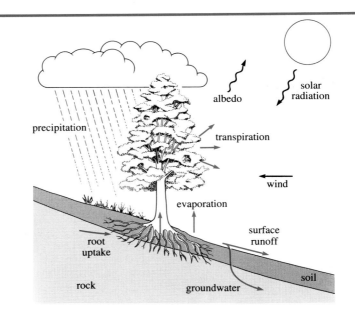

To crystallize your thoughts on Activity 2.5, Figure 2.33 depicts a *steady-state* cycle: none of the reservoirs involved either grows or diminishes. But at the same time, the figure captures the overall movement of water from the oceans to the atmosphere (through *net* evaporation), whence it is carried by winds over the land and deposited (as *net* precipitation), and then flows back into the oceans via the world's rivers.

For any steady-state cycle (and you will meet another example in Chapter 4), the *average* time the substance (or whatever) in question spends in a given reservoir is called the **residence time**. It can be calculated as follows:

$$\text{residence time} = \frac{\text{reservoir size}}{\text{rate of input (or output)}} \tag{2.5}$$

▷ According to Figure 2.33 and Activity 2.5a, what is the residence time for water in the atmosphere?

▶ The residence time for water in the atmosphere is

$$\frac{[(11 + 4.5) \times 10^3\,\text{km}^3]}{(505 \times 10^3\,\text{km}^3\,\text{yr}^{-1})} = 0.031 \text{ yr, or around 11 days.}$$

Residence times in other compartments are generally much longer than this — over 3 000 years for the oceans, for example. For our purposes here, the points to register are that the atmosphere holds very little water, and such water as it does hold stays there only briefly. As a result, the *actual* moisture content of air is highly variable — sensitive to relatively *local* variations in the flow (or flux) of water to and from the underlying surface. Thus, virtually all the precipitation over maritime and monsoon regions (such as southeast Asia, Section 2.3.2) does indeed come from ocean sources — in line with the globally-averaged picture in Figure 2.33, that is — as does the precipitation over the sea itself. Further inland, however, terrestrial evaporation and transpiration (collectively dubbed **evapotranspiration**) can be equally important — effectively recycling the 'life-blood of the biosphere' on a regional scale. In short, trees and other vegetation can have a critical influence over the 'water budget' — and hence climate — of a particular region.

Water is vital for life. The hydrological *cycle* is a vital part of the overall climate system, intimately linked to the dynamics of the atmosphere and the global energy budget. For example, evaporation (and evapotranspiration) is greatest at equatorial latitudes — both from the oceans and from areas of tropical rainforest. Here, the high input of solar energy at the surface fuels strong convection in the overlying air (Figure 2.24). Working together, these factors drive the transfer of moisture to the atmosphere (recall Question 2.1): its latent heat is released in the towering cumulonimbus clouds typical of these latitudes (Box 2.3).

Elsewhere too, convection (or indeed, any turbulence) in the lower atmosphere strongly influences the transfer of water, and hence heat, from the underlying surface — be it ocean or land (a link touched on in the caption to Figure 2.34). Winds carry moisture around. And cloud formation is inherently bound up with vertical motion in the atmosphere — be it ascent over a mountain barrier, or the gradual uplift of air over a wide area associated with the low-pressure systems characteristic of our own temperate latitudes (and often marked by banks of stratocumulus, Box 2.3 again).

Finally, clouds (however ephemeral) play a crucial role in the Earth's radiation balance — both globally (the point stressed in Section 2.2.4) and regionally, through the geographical distribution of different types of cloud cover (Section 2.3.1), evident in Plate 2.2. And so does atmospheric moisture — itself highly variable in both space and time — since water vapour is the most important natural greenhouse gas. In short, the hydrological cycle vividly exemplifies the 'interconnectedness' of the Earth's climate system. That is the theme on which we close this chapter.

2.4 Linking the climate system together

Most of the weather statistics that go to make up the 'climate' of a given region have to do with the atmosphere — air temperatures, rainfall, snowfall, cloudiness, etc., and their variations through the year. That everyday notion of climate was the starting point for this chapter. By this stage, however, you should have a growing awareness that the overall climate *system* is not just the atmosphere and its general circulation. On the contrary, atmospheric processes both influence, and are influenced by, a multitude of interactions between the atmosphere and the Earth's surface, be it land, sea or ice — a message manifest in the workings of the hydrological cycle. To take that 'interconnectedness' story on a stage, recall the global distribution of surface temperatures recorded in Figure 2.16: this is determined by the energy balance at the planetary surface, and the way this varies around the world. Activity 2.6 gives you a chance to draw together what you have learnt about the main factors involved here.

Activity 2.6   *You should spend up to 30 minutes on this activity.*

Drawing on material in this chapter (and your own everyday experience) summarize the main factors that influence the following components of the surface energy balance, and the way they are likely to vary around the Earth.

(a)   The solar radiation *absorbed* at the surface (about *200 words*).

(b)   The longwave radiation emitted by the surface (about *50 words*).

(c)   The longwave radiation absorbed by the surface. (Don't worry if you find this tricky. Just think for a moment about the points in the final paragraph of Section 2.3.4.)

(d)   The transfer of latent and sensible heat (about *100 words*).

There is one all-important way in which the *oceans* help to shape the climate, both globally and, crucially, on a regional scale, that was not brought out in the answer to Activity 2.6 (although you may well have thought of it). The oceans also store and 'redistribute' the solar energy they absorb, before releasing it to the atmosphere — mainly through the evaporation of water. Thus, the surface energy balance in a region of ocean is also affected by heat brought in (or lost) by currents and mixing (including the upwelling and sinking of water) *within* the ocean. In this way, the major warm currents in the upper ocean — and the 'weather systems' (mesoscale eddies) associated with them — make a significant contribution to the net transport of heat from low to high latitudes (Section 2.3.3). Recall, for example, the effect of the Gulf Stream and the North Atlantic drift on the distribution of sea-surface temperatures in the North Atlantic (apparent in Figure 2.16) and the benign influence that, in turn, has on the climate of Britain and western Europe.

Heat transport within the oceans primarily results from the turbulent flow and mixing of water masses with different temperatures: in short, the general circulation of the oceans. That circulation is, in turn, strongly 'coupled' to the atmosphere. Ultimately, it is driven by the exchange of heat and water (which are themselves interconnected, Section 2.3.4) and 'momentum' with the atmosphere. Winds transfer momentum to the ocean at the sea-surface. Together with the distribution of continental land masses, the pattern of prevailing winds at the surface (*themselves a manifestation of the general circulation of the atmosphere*) is largely responsible for the major current systems in the upper ocean (Section 2.3.3). Winds also produce turbulent mixing in this zone — together with the downwelling of surface waters, and upwelling of subsurface waters that occurs throughout the oceans, both at coastal boundaries and away from them.

The vertical (thermohaline) circulation (Figures 2.31 and 2.32), which moves cold surface waters down into the deep ocean, essentially depends on the density of different water masses, which in turn depends on the temperature and salinity of the water. Sea-surface temperatures are controlled by the local energy budget, as noted above. Similarly, the local 'salinity budget' is determined by the removal or addition of freshwater — mainly through the balance between evaporation and precipitation (i.e. exchange with the atmosphere), but also through river inputs (Figure 2.33) and via mixing (with more or less saline waters) within the ocean.

▷ What other process is crucial to the movement of surface waters into the slow circulation of the cold deep ocean?

▶ The major input of surface waters into the deep ocean circulation occurs at high latitudes (i.e. in the North Atlantic and around Antarctica) in winter. Here, the formation of sea-ice leaves behind cold, saline water which is dense enough to sink to the deep ocean (Figure 2.31).

This deep-water formation — the driving force behind the thermohaline circulation — stems from an *interaction* between the atmosphere, ocean and sea-ice. In general, the atmosphere and the oceans are *both* influenced by the **cryosphere** — the part of the Earth covered with ice or snow. This is not just sea-ice: it also takes in the vast ice-sheets of Greenland and Antarctica, mountain glaciers and snow and ice cover elsewhere. Seasonal variations in continental snow cover affect the surface energy balance (Activity 2.6a) — just as the growth and retreat of sea-ice is bound up with the oceanic circulation (Section 2.3.3).

Climbing back out of the sea, the physical transfers that link the land surface with the atmosphere are essentially the same as those that link the atmosphere with the oceans — the exchange of heat, moisture and momentum. Overall, frictional 'dissipation' at the Earth's surface tends to slow down the general circulation of the atmosphere, but the detailed picture is enormously complicated by the great diversity of the continental landscape. In particular, the flow of air close to the surface is strongly influenced by the detailed topography of the underlying terrain — not just the contrast between land

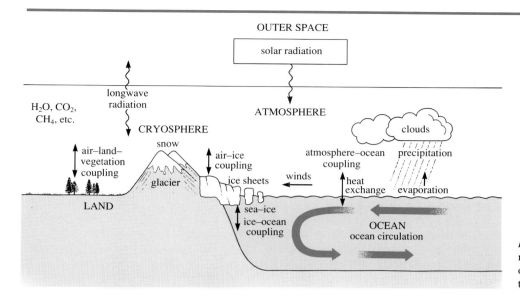

OUTER SPACE

solar radiation

longwave
radiation

H_2O, CO_2,
CH_4, etc.

ATMOSPHERE

CRYOSPHERE

snow

air–land–
vegetation
coupling

glacier

air–ice
coupling

ice sheets

clouds

atmosphere–ocean
coupling

precipitation

winds

heat
exchange

evaporation

LAND

sea–ice
ice–ocean
coupling

OCEAN
ocean circulation

Figure 2.35 A schematic
representation of the various parts
of the overall climate system, and
the links between them.

and sea or the presence of major mountain ranges, say, but also smaller-scale features
(collectively known as 'surface roughness') and the type of vegetation it carries
(forest, as opposed to open grassland or desert, for example). In turn, turbulent mixing
of the overlying air is one of the many interrelated factors (assembled in Figure 2.34)
that together determine the water budget and surface energy balance of different
regions. Notice again how the type of vegetation involved comes into that equation.

In summary, building on the discussion in Section 2.3.4, this brief review has sought
to emphasize the *holistic* nature of the Earth's climate system. Or to put it slightly
differently, it has stressed how the exchange of heat, moisture and momentum across
the surface–air boundary links the atmosphere, and *its* behaviour, to the oceans,
cryosphere and land surface — and to the vegetation that grows there. Figure 2.35
attempts to illustrate this coupled, interacting system in a highly schematic way. It is
this interconnected system that produces the pattern of climatic conditions around the
world which determines — and is itself influenced by — the global distribution of
biomes shown in Figure 2.1.

Or at least it does as long as certain 'parameters' are fixed. Implicit in the discussion
in this chapter are factors like the Sun's output, our planet's orbit and rotation, the
land–sea distribution, and the atmospheric burden of various greenhouse gases. The
central thrust of this book is toward the potential consequences of human-induced
changes in the last factor: the others in our list are clearly beyond human interference!
But can anything be learnt from how the climate system responds to *natural* changes
in these other factors? This is where the study of the Earth's *past* climatic history
comes into our story.

Summary of Chapter 2

1   A proportion (the planetary albedo) of the shortwave solar radiation intercepted by
the Earth is reflected directly back to space: the remainder is absorbed by the
Earth–atmosphere system, the bulk of it at the Earth's surface.

2   Outgoing longwave radiation from the Earth's surface is repeatedly absorbed and
re-emitted by molecules of certain trace constituents naturally present in the atmosphere — the greenhouse gases (mainly water vapour and carbon dioxide, but also
ozone, methane and nitrous oxide): ultimately, it is re-radiated to space from higher,
colder levels, thus maintaining an overall radiation balance at the top of the atmos-

phere. The 'trapping' of longwave radiation by greenhouse gases (and clouds) is the origin of the Earth's natural greenhouse effect: together with the turbulent mixing of the lower atmosphere (the troposphere) — and the consequent redistribution of sensible and latent heat — this keeps the planetary surface a vital 33 °C warmer than it would otherwise be.

Important: You should be able to interpret a schematic representation of the global energy balance, like the one in Figure 2.14; Activity 2.3 is a good guide here.

3   The chemical and photochemical processes that maintain the ozone layer in the stratosphere both 'filter' out (potentially damaging) shorter uv wavelengths in the incoming solar radiation, and heat this region *directly* — whence the 'reversal' in the Earth's temperature profile at the tropopause. Stratospheric ozone also absorbs and re-emits outgoing longwave radiation.

4   The climate for any part of the Earth varies mainly with latitude and season. There is a net gain of radiant energy by the Earth–atmosphere system at low latitudes and a net loss of radiant energy at high latitudes. Clouds are important in the reflection of the incoming solar radiation back to space. The albedo of the Earth varies with latitude, being greater in the polar regions, due to the snow or ice cover. The albedo of land surfaces is usually greater than the ocean albedo. Heat from low latitudes is transferred to high latitudes by winds and ocean currents.

5   Driven largely 'from below', the general circulation of the atmosphere results from the differential heating of the planet, coupled with its rotation: the net effect is to transport heat towards the poles. An important contribution to this heat transport comes from the transient 'weather systems' — cyclones and anticyclones — generated as instabilities in the general westerly flow at mid-latitudes. Elsewhere, the main surface wind systems are the trade winds (at low latitudes) and polar easterlies. Some surface winds — the monsoons — reverse direction seasonally.

6   Driven by the pattern of prevailing winds at the surface, the major current systems in the upper ocean make a significant contribution to the net transport of heat from low to high latitudes. Winds also produce turbulent mixing in the upper ocean — together with the downwelling of surface waters and upwelling of subsurface waters. The deep-water thermohaline circulation (which links the world's oceans together) is driven by the sinking of cold, saline water at high latitudes in winter.

7   The movement and storage of water around the world — the hydrological cycle (Figure 2.33) — is intimately linked to the dynamics of the atmosphere and the global energy budget. Ultimately, it is driven by the solar energy used in the evaporation of water from the Earth's surface. Globally, this is the main process whereby heat is transferred to the atmosphere — released when water vapour subsequently condenses to form clouds, and falls as rain (or snow). Atmospheric moisture — and indeed freshwater availability in general — is highly variable, both in space and in time. Vegetation plays an important part in the regional hydrological cycle (through evapotranspiration) — as well as the surface energy balance — and hence in shaping the climate on this scale (Figure 2.34).

8   The pattern of climatic conditions around the world, and hence the geographical distribution of 'natural' vegetation (biomes, Figure 2.1) results from the workings of the whole interconnected climate system. This takes in the atmosphere, oceans, cryosphere, land surface and terrestrial vegetation — and all the many processes that link these 'components' together.

Important: Given a schematic representation of the climate system (like the one in Figure 2.35) you should be able to describe briefly the main links between the various components, as summarized in Sections 2.3.4 and 2.4.

3 Causes of climatic change

In the last chapter we looked at the overall energy balance of the Earth and at how geographical imbalances in it drive the atmospheric and oceanic circulation. Changes in these circulations, in the radiation balance at the top of the atmosphere, or in the composition of the atmosphere, can cause changes in the Earth's climate. In this chapter we will examine how and why these controlling factors change naturally to give you an understanding of the reasons for, and the past extent (and future prediction) of, *natural* climatic change. This is needed for an understanding of how climate may be changed by human activities and for consideration of whether the size and rate of anthropogenic climatic change is significant compared with natural climatic change. As you study this chapter, try to extract and note down, for each climatic factor discussed, both the size and rate of climatic change that it produces, in preparation for Activity 3.4.

Five factors are discussed in this chapter: lithospheric plate movements, which change the oceanic circulation; variations in the Earth's orbit around the Sun; and changes in the solar constant, all of which change the radiation balance at the top of the atmosphere; volcanic activity which affects the radiation balance within the atmosphere; and changes in atmospheric composition. Before embarking on that discussion, however, we first look at *how* the climate has changed in the past, as a basis for studying *why* it has changed. How much has it changed, how fast, and how do we know it has changed? Is change continuous, cyclic, or something else? We will investigate these questions in Section 3.1.

3.1 Past changes in climate

Before we look at how climate has varied in the past, it is necessary to recall for how long climatic changes have been taking place on the Earth — how old is the Earth? Box 3.1 summarizes the main points about geological time.

Box 3.1 Geological time and its terminology

Geological time is usually expressed in millions of years (the unit **Ma**; 'a' is used as a unit to represent a year for ages in geology instead of year, and comes from the Latin *annus* for year) or for the very recent geological time used in consideration of climate, in thousands of years (the unit **ka**). Both refer to years 'before present', which is written as BP. This is always left off the unit Ma, but may or may not be left off the unit ka, depending on the preference of the author. In this book it will always be left off, so that an age given as 18 ka means 18 thousand years before present. You may also find others ways of expressing time in articles or scientific papers about climatic change, such as 1 000 BP, meaning 1 000 years before present, or BC or AD, meaning

before or after the time of the birth of Christ. If a date has no units given, (e.g. 1850) it is assumed to mean AD (i.e. 'normal' time).

The Earth formed 4 600 Ma ago. The oldest geological **Era** occupies most of geological time, between 4 600 and 590 Ma (the Precambrian). The younger three Eras (the Palaeozoic, Mesozoic and Cainozoic) are subdivided into eleven **Periods** (Figure 3.1). You do not need to remember the names of the Periods, or their ages, or order, but you should refer to Figure 3.1 as necessary when Periods are mentioned in this book. The Tertiary and Quaternary Periods (the two Periods in the youngest Era, the Cainozoic) are further subdivided into divisions called **Epochs**. ■

3.1

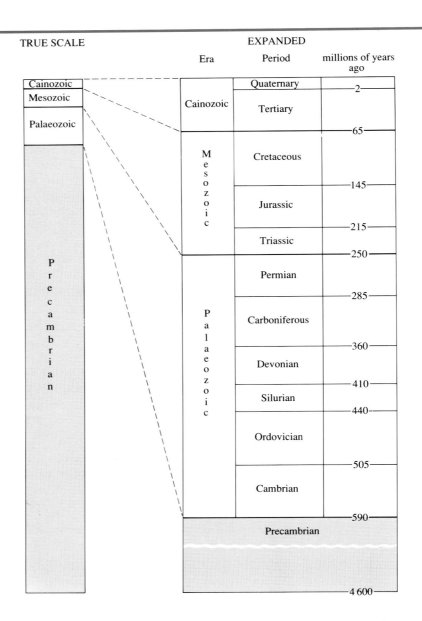

TRUE SCALE

EXPANDED

Era	Period	millions of years ago

Figure 3.1 The division of geological time into Eras and Periods. The dates for the beginning and end of each Period are in the column on the right. The Eras shown on a true vertical time-scale are in the left column.

Direct measurement of temperature on the Earth, using instruments, only extends back about 150 years, so to study the climate at times earlier than this we have to use indirect information, called **proxy data**. These are natural records of climate-sensitive phenomena, such as the growth or retreat of glaciers, pollen, insect and other animal remains, and lake and ocean sediments. Much of these proxy data are imprecise, in that they cannot give, say, information that the Earth was x degrees colder y million years ago, but merely that the Earth was colder y million years ago than at present. The proxy data record becomes more sparse and more imprecise the further back in geological time we examine.

Despite this limitation, by using proxy data from various sources, it is possible to produce a reasonably confident reconstruction of how temperature has varied throughout the Earth's history (Figure 3.2).

▷ Examine Figure 3.2 and identify major times when the climate was much warmer than the present.

▶ During the earliest part of Earth history, in the Precambrian before about 2 400 Ma; from about 2 000 to 1 000 Ma; and from the late Mesozoic to early Tertiary (Cretaceous–Eocene).

It is generally believed that the high temperatures before 2 400 Ma resulted from the greater abundance of carbon dioxide in the atmosphere, which produced an enhanced *natural* greenhouse effect (as compared with the present conditions, Section 3.6).

▷ Identify five times when the Earth was colder than at present.

▶ During the Precambrian at around 2 300 Ma and 700–900 Ma, in the Ordovician–Silurian, in the Carboniferous–Permian, and in the Quaternary.

These cold periods of Earth history are called **Ice Ages**. On the geological time-scale Ice Ages are relatively rare, covering only 5–10% of the history of the Earth. Cooling of the Earth's surface at around 2 300 Ma led to the first Ice Age, recorded by widespread glacial sediments in the geological record. This lasted about 100 Ma. The next 1 000 Ma, from about 2 000 Ma to 1 000 Ma, is marked by a widespread warmer climate on the Earth. By 900 Ma there was another Ice Age, producing widespread glacial deposits. The proxy data for two Palaeozoic Ice Ages, in the Ordovician–Silurian and Carboniferous–Permian, come from the more southern continents, rather than from Europe and North America, which were then at low latitudes.

The Mesozoic and early Cainozoic Eras had a warm climate that extended over much of the Earth. There is no evidence of glaciation, and temperatures in the polar regions are thought to have been 10–15 °C higher than today. During the middle and late Tertiary the temperature began to decrease (Figure 3.2), finally dropping into the most recent Ice Age, called the Quaternary Ice Age.

▷ From Figure 3.2, does it look as if the Quaternary Ice Age has finished, or are we still in it?

▶ The temperature pattern shows no evidence that it is finished, so we are probably still in this Ice Age.

This may be an unexpected statement, as the common view of an Ice Age has Britain covered with an ice-sheet and inhabited by mammoths. However, if you look at Figure 3.2 you will see that the Quaternary Ice Age is characterized by many fluctuations in temperature. At the moment we are in one of those relatively warm periods, called an **interglacial**, within the Quaternary Ice Age. The cooler periods are called **glacials**. Glacials are occasionally called, confusingly, 'ice ages', with lower case initial letters, in some books or papers. Another point of terminology is that the Quaternary Ice Age sometimes has 'Quaternary' dropped and is referred to as just 'the Ice Age'.

You might like to reflect on the fact that as Ice Ages are relatively rare in Earth history, we are living on an Earth which is in its less common (and possibly less stable) climatic state. Figure 3.3 shows the temperature changes during the Quaternary Ice Age in more detail.

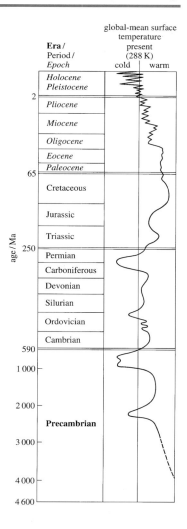

Figure 3.2 The estimated global-mean surface temperature of the Earth throughout geological time, derived from proxy data (see text for further details). The vertical time-scale is non-linear, changing scale at the double lines. This reflects our more detailed knowledge of the climate nearer to the present. The dashed line before about 3 000 Ma indicates that temperature is known poorly at this time as few proxy data are preserved.

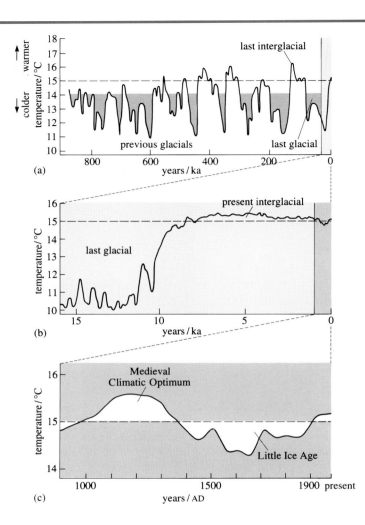

Figure 3.3 The estimated global-mean surface temperature changes derived from proxy data over (a) the past million years; (b) the past 16 000 years; (c) the past 1 000 years. The horizontal dashed line represents the global-mean surface temperature at the beginning of the 20th century. Glacial periods are shaded in (a). The demarcation between glacial and interglacial periods in (a) is defined by the mean temperature over the whole time period. These temperature changes will be discussed further in Section 3.3.

Question 3.1 Considering the part of Figure 3.3a between 500 ka and the present:

(a)   What is the average temperature change between an interglacial maximum temperature and a glacial minimum temperature?

(b)   How often do glacials (or interglacials) occur?

Details of temperature changes within a glacial and an interglacial are shown in more detail in Figure 3.3b. Between about 12 ka and 8 ka the temperature rises by about 5 °C, but not continuously: there is a temperature drop of about 1.5 °C around 10.5 ka. This 5 °C rise marks the division between the **Holocene**, which covers the period of the present interglacial (from about 10 ka to the present), and all the rest of the Quaternary Ice Age, called the **Pleistocene** (Figure 3.2).

The most accurate reconstruction of past temperatures is from the last 1 000 years or so, when written history provides good proxy data. This type of information was used to deduce the warmer climate in Europe in Medieval times and the colder centuries that followed, called (somewhat confusingly) the 'Little Ice Age' that was mentioned in Chapter 1. Figure 3.3c shows the estimated temperature changes during these times. During the Medieval Climatic Optimum between about 1000 and 1350 AD, western Europe, Iceland and Greenland appear to have been exceptionally warm; vineyards flourished in southern Britain and the Vikings colonized Greenland. However, the warm climate was not world-wide; China was cold at the time, although southern Japan was warm. The global-mean surface temperature increase during the Medieval

Climatic Optimum was quite small, less than 1 °C (Figure 3.3c), although regional temperature increases may have been of a few degrees. The Little Ice Age between about 1400 and 1850 AD was a time of cooler temperatures (Plate 1.1). Mountain glaciers advanced down valleys, icebergs became common off Norway, and the River Thames froze in winter. The climate has become warmer since the end of the Little Ice Age and at least some of this warming is believed to be a natural climatic variation, similar to other Holocene temperature changes, and not caused by human activities.

In the following sections we will examine the factors that cause the climate to change naturally, but before going on, do Activity 3.1 to consolidate your understanding of how the Earth's climate has changed naturally in the past.

Activity 3.1

Review Section 3.1, and write down what you consider to be the two most significant features of the Earth's climate in the past that will need to be explained by the following sections in this chapter.

3.2 Lithospheric plate movements

We start this section with an explanation for why the Earth occasionally switches from its stable warm state into an 'Ice Age mode' for 100 Ma or so. This seems to be related to the position of the continents on the Earth, and the corresponding shape of the ocean basins in between. We know from the theory of **plate tectonics** that the continents have changed their relative positions through geological time. The outer layer of the Earth, the crust and the upper mantle down to about 100 km (the lithosphere), is separated into rigid areas called plates (because they are thin in comparison to their horizontal extent of thousands of kilometres) which are in motion relative to each other. A plate can be destroyed by subduction — sinking into the mantle below another plate. New plates are created at ocean ridges. Continents are parts of plates, and change their relative positions as the plates move. The rate of relative motion between plates is around a few centimetres a year, which seems low, but over geological time is significant (tens of kilometres every million years).

Question 3.2 The continents of North America and Europe are presently around 3 000 km apart. They were once joined, but then split apart, forming the North Atlantic Ocean. How long ago, in Ma, did they do this? Take the rate of relative motion of the North American and Eurasian plates as 2.0 cm yr^{-1}.

Question 3.2 showed that plate tectonic processes involve changes on a time-scale of tens to hundreds of million years. This is the same order of magnitude as the length of Ice Ages.

Although it seems that plate tectonics is the factor that controls whether the Earth is in its warm or Ice Age state, exactly how it does so is more complicated and not totally understood. One requirement for an Ice Age seems to be the positioning of a large continent over one or both of the poles, which can build up a large ice-sheet influencing climate. Today, Antarctica is in the south polar region, and there is an Ice Age. During the Ordovician–Silurian Ice Age there was a very large continent (a 'supercontinent') called Gondwana in the south polar region.

However, although a polar continent seems to be a necessity for an Ice Age, the reverse is not true: there is not always an Ice Age when there is a polar continent, so there must be additional influences, probably plate tectonic, that cause Ice Ages. What these influences are, and how they work, is not clear. One factor is probably the pattern of ocean circulation, which will change as plate tectonics changes the relative positions of the continents.

There are several differences between the surface ocean currents shown on the warm-state Earth 50 Ma ago (Figure 3.4) and those on the present Ice Age Earth (Figure 2.28). First, the Panama seaway between North and South America would have allowed the Equatorial current to flow from the Atlantic into the Pacific instead of into the Gulf Stream, so the Gulf Stream may have been weaker. Second, the Atlantic Ocean basin would have been smaller so the North and South Atlantic gyres may have been slower, and there would have been no extension of the Gulf Stream into a North Atlantic drift. Third, there was likely to have been a greater interchange of surface water between the Atlantic and Mediterranean, as the Strait of Gibraltar (the sea entrance to the Mediterranean) was much wider. Finally, there would have been no seaway between South America and Antarctica and so there would have been no West wind drift.

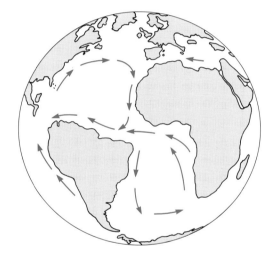

Figure 3.4 Predicted surface currents in the Atlantic Ocean (arrows) 50 Ma ago, based on the continental positions at that time. Note that (i) the Atlantic is narrower than at the present day, (ii) North and South America are not joined, (iii) the Atlantic and Pacific are separated in the South, (iv) the Mediterranean has a greater north–south extent, and (v) Europe is closer to Greenland, than at present.

The initiation of the West wind drift between 50 Ma ago and the present would have prevented warm currents from reaching the Antarctic continent, leading to cooling of the continent. These, and other changes involving the Pacific and Arctic Oceans, may have led to the gradual cooling of the Earth from about 50 Ma ago until it *switched* into the 'Ice Age mode' about 2 Ma ago.

We will now move from considering these very long-term influences on climate to a shorter-term influence; orbital variations.

3.3 Variations in the Earth's orbit

Variations in the amount of solar radiation received by the Earth can affect our climate. There are two different types of variation: one is due to changes in the orbit of the Earth around the Sun, and to changes in the tilt of the Earth, which we will look at in this section, and the other comes from changes to the solar constant, which will be examined in Section 3.4.

3.3.1 The Milankovic–Croll orbital changes

The periodic changes of climate between glacial and interglacial conditions during the Ice Age of the last 2 Ma are thought to be related to the orbital changes of the Earth. This theory was first proposed by the Scottish astronomer James Croll in the 1860s, and developed between 1920 and 1941 by the Yugoslav astronomer Milutin Milankovic. Because of their work, the effect on climate of the Earth's orbital changes is called the **Milankovic–Croll effect** (although if you read about this subject elsewhere you may find it referred to just as the Milankovic effect, ignoring Croll), and the orbital changes are known as Milankovic–Croll orbital changes.

Changes in the Earth's orbit produce seasonal and latitudinal changes in solar radiation reaching the Earth. There are three components causing the changes; eccentricity, tilt and precession.

The *eccentricity* is a measure of the shape of the Earth's orbit around the Sun. The orbit varies because of the gravitational attraction between the Earth and the other planets, which changes as the orbital positions of the planets change. The Earth's orbit varies from nearly circular (a low eccentricity) to more elliptical (a higher eccentricity, Figure 3.5). When the orbit is nearly circular, the Earth receives approximately the same amount of solar radiation each day in the year, but when the eccentricity is higher, the Earth receives more radiation on days when it is closer to the Sun. This intensifies the seasons in one hemisphere and moderates them in the other. The present eccentricity is fairly low (Figure 3.5a) so the difference in seasonality between the hemispheres is low.

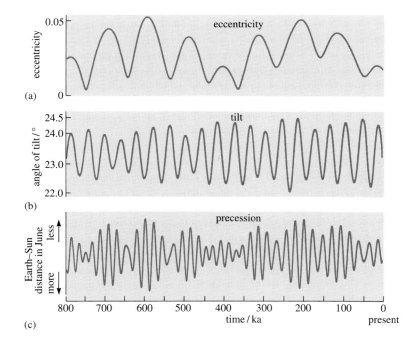

Figure 3.5 Milankovic–Croll orbital changes, based on astronomical data, with past variations in the eccentricity (a), tilt (b) and precession (c) of the Earth from 800 ka to the present. An eccentricity of 0 is a circle: the higher the value, the more elliptical the orbit. (More precisely, eccentricity is the distance between the two foci of the ellipse divided by the major axis.)

The *angle of tilt* of the Earth's axis of rotation (Figure 2.17a) varies between 21.8° and 24.4° (Figure 3.5b). The greater the tilt, the more extreme the seasons in each hemisphere become.

Precession is the change of direction in space of the Earth's axis of rotation. At present the axis points in the direction of the star Polaris, but this was not always the

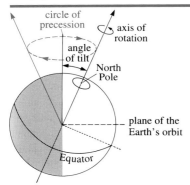

Figure 3.6 Precession is the change in direction in space of the Earth's axis. The axis is in the direction of the star Polaris at present. The centre of the circle of precession is at right-angles to the plane of the Earth's orbit. The present angle of tilt is 23.5°.

Figure 3.7 Solar radiation at the top of the Earth's atmosphere for the latitude 65° N in July from 165 ka to the present. This was calculated using the Milankovic–Croll astronomical values for eccentricity, tilt and precession, as in Figure 3.5.

case, as the axis changes direction, tracing a circle in the sky (Figure 3.6). Precession is *not* linked to the change in the *angle* of tilt: they vary independently. The precession determines the time of year when the distance between the Earth and Sun is a minimum and a maximum, and so affects the seasonality in each hemisphere. At present, the distance is a minimum in the Southern Hemisphere summer and a maximum in the Southern Hemisphere winter, so the Southern Hemisphere has more extreme seasons than the Northern Hemisphere, with slightly warmer summers and colder winters. The effect of precession, measured as the Earth–Sun distance in June, is shown in Figure 3.5c.

The Milankovic–Croll orbital changes can be used to calculate the past changes in radiation at different latitudes, for any time of the year, and for any year. Although the *total* radiation reaching the Earth over any year is about the same, the amount at a particular time of year at high latitudes has varied considerably. Figure 3.7 shows, for example, that the July solar radiation at 65° N about 10 ka ago has been calculated to be higher than at present, sufficient perhaps to melt the great northern ice-sheets and end the last glacial period. Even though the pattern of Milankovic–Croll effects in Figure 3.7 do not match the temperature changes given in Figure 3.3 in detail, it is possible to justify the earlier statement that the Milankovic–Croll orbital changes cause the climate to change. By looking at the data on which Figure 3.3 is based, we can examine the details of the climatic record over many hundreds of thousand years, and can then compare this record with that calculated from the Milankovic–Croll orbital changes.

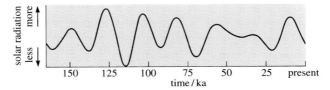

The proxy data used to produce a climate record for the Quaternary have two main sources, from cores of deep-sea sediments and from cores of ice on land in polar regions.

3.3.2 Deep-sea sediment data

Deep-sea sediments include the skeletal remains of plants and animals that have lived in the deep sea. **Micropalaeontology** (the study of preserved fossils of micro-organisms) and analysis of the oxygen isotope content of these remains can be used to provide information about past climates. The technique that uses oxygen isotopes is fairly complicated, and is described in Box 3.2. Read this box, but do not get too tied up with the details.

Box 3.2 Oxygen isotopes and the climatic record

3.2

Oxygen has three stable isotopes with mass numbers 16, 17 and 18. Over 99% of natural oxygen is made up of ^{16}O, with ^{18}O comprising most of the balance. Many marine organisms form their skeletons or shells from calcium carbonate ($CaCO_3$), taking the oxygen in the calcium carbonate from seawater. The ratio of $^{18}O:^{16}O$ in the skeletal remains of organisms preserved in sediments is a measure of the ratio of the oxygen isotopes in the seawater in which the organisms lived.

When seawater evaporates from the ocean, water molecules with the lighter isotope ($H_2^{16}O$) evaporate faster, so atmospheric water vapour is relatively enriched in the lighter isotope. When water vapour condenses and is precipitated back into the ocean, the heavier isotope ($H_2^{18}O$) condenses preferentially. Both processes deplete water vapour in the atmosphere in $H_2^{18}O$ relative to $H_2^{16}O$. When this ^{18}O-depleted water vapour is precipitated as snow in polar regions, then the snow will be depleted in ^{18}O, relative to the oceans, which will be relatively enriched in ^{18}O. The larger the ice-caps, the higher the relative proportion of ^{18}O in seawater.

The fossils in sediment cores used for oxygen isotope analysis are usually single-celled animals called foraminifera, which have calcium carbonate shells. The amount of ^{18}O in their shells is small, but the ratio $^{18}O:^{16}O$ can be measured accurately by mass spectrometry. The result is not given as a simple ratio, but as a delta (δ) value, which incorporates a comparison with a standard sample of seawater (standard seawater would have a $\delta^{18}O$ value of zero). Delta values have units of parts per thousand (‰). Snowfall in polar regions has $\delta^{18}O$ values of −30‰ to −50‰, the negative values indicating depletion of ^{18}O relative to ^{16}O. Marine sediment core $\delta^{18}O$ values, reflecting values in seawater, are usually within the range +4 to −4‰. The higher (or less negative) the $\delta^{18}O$ value from marine cores, the greater the enrichment of ^{18}O in seawater and so the larger the ice-caps on land, and the lower the global-mean surface temperature. The *reverse* is the case for $\delta^{18}O$ values from land ice-cores: lower temperatures produce a depletion of ^{18}O in ice, and therefore lower (more negative) $\delta^{18}O$ values. Lower temperatures produce *higher* $\delta^{18}O$ values in marine *sediment cores* and *lower* $\delta^{18}O$ values in *ice-cores*. Because this can be confusing, all the oxygen isotope records in this chapter are labelled warmer at the top and colder at the bottom.

There are two main complications to the interpretation of the oxygen isotope record. The first is that organisms extract a higher proportion of ^{18}O from cold water than they do from warm water, so the $\delta^{18}O$ values also vary with the water temperature. The second is that the $^{18}O:^{16}O$ ratio varies between different organisms, although the ratio is always higher in cold water. However, the same shape of oxygen isotope record is obtained from different organisms, and in different water temperatures (but with different $\delta^{18}O$ scale values) so the general interpretation that they provide a *relative* measure of the continental ice volume, and therefore of global-mean surface temperatures, is valid. ■

Figure 3.8 is a typical oxygen isotope record for marine sediments. The horizontal scale is given in terms of depth in the core, with the top (depth 0) on the right, representing present-day conditions. Converting this depth scale into a time-scale is done by using **radioactive dating** and **palaeomagnetic techniques** and is one of the major difficulties and sources of inaccuracy in using sediment core data. Figure 3.8 gives the 'best-estimate' ages from these techniques. This time-scale is discontinuous and non-linear — equal lengths of core at different depths do not represent equal periods of time, as sediment accumulation rates can vary with time.

The vertical scale of Figure 3.8 is $\delta^{18}O$, which, as we have seen, can be used as a measure of continental ice volume and therefore temperature. The less negative value near the bottom of the scale, −1‰, indicates a greater ice volume, and colder conditions, and the more negative value of the top of the scale, −2‰, a lower ice volume and warmer conditions. The present day $\delta^{18}O$ value indicates a low ice volume, as we would expect in an interglacial, with similar conditions about 125 ka ago. Between these times the ice volume was larger, indicating a glacial period.

Figure 3.8 An oxygen isotope record for a sediment core from the equatorial Pacific Ocean. Estimated ages for parts of the core are given at the top of the figure in ka. The horizontal axis is linear in terms of depth, but not time, because of differences in rates of sedimentation. On the vertical axis, colder conditions are given by less negative $\delta^{18}O$ values.

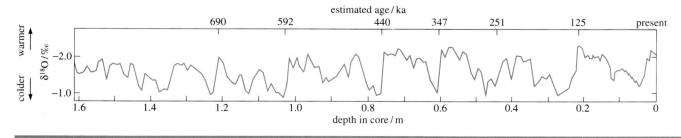

Activity 3.2

(a)   On Figure 3.8, shade in the glacial periods (as was done on Figure 3.3a).

(b)   Does this sediment core indicate the same number of glacial periods back to 400 ka as does Figure 3.3a (Question 3.1b)?

Another useful technique for deducing the climatic record from marine sediment cores is micropalaeontology. Marine organisms live in seawater of particular temperatures and hence react to changing climatic conditions. Figure 3.9a is a record of the abundance of the foraminifer *Globigerina pachyderma* (s) in a marine sediment core. This is a small animal (less than a millimetre in diameter) with a chambered shell (Figure 3.9b) that has a left-hand coil (hence the s, for sinistral, or left, after the species name, to distinguish it from the right-hand coiling version). *G. pachyderma* (s) lives at the present in the Atlantic ocean near Greenland, and is the only species of planktonic foraminifera (those that float or drift in the water) that is found in these cold waters at present. During cold periods in the past this species, together with other planktonic foraminifera, had a much more extensive range, over much of the North Atlantic. In the sediment core of Figure 3.9a, at the latitude of the British Isles, *G. pachyderma* (s) is rare at present, but at times in the past, such as about 20 ka ago, it dominated the micropalaeontological record, forming almost 100% of the planktonic foraminifera in the core. This is interpreted as indicating the presence of cold surface water at this latitude at that time — an indication of nearby glacial conditions.

Figure 3.9 (a) A palaeontological record of the foraminifer *Globigerina pachyderma* (s) as a percentage of the total planktonic foraminifera from a sediment core in the central North Atlantic Ocean at 53°N for the last 330 ka. (Note that the ages here are approximate, estimated using a uniform sedimentation rate.) This foraminifer is more abundant at the present day in colder water, so the record is considered to indicate changing temperatures at this latitude: cold water when there is a high proportion present, and warmer water when it forms a low proportion. (b) *Globigerina pachyderma* (s). (× 190)

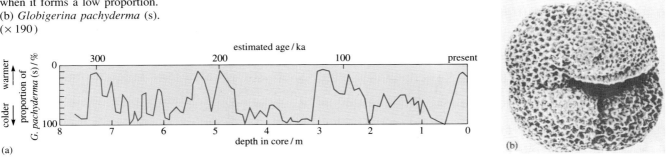

Activity 3.3

Compare the proxy data for the climatic record, from oxygen isotopes (Figure 3.8) and from micropalaeontology (Figure 3.9a). Note the similarities and differences.

3.3.3 Land ice data

The ice-sheets of the Arctic and Antarctic accumulate by precipitation of snow from the atmosphere, preserving the oxygen isotope ratio of the snow in the ice. The isotopic content of polar snow depends primarily on the temperature of formation of the ice crystals in the snow, but also on the isotopic content of the seawater (Box 3.2). Data from marine sediment cores can be used to eliminate the effect of the latter in the ice-core data so that the isotopic composition reflects only local temperature. Figure 3.10 shows the result from an ice-core from the Antarctic. As for marine sediment cores, the horizontal scale is in terms of depth in the core, in this case a very deep core, to over 2000 m. Converting this to a time-scale is as problematic as for marine sediment cores and involves an understanding of ice-flow mechanics, but the best estimate ages of parts of the core are given on the top horizontal scale. Like that of marine sediment cores, this time-scale is non-linear as snow falls and flows at different rates, and deeper parts of the core are more compressed. The vertical scale has much lower (more negative) $\delta^{18}O$ values than marine sediment cores (compare with Figure 3.8), reflecting the much lower temperature on the Antarctic continent ($-55.5\,°C$ at this location at present) than in the oceans (above $-2\,°C$ everywhere). The general pattern of the temperature record determined from the ice-core is similar to the marine sediment cores, with warm interglacials from about 10 ka to the present and 120–140 ka, separated by a longer glacial period. This ice-core is the oldest ice-core that has been drilled at the time of writing (1992), but covers a shorter period than the marine sediment cores, including just one glacial period. This is because of the difficulty of finding an area with older ice that has been essentially undisturbed by ice flow.

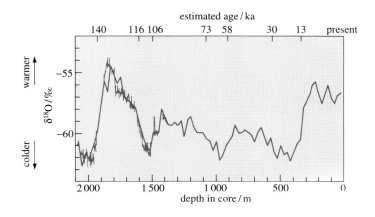

Figure 3.10 An oxygen isotope record for the last 160 ka from an ice-core at Vostock in Antarctica. The thick line gives results from measurements made every 25 m, and from 1 400 m to 2 083 m the thin line gives results from more closely-spaced sampling. Dates for parts of the core are given at the top of the figure. More negative $\delta^{18}O$ values mean colder local temperatures, which are indicators of colder global-mean surface temperatures.

Another isotope that can be used to interpret temperature records in ice-cores is the heavy isotope of hydrogen, ^2H, called deuterium (D). Hydrogen isotopes, in a similar way to oxygen isotopes, are affected by temperature and variations in ice volume, and their distribution in ice-cores is similar (Figure 3.11). The vertical scale in Figure 3.11 is δD, a measure of the ratio of deuterium to hydrogen in comparison with a standard sample of seawater. The highly negative values indicate that the ice is depleted in deuterium relative to seawater. The core was sampled and analysed at

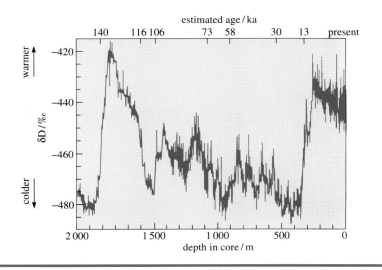

Figure 3.11 A deuterium record for the last 160 ka from the same ice-core at Vostock in Antarctica as Figure 3.10. Dates for parts of the core are given at the top of the figure.

1-metre intervals and provides a very detailed record of temperature changes over the last glacial–interglacial cycle which is in general agreement with the oxygen isotope ice record (Figure 3.10).

We have now looked at four types of proxy data for past climate, and more are available, such as the distribution of pollen species and lake sediment levels. Figure 3.12 compares three temperature records obtained from different types of data plotted with time as the horizontal scale for the last glacial–interglacial cycle. Record (a) shows a temperature rise of about 10 °C associated with deglaciation (the change from a glacial to an interglacial) in the Antarctic. Record (b) shows a summer temperature rise of about 6 °C in the sub-polar Indian Ocean associated with deglaciation. Record (c) represents the change in global continental ice volume, which is related to warmer or colder conditions (but not to specific temperatures).

All three records have similar major features — the two interglacials from 10 ka to present and around 125 ka, and the glacial in between — and have the same rapid rises at the end of a glaciation and slower fall at the end of an interglacial. Some of the minor maxima within the glacial also match, such as at around 80 ka and 100 ka. The differences in the curves are that the time of the temperature rise at the beginning

Figure 3.12 A comparison of temperatures for the last 160 ka estimated by different methods. (a) The deuterium record from Vostock, Antarctica. This uses the same data as Figure 3.11, with δD values converted to best estimates of temperature above (positive) and below (negative) the present average temperature at Vostock (−55.5 °C, the dashed line). (b) The summer sea-surface temperature record from oxygen isotope studies of a marine sediment core in the subpolar Indian Ocean, obtained by adjusting δ18O values for ice volume changes. (c) Oxygen isotope record, created by combining data from marine sediment cores from a range of locations, representing changes in continental ice volume and thus warmer or colder conditions. The horizontal scale has been converted to give time linearly, rather than depth as in Figures 3.8, 3.10 and 3.11. The vertical scales of (a) and (b) have been converted to temperature. The vertical scale of (c) is deviations in δ18O, as it cannot be interpreted in terms of specific temperatures.

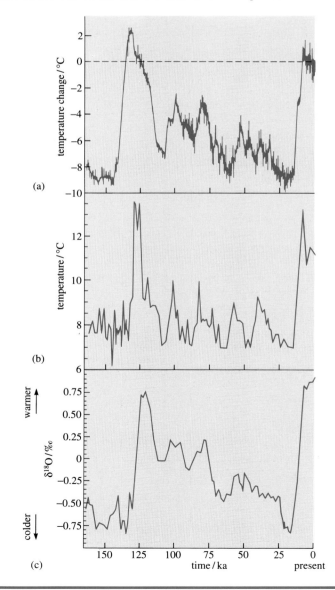

of the last complete interglacial over Antarctica (140 ka) precedes that given by ocean water (130 ka), and the ice volume decrease (125–130 ka). However, in general there is a reasonable agreement between these proxy data sets, which gives us confidence that the climatic record they represent is probably realistic.

3.3.4 A comparison of the climatic record and Milankovic–Croll orbital changes

Now we have a detailed climatic record of the glacials and interglacials in the Quaternary Ice Age (Figures 3.8–3.12) with which to compare the Milankovic–Croll orbital changes (Figures 3.5 and 3.7), using the technique of **spectral analysis**, described in Box 3.3.

Box 3.3   Spectral analysis

The records in Figures 3.3, 3.5 and 3.12 show variations in parameters with time, and are called (in mathematical terminology) **time series**. In these time series we have tried to interpret how often the pattern repeats — the **period** of the curve (e.g. Question 3.1). For a simple wave, period is easy to interpret; for example, in Figure 3.13a the period is 20 ka (the time between the peaks, or troughs of the wave). For slightly more complicated curves, however, such as the Milankovic–Croll changes in Figure 3.5, it is not so easy. It is possible to estimate roughly the main period in the tilt parameter in Figure 3.5b, about 40 ka, but some of the peaks and troughs are bigger than the others; does this mean that there is another cycle producing the bigger peaks? The period of the eccentricity is harder to determine; although the main peak repeats about every 100 ka, the larger peaks and troughs also repeat about every 400 ka. The precession period is even harder to determine; the main period is about 20 ka but there must be at least one other period present. Trying to interpret periods from the climatic record of Figure 3.12 is even more difficult: a peak about every 100 ka? How about the rest of the pattern?

However, a time series can be analysed mathematically to determine what periodicity, if any, is present. It is a complex process, but one

which can be done routinely by a computer (the details of how it is done are not necessary here). The periodicity of a wave with a single period, such as in Figure 3.13a, would be represented by Figure 3.13b. The single line indicates that there is only one period present in the wave.

A graph such as Figure 3.13b is called a **frequency spectrum** and the mathematical process of producing frequency spectra from time series is called **spectral analysis**. Frequency is the reciprocal of period:

$$\text{frequency} = \frac{1}{\text{period}}$$

so for the time series in Figure 3.13, the frequency is 1/20 ka = 0.05 cycles ka^{-1}. You may be more familiar with the unit Hz (Hertz) for frequency, which is 1 cycle s^{-1}, but for climatic change this unit is less appropriate, as changes occur much more slowly. The horizontal axis of frequency spectra is usually represented in terms of frequency, not period (hence the name) but period is usually added to this axis for climatic change as it is a more useful measure than frequency. If the frequency scale is linear, the period scale will not be because of the inverse relationship given above. ■

Figure 3.13 (a) A periodic time series. (b) A frequency spectrum of the time series in (a). The horizontal scale is linear for frequency but not period, and longer periods are towards the left.

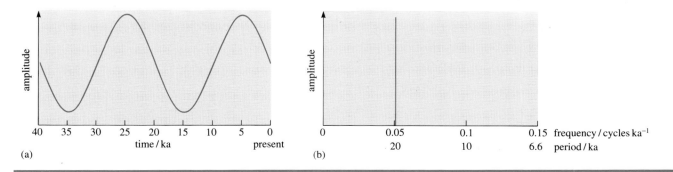

(a)

(b)

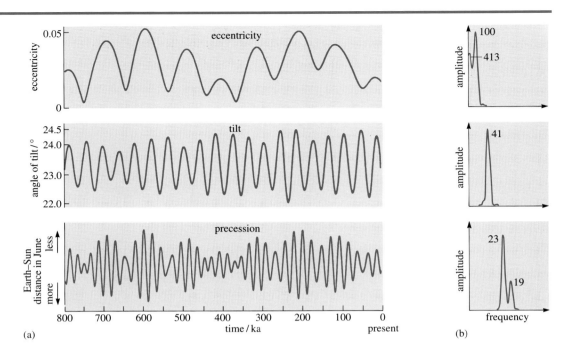

(a)

(b)

Figure 3.14 Milankovic–Croll orbital changes. (a) This is a repeat of Figure 3.5. (b) Frequency spectra for (a). The numbers next to the peaks are periods in ka. Longer periods are towards the left.

Figure 3.14b shows the frequency spectra for the Milankovic–Croll changes from Figure 3.5 (repeated as Figure 3.14a). Unlike in Figure 3.13, none of the spectra show a single line, indicating just one period, but instead the line has broadened into one or more peaks, showing that although there are one or more main periods there are also periods of lesser amplitude with values just above and below the main periods. This is the reason that even the graph of the tilt, which seems to produce the most regular effect, has peaks and troughs with different amplitudes; although 41 ka is the dominant tilt period, the time series is modified by other periods close to 41 ka.

The eccentricity has two peaks in its frequency spectrum, one at 100 ka, which is the obvious one, but also a lesser one at 413 ka.

▷   Can you see any evidence for this 413-ka period in the eccentricity curve in Figure 3.14a?

▶   The largest peaks, and the lowest troughs, repeat about every 400 ka.

The precession also has two peaks, the main one at 23 ka and a lesser one at 19 ka.

Now we can compare these periods in the Milankovic–Croll orbital changes with periods in the climatic record. Figure 3.15 is a frequency spectrum for marine oxygen isotope data from the Indian Ocean. This is more complicated than the spectra for the individual Milankovic–Croll changes (Figure 3.14b), but a number of distinct peaks, corresponding to dominant periods, can be distinguished.

▷   What are the four main periods shown on Figure 3.15, and how do these compare with the Milankovic–Croll periods?

▶   The four main periods on Figure 3.15 are 100 ka, 43 ka, 24 ka and 19 ka. The four shorter Milankovic–Croll periods seem to be present, although for two of them the periods differ slightly; 43 ka instead of 41 ka and 24 ka instead of 23 ka. The 413 ka Milankovic–Croll period is absent, but a record of only 500 ka would not be expected to show a period as long as 413 ka. As well as the four main peaks there are other, lower amplitude peaks in the data, at shorter periods from about 12 to 5 ka, which do not relate to Milankovic–Croll periods.

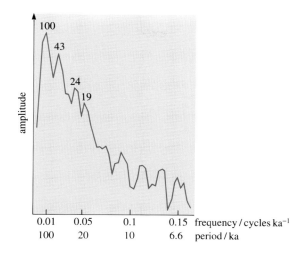

Figure 3.15 A frequency spectrum of the climatic record for the past 500 ka, from oxygen isotope data of two Indian Ocean sediment cores, including data from Figure 3.12b. The numbers against the peaks are the periods in ka.

Figure 3.16 is the frequency spectrum of the Vostock deuterium isotope data. Here the spectrum is clearer than that of the marine sediment data. There are three main peaks at 107.5 ka, 45.7 ka and 25.3 ka. These correspond approximately with the 100 ka, 41 ka and 23 ka Milankovic–Croll periods, although there is no corresponding 19 ka period present. The dominant period here is the one near 41 ka, whereas in the marine sediment data the 100 ka period was dominant. This could be caused by the age of the Vostock core, up to only 160 ka, whereas the marine sediment core was up to 500 ka, sufficient for five 100 ka cycles to be represented instead of just over one in the 160 ka ice-core.

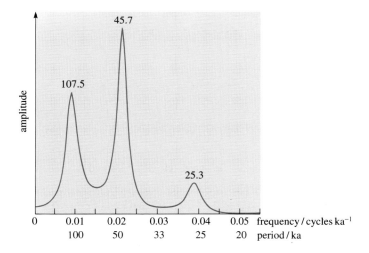

Figure 3.16 A frequency spectrum of the climatic record over the past 160 ka from deuterium isotope data from the Vostock ice-core (Figure 3.11). The numbers against the peaks are the periods in ka.

Spectral analysis provides convincing evidence that the Milankovic–Croll orbital changes are the driving force for glacial and interglacial cycles, in particular for the 100-ka cycle of glaciation and deglaciation. Unfortunately, however, that is not the end of the matter. Although the orbital changes are driving the timing of climatic changes, the changes in solar radiation caused by the orbital changes are not large enough in themselves to cause the *size* of temperature changes deduced from the proxy data. There must be one or more other factors acting in addition to the

Milankovic–Croll effects. However, as the timing of climatic change is set by the orbital changes, the Milankovic–Croll climatic effects must be setting the timing of the other factors, so that the other factors are *amplifying* the Milankovic–Croll effects. Amplification is a **feedback process**, which is discussed in Box 3.4.

Box 3.4   *Feedback processes*

A feedback process is one that acts to produce further change in response to a change in a system. Feedback can be positive or negative; **positive feedback** *amplifies* (increases) change to the system, and **negative feedback** acts to *counter* (reduce) change to the system.

For example, water vapour provides positive feedback for temperature changes. As tem-

perature increases, more water evaporates, increasing the concentration of water vapour in the atmosphere. Water vapour is a greenhouse gas, so the temperature rises further, causing more water to evaporate and so on. (In everyday terms, positive feedback is a vicious circle.) Figure 3.17a shows this process, and Figure 3.17b shows a generalized positive feedback loop. ■

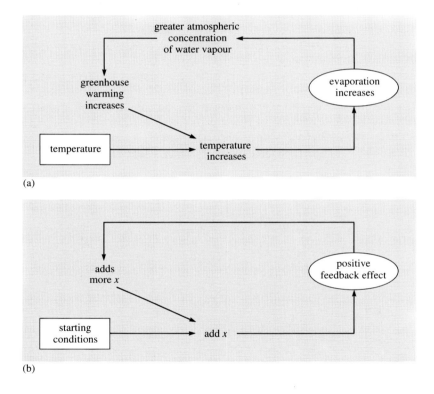

Figure 3.17 (a) The positive feedback of water vapour in the greenhouse effect. (b) A generalized positive feedback loop.

There are a number of possible factors that could act to amplify the Milankovic–Croll effects, and some of them will be introduced here, but detailed examination will be left to later sections of this chapter or later chapters.

One feedback factor is caused by the growth of ice-sheets.

▷ Is the albedo of ice high or low?

▶ High, 80–90% (Table 2.2).

When the Earth cools due to orbital changes, ice-sheets increase in size, reflecting more of the solar radiation and reducing the absorption of solar radiation by the Earth, increasing the cooling effect.

▷   Is this positive or negative feedback?

▶   Positive feedback.

Another feedback factor is the atmospheric concentration of carbon dioxide. If a rise in temperature caused by orbital changes causes the concentration of carbon dioxide in the atmosphere to increase, the greenhouse effect increases, producing a further temperature rise. This is an extremely important positive feedback — some estimates have given it a greater effect on climatic change than orbital effects. We will look at the evidence for past changes in the concentration of atmospheric carbon dioxide in Section 3.6.

A major change in the oceanic circulation system could be another feedback factor. At the present time, ocean currents transport heat into the North Atlantic Ocean, warming this area (Sections 2.3.1 and 2.3.3). If falling temperatures cause this conveyor belt of heat to the North Atlantic to shut down, this would cool this area even further, perhaps leading to glaciation in the North Polar region. There is evidence that this may have occurred in the past and we will examine this in Chapter 7.

The Milankovic–Croll orbital changes can be calculated not only for the past but also for the future. We can use these values, with the best estimates of amplification by the feedback processes, to predict future climatic change due to natural processes. Figure 3.18 shows a prediction in terms of continental ice volume. The peak of the last interglacial was 120 ka ago, and the glacial minimum (the ice maximum) was 20 ka ago. At present we are near the Holocene interglacial maximum (and ice minimum) with the temperature set to decrease to a minor minimum in about 20 ka time and full glacial conditions by 60 ka in the future. These changes in climate are natural ones, and this prediction ignores anthropogenic changes, which could alter our climatic pattern significantly.

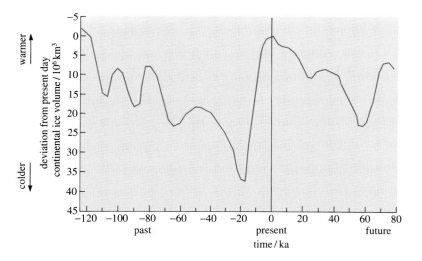

Figure 3.18 Continental ice volume variations over the last 125 ka and predictions for the next 80 ka, based on the Milankovic–Croll effects and feedback factors. The volume of the present-day continental ice is the baseline zero, with positive values indicating more ice and colder conditions. The prediction is for the Northern Hemisphere ice-sheets only.

3.4 Variations in the solar constant

In Section 2.2.1 we introduced the *solar constant* (or solar irradiance), which is the energy flux from the Sun at the top of the atmosphere, incident at right angles to the Sun's rays, and we gave it a value of approximately $1\,370\,\mathrm{W\,m^{-2}}$. Because it is called a *constant* it might be expected to have an unchanging value, but this is not the case;

the radiation output from the Sun does vary slightly on a wide range of time-scales, from days to millions of years, so the solar constant also varies.

On a very long time-scale, the solar constant is thought to have increased from an initial level of about 70% of its current value 4 600 Ma ago (the age of the Sun and of the Earth) to the present-day value. There is no direct evidence for this (obviously), but this change is a consequence of stellar evolutionary theory. The theory is too complex to examine here, but the increase in solar output relates to the increase in the average mass number of the Sun with time as nuclear fusion has changed more of the hydrogen in the Sun to helium.

This increase from 70% to 100% is an enormous change, and could be expected to show up in the climatic record. However, proxy data do not support this long-term increase in solar output. A 'faint' Sun, with only 70% of its present output, would result in a frozen Earth, so the early history of the Earth, in the Precambrian, should have been a massive and lengthy Ice Age. Set against this reasoning, geological evidence suggests that the early Earth was generally *warmer* than today (Figure 3.2). This phenomenon, with solar physicists predicting a faint early Sun and a frozen Earth, but geologists having proxy data indicating a warm Earth, is known as the 'faint Sun paradox'. A possible explanation of this conflict involves the composition of the early Earth atmosphere, which will be examined in Section 3.6.

Beyond the long, slow evolution of the Sun, there is direct observational evidence for shorter-term variations in solar irradiance — but only for the most recent past. Ongoing measurements of the solar constant (by satellite-borne instruments) have been made since 1978 (see Figure 3.19).

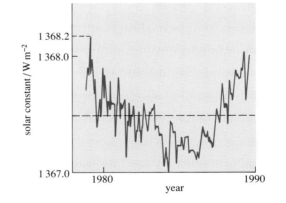

Figure 3.19   The solar irradiance at Earth (i.e. the solar constant) over the period 1978–1989, as measured by satellite-borne instruments. The horizontal broken line is the average value over this period (1 367.5 W m^{-2}).

Question 3.3   According to Figure 3.19, what is the percentage change in the solar constant over the period shown (i.e. the *difference* between the maximum and minimum values as a percentage of the average value of the solar constant)?

This pattern of change in the solar constant follows a long-known 11-year cycle of **sunspot numbers** — the maximum output over the period in Figure 3.19 (in 1979) being associated with high sunspot numbers. Since sunspots are darker and *cooler* areas of the Sun — with a lower than average radiation output — this would seem to be the reverse of what might be expected. The explanation lies in a simultaneous increase in *bright* areas, called **faculae**. Like sunspots, faculae are associated with activity in the Sun's outer layer. It has been found that the increased irradiance due to faculae more than offsets the decreases due to the cooler sunspots: consequently, *high sunspot numbers are associated with high solar output.*

The fluctuations in solar irradiance linked to the 11-year sunspot cycle are thought to have relatively little effect on the Earth's climate. Not only are the changes involved quite small (less than 1% of the total solar constant), they are also too short-term to influence the more 'slowly-responding' parts of the climate system — such as ice sheets or mountain glaciers, for example (or even the oceans, more on which in Chapters 5 and 6). However, there has been much speculation and debate about the influence on climate of possible *larger* and *longer-term* (a century or so) — variations in the solar constant. Given the shortness of the satellite record, there is no *direct* observational evidence for such changes. On the contrary, the existing evidence is *indirect*, based on the *hypothesis* that century time-scale fluctuations in solar irradiance are responsible for a characteristic feature of the palaeoclimatic record for the present interglacial (i.e. the Holocene) — specifically, the 'wiggles' in global-mean surface temperature just evident in Figure 3.3b.

The main evidence for these *global-scale* temperature fluctuations (they are clearer in the 'expanded' section in Figure 3.3c) comes from data that record the periodic advance and retreat of mountain glaciers around the world. Direct observational evidence over the past 150 or so years indicates that the ebb and flow of such glaciers reflects trends in annual-mean temperature. Thus, records of glacier advance and retreat in *the past* — combined on a regional, then hemispheric, and finally global basis — can be cautiously interpreted as a proxy for changes in global-mean surface temperature.

The reconstructions of climatic conditions during the Holocene in Figure 3.3 (parts b and c) were assembled in this way — the temperature scale being based on correlations between glacier data and *direct* temperature records over the past century or so. The 'wiggles' referred to above mark the recurrence during the Holocene of relatively cold periods (with glaciers advancing) — more or less global in extent, and sometimes lasting for centuries — interspersed by longer warmer intervals (with glaciers retreating). This overall picture of the Holocene can be represented as shown in the top half of Figure 3.20 (ignore the bottom half for now) — the most recent of the cold periods depicted there being the Little Ice Age mentioned in Chapter 1 and Section 3.1.

The global-scale cooling associated with the series of 'Little Ice Age' type events shown in Figure 3.20 appears to have averaged some 0.4–0.6 °C. Several possible explanations have been put forward: the suggested link with *century* time-scale reductions in solar irradiance is just one of these. Here, the chain of reasoning starts with indisputable evidence that some characteristics of the Sun's behaviour *have* varied on this century time-scale during the Holocene. Specifically, there have been prolonged fluctuations in solar *magnetic* activity throughout this period. These fluctuations are known to leave a characteristic 'trace' on Earth: they are responsible for marked changes in the **radiocarbon** (i.e. ^{14}C) content of the atmosphere. And such changes, or '**^{14}C anomalies**', can be detected. That story is explained briefly in Box 3.5: give this a quick read through now.

Figure 3.20 Schematic representation of major changes evident in the climatic record (top) and ^{14}C anomaly record (bottom) during the Holocene. The upper half depicts the timing and duration of cold periods like the Little Ice Age (the rectangles). The lower half indicates (as triangles) maxima in the ^{14}C anomaly record.

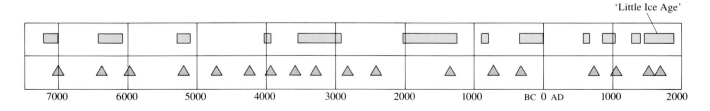

Box 3.5 ^{14}C anomalies

'Radiocarbon' (^{14}C) is a radioactive isotope of carbon. It is generated through the interaction of incoming cosmic radiation (mostly high-energy protons) with the upper atmosphere. This produces showers of secondary radiation — including neutrons ($^{1}_{0}n$) — in the upper atmosphere. Most of the neutrons collide with atmospheric nitrogen atoms and are captured by the nitrogen nucleus to produce ^{14}C (and a proton $^{1}_{1}H$):

$$^{1}_{0}n + ^{14}_{7}N \rightarrow ^{14}_{6}C + ^{1}_{1}H$$

Once formed, ^{14}C atoms are rapidly oxidized to $^{14}CO_2$ and mixed up with the rest of the CO_2 in the atmosphere — the bulk of which contains the more abundant 'normal' isotope of carbon (^{12}C). Thereby, ^{14}C is 'fed' into all the pathways that continually cycle the global inventory of carbon through various 'reservoirs': more on that global 'carbon cycle' in Chapter 4. Suffice it to say here that plants take up ^{14}C (along with ^{12}C) from the atmosphere during photosynthesis, and thus assimilate it into their tissues.

Through a continual exchange of 'new' CO_2 with the atmosphere (as old cells die and are replaced), the '^{14}C content' (i.e. ^{14}C as a fraction of total carbon) of *living* plant tissue is the same as that in the atmosphere. But the exchange and replacement of ^{14}C from the atmosphere stops when the plant dies. From then on, its ^{14}C content begins to fall off as the ^{14}C decays to nitrogen, with the release of a β-particle (an electron, $^{0}_{-1}e$):

$$^{14}_{6}C \rightarrow ^{14}_{7}N + ^{0}_{-1}e$$

In short, the death of a plant (or indeed any organism) activates a 'clock': henceforth, its ^{14}C content is purely a function of time.

The 'pace' of this clock is precise — governed by the half-life of ^{14}C (5 700 years). That is the basic principle behind *radiocarbon dating* — one of the most useful techniques for dating samples of recently fossilized plant material. Put simply, the age of such material can be calculated by comparing its ^{14}C content with that in the present atmosphere.

A fundamental assumption behind radiocarbon dating is that the proportion of ^{14}C in the atmosphere has been essentially constant throughout the period useful for dating (limited by the half-life of ^{14}C). If that assumption is invalid — if the ^{14}C content of the atmosphere was in fact higher (or lower) than average when the plant was alive — this produces an error in the radiocarbon date.

Turning that argument on its head, such errors can be a useful *indicator* of fluctuations in atmospheric ^{14}C, if there is also another, independent, way of dating the fossil plant material. Fortunately, there is such a technique — for much of the Holocene, at least. *Dendrochronology* gives an age based on counting the number of annual growth rings in trees (whether living or fossil). The difference between the radiocarbon and dendrochronological dates of tree-ring samples is called the **^{14}C anomaly**.

The link between anomalous levels of atmospheric radiocarbon and the Sun is through the process that generates ^{14}C. *Reduced solar magnetic activity allows an increase in the intensity of cosmic radiation incident on the Earth's upper atmosphere, thus increasing the production of radiocarbon, and so increasing the overall ^{14}C content. And vice versa.* ■

Limited mainly by the preservation of suitable fossil trees, the ^{14}C anomaly record stretches back nearly 9 000 years. Close scrutiny of that record reveals a number of '^{14}C maxima' — periods (usually lasting 100–200 years) when the ^{14}C content of the atmosphere was significantly *enhanced* (implying reduced magnetic activity on the Sun — Box 3.5). That much is clear. But were the fluctuations in solar magnetic activity that were responsible for these ^{14}C maxima accompanied by parallel changes in solar *irradiance*? Here, the evidence for a link is more circumstantial. It draws on the close correspondence (in time) between the three most recent ^{14}C maxima and three *prolonged* periods of abnormally *low* sunspot activity during the past 1 000 years. Known as '**sunspot minima**', all three are well-documented in historical records.

▷   How does this add weight to the hypothesis implicit in our question?

▶   The satellite data referred to earlier confirm that solar irradiance does vary in step with sunspot activity — or at least, it does over the 11-year sunspot cycle.

On that basis, sunspot minima — and hence ^{14}C maxima — may well represent prolonged periods of *reduced* solar irradiance. If so — *and if such changes were indeed responsible for the recurrent cool periods during the Holocene* — then there should be some correspondence between the timing of these climatic events and the maxima in the ^{14}C anomaly record. Depicted in visual form, the required comparison is that between the upper and lower halves of Figure 3.20. By eye, the correspondence is not overly compelling! Following a more detailed analysis, the authors of the study behind Figure 3.20 were themselves somewhat equivocal — concluding that the correlation between the two records was 'statistically significant', but not fully convincing.

Further — and this is an important general point — the existence of a correlation does not, by itself, *prove* cause-and-effect. As noted earlier, there are alternative explanations for the Little Ice Age (and the earlier cold periods in Figure 3.20) — one of which is touched on in Section 3.5. And there are other caveats as well. For example, there exists a physically-based model of the mechanism responsible for changes in solar irradiance during the 11-year sunspot cycle. Applied to the well-documented level of sunspot activity during the most recent sunspot minimum (the 'Maunder Minimum', 1645–1715), the estimated change in solar irradiance is a 70-year-long reduction of some 0.14%. Studies with climate models (more on which in Chapters 5 and 6) suggest that such a drop would be neither large enough, nor long enough to explain the observed cooling during the last Little Ice Age.

To sum up: the evidence for a *causal* link between century time-scale solar variability (manifest as ^{14}C anomalies) and global-scale fluctuations in climate during the Holocene is, at best, 'highly suggestive'. *Assuming* the reality of such a link implies that significant, and prolonged, reductions in solar irradiance occur in parallel with the solar changes responsible for ^{14}C maxima. Where records exist, the latter are roughly contemporaneous with long periods of reduced sunspot activity — yet according to current theory, the associated drop in solar irradiance is too small to explain the observed global cooling.

This brief resumé exemplifies well an important general point. Putting together a *record* of the Earth's climatic history is itself a difficult and uncertain business. *Interpreting* that record, i.e. identifying the factors responsible for changes on a variety of different time-scales, can be even more problematic. On a more specific note, remember that we are living *in* the Holocene — a period apparently characterized by significant (0.4–0.6 °C) century time-scale fluctuations in global-mean surface temperature. Whatever the *natural* forces actually behind that pattern of change — and long-term variations in solar irradiance remain one of the more plausible candidates — *they are doubtless still at work*. The full implications of this remark will become apparent in Chapter 6, when we grapple with the tricky problem of interpreting the Earth's more immediate climatic past — the observed global warming over the last century or so (referred to in Figure 1.2). For now, we turn to one of the most dramatic — if short-term — natural influences on climate.

3.5 Volcanic activity

Volcanic eruptions can have devastating effects: explosive eruptions of ash and lava, ashfalls, lava flows, mudflows and flooding. One of the best known eruptions in recent years was that of Mount St Helens in Washington State, USA, which started

Figure 3.21 The explosive eruption of Mount St Helens in May 1980 sent a cloud of dust into the stratosphere.

with an explosion on 18 May 1980 that devastated the surrounding area, sent a cloud of dust as high as the stratosphere (Figure 3.21) and triggered a huge avalanche and mudflow, causing the deaths of 57 people. Apart from local cooling the next day for areas within or under the ash cloud, there were no significant climatic effects from the eruption. However, some volcanic eruptions have had not just a local effect on climate, but also regional or global effects. To have a climatic effect, a volcano must inject large amounts of material to stratospheric heights.

There are two principal types of particle injected into the stratosphere by volcanoes that can have an effect on climate. The first type is particles of silicate dust (volcanic ash), derived from cooling of molten rock to solid rock and its fragmentation in an explosion. The second type is aerosols (tiny droplets of liquid) of sulphuric acid. These **sulphate aerosols** are produced from sulphur dioxide, one of the volcanic gases released during an eruption. Water vapour is the most abundant volcanic gas, followed by carbon dioxide, nitrogen and sulphur dioxide. The first three volcanic gases have no measurable effect on climate, as although water vapour and carbon dioxide are greenhouse gases, the amount produced during even the largest volcanic eruption is minute in comparison with the amounts already in the atmosphere. The sulphur dioxide is converted to small aerosol droplets of sulphuric acid. Most of the volcanic ash falls out of the stratosphere within a few months, but the aerosol droplets may remain in the stratosphere for several years.

Stratospheric dust and aerosols affect the global energy budget in two ways. The most important effect is by back-scattering, reflecting back incoming solar radiation to space, increasing the Earth's overall albedo (Figure 2.14). A smaller effect is the absorption of radiation by the dust and aerosols which results in warming of the stratosphere. Both effects cause a cooling of the Earth's surface.

Aerosols have a much greater effect than dust because of their longer residence time in the stratosphere. This means that the climatic effect of a volcanic eruption depends mainly on the amount of sulphur dioxide it injects into the stratosphere, which is not necessarily related to the violence of the eruption or the amount of ash or lava it produces. This appears to be the reason for the absence of observable climatic effects from many major volcanic eruptions: the eruptions produced relatively small amounts of stratospheric sulphur dioxide.

One eruption that did produce a lot of sulphur dioxide and caused a significant climatic change was that of the Indonesian volcano Tambora, in 1815. This is the largest volcanic eruption in historically recent times. The eruption is not generally well known, but its effect on climate is well documented.

Tambora is believed to have erupted over $150 \, km^3$ of ash, producing columns of ash and gas that reached heights of 43 km, far into the stratosphere. The volcanic cloud quickly travelled around the world at tropical latitudes, and its effect extended to higher latitudes, with the following year, 1816, being documented as the 'year without a summer'.

> *The bright sun was extinguish'd, and the stars*
> *Did wander darkling in the eternal space,*
> *Rayless, and pathless, and the icy earth*
> *Swung blind and blackening in the moonless air;*
> *Morn came and went — and came, and brought no day,*
> *And men forgot their passions in the dread*
> *Of this their desolation*
>
> *(Lord Byron, 1816, Darkness)*

Studies of weather records show significant decreases in regional temperature, by as much as 6 °C in North America (Figure 3.22), with reports of a dry fog, or dim sun. This haze must have been located in the stratosphere, as surface winds or rain did not disperse it. Europe was also cooler, leading to crop failures and famine, with summer temperatures in central England about 1.5 °C cooler in 1816 than in 1815. The low temperatures lasted for about 2 years (Figure 3.22). The estimated average decrease in temperature throughout the Northern Hemisphere was 0.5 °C.

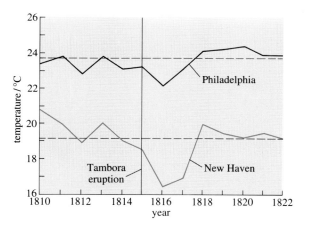

Figure 3.22 Climatic response in the United States to the 1815 eruption of the volcano Tambora. The upper curve is the average summer temperature for Philadelphia, Pennsylvania (40° N); the dashed horizontal line is the 224-yr average at Philadelphia. The lower curve is the average June temperature for New Haven, Connecticut (41° 15′N); the dashed horizontal line is the 145-yr average at New Haven.

The climatic effects from volcanic eruptions before Tambora's time are not so well documented, and rely on proxy data, which are not as precise, hence the absence of a value for the temperature decrease for the two oldest and largest eruptions in Table 3.1 (*overleaf*). Proxy data include tree ring widths, frost damage rings in trees, changes in treelines, and acidity anomalies in ice-cores.

Ice-cores can be used to detect historic and pre-historic eruptions by measurement of the sulphate concentration in the ice. The sulphur dioxide or sulphate aerosol from an eruption is gradually precipitated out of the atmosphere, and is preserved in glacial

Table 3.1 Estimates of the amounts of stratospheric aerosols (millions of tonnes, Mt) and Northern Hemisphere average temperature decreases (ΔT) produced by some major volcanic eruptions. (The volcanoes that are in the Southern Hemisphere produce greater temperature decreases in the Southern Hemisphere, but there are no good estimates of these.)

Volcano	Latitude	Yr	Stratospheric aerosols / Mt	Northern Hemisphere ΔT / °C
St Helens, USA	46° N	1980	0.3	<0.1
Agung, Indonesia	8° S	1963	10–50	0.3
El Chichón, Mexico	17° N	1982	20	0.2
Pinatubo, Philippines	15° N	1991	20–30	0.5
Krakatau, Indonesia	6° S	1883	50–93	0.3
Tambora, Indonesia	8° S	1815	200–300	0.5
Rabaul, New Guinea	4° S	536	300	large?
Toba, Indonesia	3° N	75 000 BP	1 000?	large?

ice. Analysis of an ice-core can detect this volcanic sulphate. Figure 3.23a is an ice-core record spanning the time of the Tambora eruption, and the high sulphate value corresponding to the eruption is very clear. Extending the record to greater depths identifies earlier eruptions, such as that in Figure 3.23b, a very distinctive sulphate value thought to be caused by the volcanic eruptions of Laki in Iceland in 1783. The size of the sulphate value is a measure of the amount of aerosol produced by the eruption, and so is also an indication of the temperature decrease.

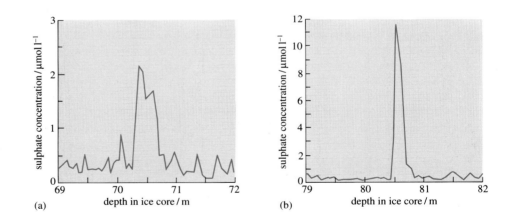

Figure 3.23 Sulphate concentrations in an ice-core from Greenland relative to the core depth. (a) includes the Tambora eruption in 1815, and (b) includes the year 1783. Each 1 m of core in (a) and (b) corresponds to about 3 years. The sulphate concentration is corrected for the amount present due to sea salt.

Ice-core data extend our knowledge of volcanic eruptions back in time by producing estimates of stratospheric aerosols such as that for the two oldest eruptions in Table 3.1. The eruption of Rabaul was a Tambora-size great eruption, whereas the Toba eruption at 75 ka seems to have been even larger.

▷ From Table 3.1, is the estimated decrease in temperature related to the estimated amount of stratospheric aerosols generated by the eruption?

▶ Generally yes: Mount St. Helens, with a low aerosol production, produced a temperature decrease of less than 0.1 °C (that is an insignificant temperature decrease, within the inter-annual variability); Tambora, with a large aerosol production, produced a 0.5 °C decrease, and the three volcanoes with moderate aerosol production gave decreases of between 0.3 °C and 0.5 °C. However, there is not a linear relationship; Agung produced the same temperature decrease as Krakatau, but had only around one-fifth of Krakatau's aerosol production, and Pinatubo produced the same temperature decrease as Tambora, despite an aerosol production of only about one-tenth that of Tambora.

So a major volcanic eruption can have a significant impact on climate, but only on a short time-scale — a few years. Eruptions of the size of Tambora are rare, occurring only once every thousand years or so, with most eruptions being much smaller (Table 3.1). Even the Krakatau eruption was about five times smaller than Tambora, and Mount St Helens more than a hundred times smaller.

Putting all the direct and proxy data together, a number of tentative conclusions can be reached about volcanic eruptions and their effects on climate:

o   A moderate, once-a-decade size eruption (an Agung or El Chichón) may give a measurable hemispheric temperature decrease of 0.2–0.3 °C;

o   A large, once-a-century size eruption (a Pinatubo), may produce a slightly larger temperature decrease of about 0.5 °C;

o   A great, once-a-millenium size eruption (a Tambora or a Raboul), may produce a temperature decrease of up to 1 °C;

o   Climatic effects from volcanic eruptions last for up to 1–3 years;

o   Regional climatic changes are much more extreme than average global changes, especially in higher latitudes.

Investigations of the climatic and volcanic record have also been made to see whether great eruptions, or groups of smaller eruptions, have produced longer-term effects on climate. Some historic cool intervals in the Holocene, such as the Little Ice Age, correspond to periods of enhanced ice-core sulphate values, so there may be a link between volcanism and climatic change on the decade to century time-scale. However, the global cooling produced by volcanic activity seems insufficient to cause the recorded cooling on this time-scale so this link is unproven.

3.6 Atmospheric composition

Changes in the proportion of greenhouse gases in the atmosphere are one of the fundamental factors that influence climate. For anthropogenic changes this is the heart of the debate about global warming. However, there is evidence that the composition of the atmosphere has also changed in the past *without human intervention* — and on a variety of different time-scales. The focus here will be on such changes in the carbon dioxide content of the atmosphere, and the link with climate.

The Earth's atmosphere mainly originated from gas brought to the surface from the Earth's interior by volcanic activity. Volcanoes have continued to contribute gases to the atmosphere through time.

▷   What are the two main volcanic gases?

▶   Water vapour and carbon dioxide (Section 3.5).

The early atmosphere is therefore believed to have consisted mainly of these two gases, both of which are greenhouse gases, with a carbon dioxide concentration much higher than that of today. Given that, we might expect that the early Earth had a far higher surface temperature than at present. However, geological evidence suggests that although the early Earth may have been slightly hotter than now, the global-mean surface temperature, currently about 15 °C, has not varied outside the range 7–27 °C throughout the Earth's history.

So why did the higher carbon dioxide concentration in the early atmosphere not lead to much higher temperatures? There was some information in Section 3.4 that provides a possible answer — the 'faint Sun paradox'. The initial solar output is believed to have been only about 70% of the present-day level, which reduced the effective radiating temperature of the Earth. The global-mean surface temperature was still high, however, because of the increased greenhouse effect due to the higher atmospheric carbon dioxide concentration. In other words, the influence of the faint early Sun was offset by the increased greenhouse effect. This provided conditions for life to evolve, and in doing so, drastically changed the composition of the atmosphere.

We shall not pursue the details of that story here. Suffice it to say that during the course of geological time, most of the carbon dioxide in our planet's early atmosphere has been locked up in rocks in the Earth's crust, through the processes illustrated schematically in Figure 3.24. The figure depicts *part* of the **biogeochemical carbon cycle**, the detailed workings of which will be explored more fully in the next chapter.

For now, notice that the processes shown in Figure 3.24 'start' with rainwater dissolving atmospheric carbon dioxide — forming a dilute solution of carbonic acid. Falling onto land, this reacts with rocks containing calcium minerals, releasing calcium ions and *bicarbonate* ions into solution in river water and groundwater, by a process known as chemical weathering. These ions eventually reach the sea, where plants and animals can use them to build shells of calcium carbonate. When the organisms die, their shells settle on the sea floor, forming calcium carbonate sediments, which with time become buried and compacted to form carbonate rocks — a process which effectively removes carbon dioxide from the atmosphere.

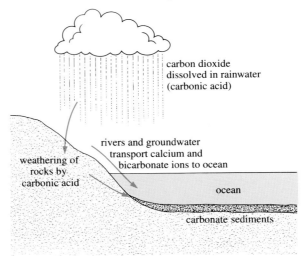

Figure 3.24 Part of the biogeochemical carbon cycle; the rest will be considered in Chapter 4.

An indication of what the Earth could have been like if carbon dioxide had not been removed from the atmosphere by the processes outlined above can be obtained by considering what has happened to another planet — Venus. The early atmosphere of Venus is thought to have been similar to that of the early Earth, and comprises mainly water vapour and carbon dioxide. Venus is closer to the Sun, so its surface temperature was higher than that of the Earth. The atmospheric water vapour did not condense into rain, forming oceans and removing carbon dioxide into rocks, but remained in the atmosphere, slowly dissociating into hydrogen and oxygen, which escaped into space. This has left Venus with an atmosphere of about 97% carbon dioxide, and a thick cover of sulphuric acid clouds. The gigantic greenhouse effect on Venus produces a surface temperature of about 460 °C — not suitable for life and distinctly hellish. Unlike Venus, which was the victim of a 'runaway' greenhouse effect, with no system to reduce the carbon dioxide in the atmosphere, the Earth has a moderate greenhouse effect, making it habitable.

What evidence is there that changes in atmospheric composition have *caused* past changes in surface temperature? The direct evidence is limited to the fairly recent past, up to about 160 ka, and comes from polar ice-cores. As snow is added to ice-sheets, air is trapped in the pores of the newly formed ice, becoming isolated from the atmosphere. The atmospheric carbon dioxide concentration in the past can therefore be measured from the air in the ice pores. The process is not as precise as the measurement of deuterium or oxygen isotopes in the ice itself, as the pores remain interconnected for between 10 and 1 000 years after snow deposition, so a sample represents the atmospheric composition averaged over this time interval.

Figure 3.25 is the record of temperature (determined from deuterium isotopes) and carbon dioxide concentration from the ice-core at Vostok, Antarctica, that we studied in Section 3.3.3. Fewer samples and measurements were taken for carbon dioxide than for temperature, because of the averaging effect of interconnected air pores: this explains why the temperature record looks 'hairier' than the carbon dioxide record. Apart from this superficial difference, there are great similarities between the two records, with the carbon dioxide concentration rising as temperature rises and falling as temperature falls. So there is good evidence that temperature and atmospheric carbon dioxide concentration are connected. However, are the changes in carbon dioxide concentration caused by temperature changes or are temperature changes caused by changes in carbon dioxide concentration? In other words, which comes first — the temperature change or the atmospheric change? This can be determined — to a limited extent — by careful analysis of the records, using a variation of the spectral analysis technique described in Box 3.3. The limitations arise mainly from the number of carbon dioxide measurements made, and to a lesser extent from the uncertainties in the carbon dioxide concentrations and the age difference between the air trapped in the ice and the ice itself, so the determination of a time difference between the two records in

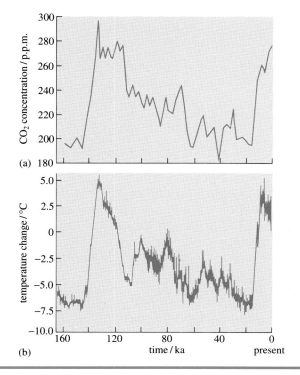

Figure 3.25 (a) Carbon dioxide concentrations, in p.p.m. (parts per million) in the Vostock ice-core. (b) The deuterium record determined from deuterium isotopes, expressed as deviations from the present temperature. This deuterium temperature record was also in Figure 3.12a.

73

Figure 3.25 is only possible for differences greater than about 3.5 ka. Within this uncertainty, the results indicate that temperature and carbon dioxide change at the same time during the change from a glacial to interglacial (a warming), but that carbon dioxide *lags* behind the temperature change during the change from the interglacial to the last glaciation (a cooling).

▷　Do these results provide any indication of whether the temperature change or the carbon dioxide change came first?

▶　The lag of the carbon dioxide behind the temperature change on cooling suggests that, at least on cooling, the temperature change occurred first.

▷　If these climatic temperature changes were not *triggered* by atmospheric carbon dioxide changes, what did trigger them?

▶　The orbital changes that we looked at in Section 3.3 were the likely trigger.

However, the relatively weak Milankovic–Croll effects were *strongly amplified* by the induced atmospheric carbon dioxide changes; the carbon dioxide produced a *positive feedback* on orbitally-induced temperature changes. In other words, orbital changes came first, and caused a small temperature change that changed the carbon dioxide concentration, to produce a larger temperature change.

So far we have not considered exactly how temperature changes manage to change the concentration of carbon dioxide in the atmosphere. Unfortunately there is no scientific consensus on the mechanism. Most suggestions are based on a link with changes in the biological productivity of the oceans (which controls the supply of carbonate to the deep sea), but there are various possibilities for the mechanisms driving these variations in productivity. We will look at these mechanisms in more detail in later chapters.

Activity 3.4

Make a list of the factors that affect climatic change on:

　　a long time-scale (hundreds of million years);

　　a medium time-scale (hundreds of thousand to tens of thousand years);

　　a short time-scale (hundreds of years to a year).

Some factors will appear more than once in your list; where this occurs make a note of how the factor works on the time-scale you are considering. For example:

Long time-scale Atmospheric composition (early Earth's atmosphere had much more carbon dioxide so there is a much greater greenhouse effect).

Summary of Chapter 3

1　Factors that can cause natural climatic change are: lithospheric plate movements, orbital variations, changes in the solar constant, volcanic activity and atmospheric composition.

2　Proxy data (indirect data) are used as a record of past climate.

3　The Earth's past climate has mainly been warmer than at present, but there have been cooler times, called Ice Ages, which last for 100 Ma or so. Within an Ice Age, there are glacials (cold periods) and interglacials (warm periods). At the moment we are in an interglacial of the Quaternary Ice Age. The global-mean surface temperature change between glacials and interglacials is about 5 °C. Glacials (and interglacials) occur about every 100 ka within an Ice Age.

4 Plate movements affect climate on a long time-scale, hundreds of millions of years, and are thought to be the factor controlling whether the Earth is in its warm state or its Ice Age state.

5 Variations in the Earth's orbit produce seasonal and latitudinal changes in solar radiation. There are three types of orbital changes: eccentricity, tilt and precession. Their effects on climate are called the Milankovic–Croll effects. These effects are the triggering force for glacial and interglacial cycles.

6 Positive feedback effects amplify the Milankovic–Croll effects.

7 Solar irradiance (and hence the solar constant at Earth) has increased substantially during the lifetime of the Earth. On shorter time-scales, direct observations reveal small (less than 1%) changes in solar irradiance, in step with the 11-year sunspot cycle. Larger, century time-scale fluctuations in solar irradiance may be responsible for the series of global-scale 'Little Ice Age' type events during the present interglacial (the Holocene), but the evidence for such a link is both indirect, and 'highly suggestive', at best.

8 Large volcanic eruptions can reduce the global-mean surface temperature by up to 1 °C for up to 3 years.

9 The composition of the atmosphere has changed significantly during the lifetime of the Earth, particularly with regard to carbon dioxide concentration, with a consequent change in the greenhouse effect.

10 On a glacial–interglacial time-scale, atmospheric carbon dioxide changes, which appear to be triggered by temperature changes, act to strongly amplify Milankovic–Croll effects on climate.

4 The changing atmosphere

Figure 4.1 (a) The instrumentation needed to measure atmospheric CO_2 was developed by Charles Keeling (then a student of Roger Revelle and Hans Suess — Chapter 1): it was installed at the Mauna Loa climate observatory in Hawaii during the International Geophysical Year in 1957. Located at an altitude of about 11 000 feet, the station is geographically remote from any local sources of industrial pollution. (b) Concentration, in parts per million (p.p.m.), of atmospheric CO_2 measured at Mauna Loa: annual oscillations arise from seasonal changes in photosynthesis and other biological processes. The overall trend apparent here has since been confirmed at other monitoring stations scattered around the globe. Parallel programmes have revealed upward trends in the atmospheric concentrations of (c) methane, and (d) nitrous oxide, recorded here as parts per billion (10^9), p.p.b.

One message is clear from the previous chapters. Any factor that can perturb the balance between the incoming solar radiation absorbed by the Earth–atmosphere system, and the longwave radiation it emits to space, has the potential to alter the climate. From now on, we focus on the factor at the heart of current concern about global warming — the increasing atmospheric burden of greenhouse gases.

4.1 Introduction

There is no doubt that the chemical composition of the atmosphere is changing. The longest-running continuous monitoring of carbon dioxide (CO_2) levels is that carried out at the Mauna Loa climate observatory in Hawaii (Figure 4.1a): that study records a steady increase in the atmospheric concentration of CO_2 since measurements began in 1957 (Figure 4.1b). More recently-established monitoring programmes also reveal a build up of two other 'natural' greenhouse gases — methane (Figure 4.1c) and nitrous oxide (Figure 4.1d). And there is some evidence that ozone concentrations in the *troposphere* are increasing as well — at least near industrial regions in the Northern Hemisphere. In addition, the atmosphere now contains rising concentrations (albeit only at the level of a few tens to hundreds of parts per *trillion*, 10^{12}) of a whole range of infrared-absorbing **halocarbons** that do not occur naturally.

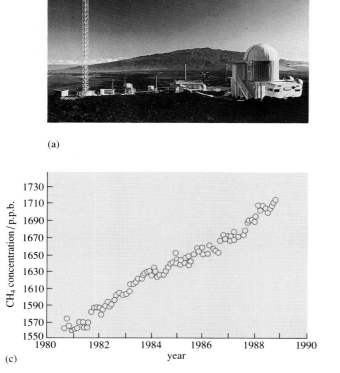

(a)

(b)

(c)

(d)

At present, the most important of these 'unnatural' compounds are two **chlorofluorocarbons** (**CFCs**), usually known (in an arcane nomenclature, reputedly devised by the American company Du Pont to confound the opposition) as **CFC-11** ($CFCl_3$) and **CFC-12** (CF_2Cl_2); see Figure 4.2. As a class of compounds, the CFCs first became notorious for their role in depleting the ozone layer *in the stratosphere*. However, they are also potent greenhouse gases; for example, molecule-for-molecule, CFCs-11 and -12 are currently some 10^4 times more 'effective' than CO_2 at trapping outgoing longwave radiation. Basically, this can be traced back to the fact that they absorb strongly at wavelengths within the 'atmospheric window' identified in Chapter 2 (Figure 2.7b), where absorption by water vapour and CO_2 is weak.

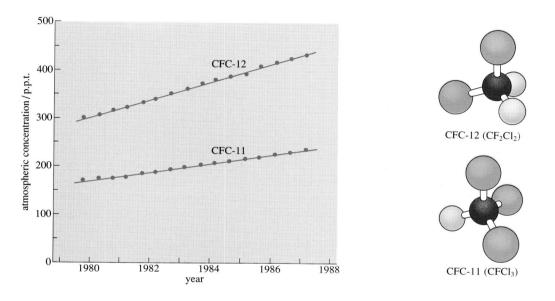

Figure 4.2 Trends in the atmospheric concentrations of two CFCs, CFC-11 and CFC-12, observed at mid-latitudes in the Northern Hemisphere, recorded as parts per trillion (10^{12}), p.p.t.

Clearly, the atmospheric burden of CFCs — and of other similar 'manufactured' halocarbons that are also building up — can be wholly ascribed to human activities. But what of the greenhouse gases that do occur naturally? Chief among these is water vapour (as noted in Section 2.2.2). It is, however, unique among its fellows in that its atmospheric concentration is dependent on temperature — and on very little else. With this is linked its crucial role in cloud formation, and in the transport of latent heat through the atmosphere, and between air and sea (as discussed in Section 2.3.4). Because of this, water vapour is normally considered as part of the climate system, rather than as a separate greenhouse gas. We shall consider the effect of changing levels of water vapour, in that context, in Chapter 5.

All of the remaining gases — CO_2, methane (CH_4), nitrous oxide (N_2O) and tropospheric ozone (O_3) — have natural **sources** and **sinks**: that is, there are natural mechanisms that release the gas into, and remove it from, the atmosphere. For each gas, a *changing* atmospheric concentration implies an *imbalance* between its sources and sinks. Put more precisely, at any given time, the *rate* at which the atmospheric concentration of a gas is changing is determined by the difference between its rates of release to and loss from the atmosphere, i.e.

rate of change of atmospheric concentration = release rate – loss rate   (4.1)

A gas will go on accumulating in the atmosphere as long as the release rate outstrips the loss rate. But to what extent is the imbalance evident at present (Figures 4.1b–d) influenced by human activities? Certainly, levels of CO_2 have fluctuated markedly in the past, in the *absence* of human intervention; here the Vostock ice-core provides the most dramatic, and long-term, record (Figure 3.25a).

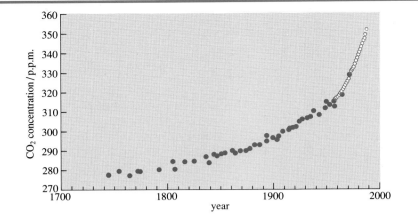

Figure 4.3 Increases in the concentration of CO_2 in the atmosphere over the past 250 years, as indicated by analysis of air trapped in ice from Siple Station, Antarctica (●), and direct atmospheric monitoring at Mauna Loa (○).

One strong line of evidence that we are now witnessing something *other than* natural variation again comes from ice-core data, but from samples that capture a more detailed picture of the past thousand or so years. For CO_2, for example, Figure 4.3 indicates that the record from Mauna Loa continues a rising trend that seems to have started toward the end of the 18th century. Analysis of longer-term ice-core records reveals that for 800 years before that, the level of atmospheric CO_2 fluctuated little (some 10 p.p.m. on a 100-yr time-scale), about a mean value close to 280 p.p.m. Similar patterns emerge for both methane and nitrous oxide. The so-called 'pre-industrial' atmospheric concentrations determined from ice-core data are included in Table 4.1. These figures are commonly taken as a benchmark against which to measure the increased atmospheric burden of greenhouse gases wrought by human actions over the past 200 years or so.

Table 4.1 Information on the key greenhouse gases influenced by human activities[*].
Note: p.p.m. = parts per million; p.p.b. = parts per billion (10^9); p.p.t. = parts per trillion (10^{12}).

	CO_2/ p.p.m.	CH_4/ p.p.m.	CFC-11/ p.p.t.	CFC-12/ p.p.t.	N_2O/ p.p.b.
pre-industrial atmospheric concentration (1750–1800)	280	0.8	0	0	288
current (1990) atmospheric concentration	353	1.72	280	484	310
current annual rate of accumulation (as a percentage of the current concentration)	1.8 (0.5%)	0.015 (0.9%)	9.5 (3.4%)	17 (3.5%)	0.8 (0.25%)

[*] Tropospheric ozone is not included because precise data are lacking: more on this in Section 4.3.2.

Some human activities clearly release natural greenhouse gases into the atmosphere. An obvious example is CO_2, the release of which is linked to the explosive growth in the burning of fossil fuels (coal, oil and gas) since the mid-19th century, as depicted in Figure 4.4. The use and extraction of fossil fuels also releases methane through leakage from natural gas pipelines, and by venting to the atmosphere at oil and gas production sites and from coal mines. These 'anthropogenic' releases or *emissions* effectively add a new source of the gas. But there is a whole range of human activities that can influence the natural balance in more subtle ways. To assess the impact of such activities (past, present and future) it is first necessary to build up a

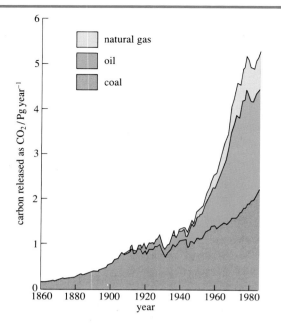

Figure 4.4 Global annual emissions of CO_2 from combustion of fossil fuels (natural gas, oil and coal) since the mid-19th century, expressed in terms of the mass of *carbon* released as CO_2 in petagrams, usually written as PgC (where $1\,Pg = 10^{15}\,g$).

detailed understanding of the natural control mechanisms. This is a formidable task. The awesome scale of the problem was touched on in Chapter 1: it is best conveyed through the IPCC description of the **International Geosphere–Biosphere Programme (IGBP)** established in 1986:

> *... an inter-disciplinary research initiative of the International Council of Scientific Unions, to describe and understand the interactive physical, chemical and biological processes that regulate the total Earth system, the unique environment that it provides for life, the changes that are occurring and the manner in which changes are influenced by human actions. A central objective of the IGBP is to establish the scientific basis for quantitative assessments of changes in the Earth's biogeochemical cycles, including those which control the concentration of carbon dioxide and other chemicals in the atmosphere.*

We can only scratch the surface of the problem here — sufficient, we hope, to give you a sense of its complexity, and the many challenging and unanswered questions it continues to pose.

We start with, and dwell at greatest length on, CO_2. Although many of the other greenhouse gases are currently accumulating in the atmosphere more rapidly than CO_2 (Table 4.1), its role in the greenhouse effect is still second only to that of water vapour.

4.2 Carbon dioxide and the global carbon cycle

Atmospheric CO_2 is just part, albeit a vital part, of the grand biogeochemical 'machine' that continuously cycles the global inventory of carbon between various reservoirs or 'compartments' — the atmosphere, oceans, living things, soils, sediments and rocks.

Important: You should study Box 4.1 at this point if you are at all uncertain about the workings of the biological carbon cycle on land.

Box 4.1   The biological carbon cycle on land: photosynthesis and respiration

1   Plants are autotrophs (literally 'self-feeders'). Using sunlight, they take up CO_2 from the air and combine it with the hydrogen in water to produce molecules of a simple organic compound (glucose) and oxygen — the process of **photosynthesis**. It can be represented as follows:

$$6CO_2 + 6H_2O \xrightarrow{\text{sunlight}} \underset{\text{glucose}}{C_6H_{12}O_6} + 6O_2 \quad (4.2)$$

2   A proportion of the CO_2 that plants take up is returned to the air through their own (autotrophic) **respiration** — a slow form of burning which is essentially the reverse of Equation 4.2. This provides energy for the biochemical reactions which convert glucose to a host of other, more complex, organic compounds. The fixed carbon *not* released back into the atmosphere via plant respiration is called the **net primary production (NPP)**, that is:

NPP = (carbon taken up via photosynthesis)
    – (carbon lost during plant respiration) (4.3)

3   There are two fates for plant NPP. Part may be stored within plants, manifesting itself as growth — an increase in plant **biomass**. The remainder enters heterotrophic food chains as either living material (eaten by herbivores) or dead material (litter or detritus). Heterotrophs are living organisms that cannot photosynthesize. The term encompasses herbivores, and the flesh-eaters that may consume them (and each other!), together with all the small animals and decomposers (fungi and bacteria) that feed on, and live in, the dead organic matter in detritus and the soil. Heterotrophic respiration, like plant respiration, converts organic carbon back into CO_2 and returns it to the air.

▷   Suppose that averaged over a whole year, the total *living* biomass in a given ecosystem (an area of woodland or forest, say) is constant. What does this imply?

▶   During the course of the year, any production of *new* plant or heterotroph biomass must be balanced by an equivalent loss.

In other words, *all* of the carbon added to the 'living' reservoir (through the annual plant NPP) must be balanced by an equivalent loss of carbon from that reservoir. In general, part of the latter may go to increase the store of dead organic matter; the remainder passes back to the atmosphere as CO_2 through heterotrophic respiration.

▷   But what if there is also no *net* accumulation of dead organic matter over a year?

▶   Then all the carbon fixed by plant NPP must be balanced by carbon returned to the atmosphere as CO_2.

In practice, the respiration of 'higher' animals comprises only a small fraction of the total return flux of CO_2; the major input comes from the activities of the decomposers. So in the 'unperturbed' ecosystem envisaged here, there is also a rough annual balance between NPP and the formation of dead organic matter, on the one hand — and on the other, the breakdown of dead organic matter and return to the atmosphere of its carbon content via the respiration of decomposers. This balanced state can be represented as shown in Figure 4.5; carbon flows around a closed cycle, and the three reservoirs involved neither grow nor diminish. ∎

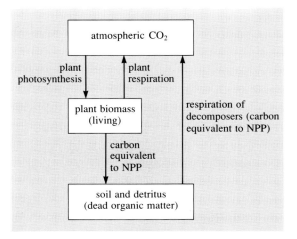

Figure 4.5 The biological carbon cycle for a 'balanced' terrestrial ecosystem, as described in Box 4.1.

4.2.1 The natural carbon cycle: time-scales

A crude breakdown of the major carbon reservoirs is shown in Figure 4.6, together with an indication of their sizes and the annual exchanges between them. All of the figures are *global* estimates. For example, Figure 4.6 incorporates a land-based biological cycle (cf. Figure 4.5), but with two carbon reservoirs — one 'living' and one 'dead' — that encompass all terrestrial ecosystems, everywhere. Because plants drive the cycle of CO_2 exchange with the atmosphere, the 'living' terrestrial reservoir is usually equated with the carbon stored in plant biomass, as indicated in Figure 4.6. The size of this reservoir can be estimated by sampling representative areas of different ecosystems, together with surveys of the world-wide distribution of each type (recall Figure 2.1). A figure for the total amount of carbon stored in soil and detritus can be assembled in the same way, as can global estimates of the annual rate of photosynthesis, NPP, etc. Although ecologists differ about the details of such assessments, several recent estimates fall close to the values recorded in Figure 4.6. Apart from the atmospheric reservoir (which is now well characterized by routine monitoring), similar difficult and uncertain analyses underlie the other estimates in Figure 4.6.

Question 4.1 According to Figure 4.6, what is the *global* annual NPP of terrestrial ecosystems?

In one important respect, the picture of the present world captured in Figure 4.6 is misleading; it shows a rough balance in the annual exchange of CO_2 between the atmosphere and on the one hand, terrestrial ecosystems, and on the other, the surface ocean. In other words, it effectively represents a 'steady-state' cycle in the sense defined in Section 2.3.4. For the moment, we have ignored current estimates of any imbalance in the overall system — and neither have we included anthropogenic emis-

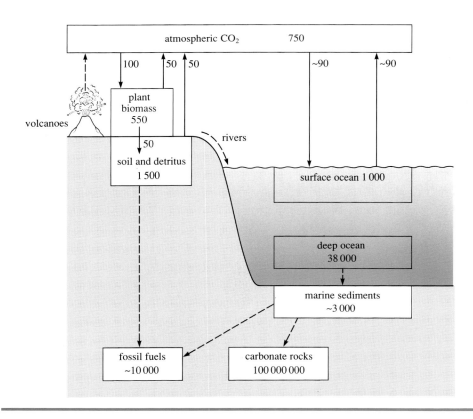

Figure 4.6 A schematic representation of the major global carbon reservoirs and annual fluxes between them (arrows). Reservoir sizes represent the mass of carbon in PgC: fluxes are in PgC per year. Anthropogenic contributions and current *imbalances* in the overall system are *not* included.

sions. This somewhat artificial device allows us to focus on the time-scales that characterize the various natural controls over the level of atmospheric CO_2. And these time-scales are important.

Question 4.2 Use the numbers in Figure 4.6 to estimate the average residence time (Equation 2.5 in Section 2.3.4) of carbon in each of the following reservoirs: the atmosphere; plant biomass; soil and detritus; the surface ocean.

The important general point, then, is that with relatively small stocks and large annual fluxes, carbon moves around this set of reservoirs on a time-scale of years to decades. These transfers are the fast wheels that spin within the overall biogeochemical cycle. They are 'geared' into that cycle by a series of much slower 'leaks' — some of which are represented by broken lines in Figure 4.6. These slow processes include the cycle of *chemical* weathering (which releases carbon into the freshwater system as bicarbonate and transports it to the oceans) and sedimentation (which dumps it on the sea-bed) that were mentioned in the previous chapter (Section 3.6). Over the course of geological time, a *net* transfer along this route has locked up most of the Earth's carbon — largely as calcium carbonate in sediments and rocks, but also as fossil fuels[*]; this is perhaps the most striking feature of Figure 4.6.

On time-scales that range from years to a few centuries, however, it is generally assumed that these, and other even slower natural transfers (like the outgassing of CO_2 from the Earth's interior, for example, most violently during volcanic eruptions), have a negligible effect on the level of atmospheric CO_2. In particular, most attempts to analyse the rapid changes of the past two centuries — and to predict how they may evolve into the next one — take no explicit account of these transfers; on this time-scale, the atmosphere, oceans and terrestrial ecosystems are taken to be the only 'active' reservoirs of carbon. This simplifies a problem of daunting complexity, but you should always bear in mind that it is an assumption.

However (as noted in the answer to Question 4.2), there is one process not shown in Figure 4.6 that *is* crucially important on the decade-to-century time-scale; the exchange of carbon between the surface ocean and the deep ocean.

4.2.2 Ocean–atmosphere cycles: natural balances

Figure 4.7 is a repeat of the ocean–atmosphere system in Figure 4.6, but with several important refinements. First, notice that we have now emphasized the division of the ocean into two distinct reservoirs. This does scant justice to the true vertical structure of the oceans, but the simple 'two-box' ocean model that results is sufficient to get a feel for how carbon moves through the system. The boundary between the two boxes comes at the base of the warm mixed layer (between 100 and 200 m depth on average, Figure 2.29).

▷ So what does the lower box in Figure 4.7 represent?

▶ It takes in the permanent thermocline, and below that the cold deep-water masses.

---

[*] There is also a slow 'leak' from the land cycle into this reservoir. In certain ecosystems, some organic matter escapes the activities of the decomposers. The residues build up in sediments or as peat. With time, heat and pressure, they can become transformed into fossil fuels.

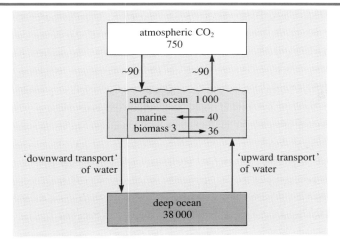

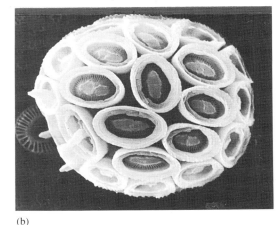

Figure 4.7 An elaboration of the ocean–atmosphere carbon system in Figure 4.6. As in that figure, reservoir sizes are in PgC; annual fluxes in PgC per year.

Since the average depth of the oceans is around 3700 m, this means that the lower box is some twenty times bigger than the upper one. In reality, the two boxes are connected by the movement and mixing of water between them, as outlined in Section 2.3.3; the '**downward transport**' of water (partly simple downward mixing, but mainly downwelling associated with the formation of deep-water masses at high latitudes in winter) is balanced over a given period (a year, say) by an equal '**upward transport**' of water (which stems mainly from widespread upward mixing, but includes localized upwelling — such as that which occurs in the Antarctic Divergence and off some coastal boundaries, for example). The important point here is that this transfer carries with it the carbon compounds *dissolved* in the water, and so provides a connection between the reservoir of carbon in each box. More on that shortly.

Returning to Figure 4.7, note that we have also put some life into the surface ocean. This does not mean that the depths are devoid of life — only that the microscopic **phytoplankton** (Figure 4.8) that drive the biological cycle in the oceans must have access to sunlight for photosynthesis. They can only grow in the **photic zone**, which rarely extends more than 200 m below the surface — and often much less. They take their CO_2 (at an estimated global annual rate of 40 PgC yr^{-1}) from that dissolved in the water around them, *not* directly from the atmosphere. This is important. It means that the *primary* exchange of CO_2 between the atmosphere and the surface ocean is mediated by physics and chemistry, not biology. Study Box 4.2 for a brief survey of this abiological system.

Figure 4.8 (a) Artist's impression of phytoplankton. These drifting microscopic plants provide the primary link between ocean biology and the atmosphere, and play an important role in the global carbon cycle. (b) A coccolith, a phytoplankton with calcified plates. (× 6000)

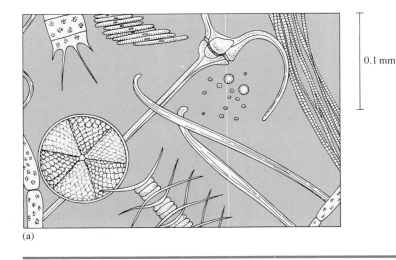

0.1 mm

(a)

(b)

4.2 Box 4.2 'Dissolving' CO_2

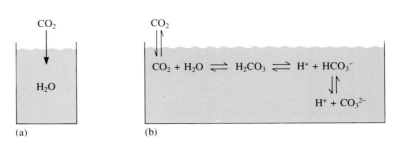

Figure 4.9 A schematic representation of the aqueous carbonate system, which is described in the text.

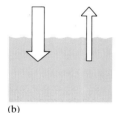

(a)

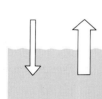

(b)

(c)

Figure 4.10 (a) At equilibrium, the exchange of CO_2 across the air–sea boundary is balanced. Changing conditions (temperature, atmospheric concentration of CO_2, or concentration of DIC in solution) — as described in the text — can upset the balance, leading to either a net uptake (b) or a net release (c) of CO_2.

The essential features of 'dissolving' CO_2 are captured in Figure 4.9. Imagine a glass of water exposed to the atmosphere. Initially, there is a flux of CO_2 into the water (Figure 4.9a). This physical transfer is rather slow, but you could speed it up by stirring the water (just as the wind and waves 'stir' the surface layers of the oceans). Once dissolved, molecules of CO_2 can react with water, forming carbonic acid (H_2CO_3). This is a weak acid: in solution it is partly dissociated into bicarbonate ions (HCO_3^-), and thence further into carbonate ions (CO_3^{2-}). Gradually, the reverse reactions get going and start to release CO_2 back into the air. Eventually, an overall equilibrium is established (Figure 4.9b) — a state of *dynamic* balance between the CO_2 in the air, and that 'partitioned' among the various components of the so-called 'carbonate system' in solution, as implied by the double half-headed arrows in the figure. All this chemical activity also goes on in the ocean.

One of the techniques used to analyse samples of seawater for carbon produces a measure of the total concentration of '**dissolved inorganic carbon**' (**DIC**), that is:

$$[DIC] = [CO_2] + [H_2CO_3]$$
$$+ [HCO_3^-] + [CO_3^{2-}] \qquad (4.4)$$

From now on, we shall adopt this collective term (and so simplify matters). Bear in mind, however, that only a tiny fraction of the total (less than 1%) is actually molecular CO_2. Concentrations of DIC are often expressed in the unit $mol\,m^{-3}$. Because *each* component of the aqueous carbonate system in Equation 4.4 contains one atom of carbon, one mole of DIC contains one mole of carbon, i.e. 12 g of carbon. The numbers (1 000 and 38 000) in Figure 4.7 are estimates of the total mass of

carbon stored as DIC in each of the two oceanic reservoirs (surface ocean and deep ocean).

As far as the ocean–atmosphere carbon system is concerned, the crucial point to grasp is that CO_2 is constantly being exchanged across the air–sea boundary. *Given constant conditions*, the flux of CO_2 into the surface ocean balances that released to the atmosphere, as depicted in Figure 4.10a. You need to be aware of three factors that can disturb this balanced state.

1 The solubility of CO_2 increases with *decreasing temperature*. In practice, this means that the concentration of DIC seawater can 'hold' — in equilibrium with a given level of atmospheric CO_2, that is — depends on its temperature. In particular, if surface waters cool down, this produces a *net* flux of CO_2 into solution (Figure 4.10b), and vice versa if they warm up (Figure 4.10c).

2 Any process *within* the ocean that drains (or adds to) the supply of DIC in surface waters will also upset the balance in Figure 4.10a — leading to a net uptake of CO_2 (Figure 4.10b), or a net release (Figure 4.10c). (One, all important, *biological* process that comes under this heading — photosynthesis by phytoplankton — is taken up in the text following this Box.)

3 Finally, increasing the concentration of CO_2 in the atmosphere disturbs the *overall* equilibrium shown in Figure 4.9b, inducing a net flux of CO_2 into solution (Figure 4.10b). Eventually, a new equilibrium would be established, with the 'extra' CO_2 partitioned between the atmosphere and the DIC in solution. As a result, the concentration of DIC would have increased. ■

Question 4.3 It is generally accepted that in the 'unperturbed' pre-industrial world the *globally-averaged* annual exchange of CO_2 between the atmosphere and the surface ocean was in the balanced state depicted in Figure 4.10a.

(a) What evidence — cited in Section 4.1 — would tend to support this view? What implicit assumption is involved?

(b) In view of point 1 in Box 4.2, would you expect this balance to hold *uniformly* over the entire surface of the oceans? (Hint: Think about the geographical distribution of sea-surface temperatures in Figure 2.16.)

But the 'physico-chemical' processes outlined in Box 4.2 are not the whole story of the ocean–atmosphere carbon system: far from it.

▷ Use the numbers in Figure 4.7 to estimate the average residence time of carbon in the marine biomass of the surface ocean.

▶ On average, about (3/40) yr — less than a month.

This short time-scale reflects the rapid recycling of carbon (and, incidentally, other nutrients) within the surface ocean. The phytoplankton are grazed by zooplankton (floating microscopic organisms) that package most of their waste products into faecal pellets, which are in turn consumed and decomposed by other organisms, including bacteria. *On a global annual basis*, the net effect is to return to the surface layers most — *but not all* — of the carbon fixed via photosynthesis, as indicated by the imbalance in Figure 4.7. A small, but crucial, fraction (some 10% or 4 PgC per year on current estimates) escapes from the photic zone. The underlying mechanism is the packaging of both organic matter and skeletal remains into particles large enough to overcome the buoyancy of seawater, and so sink down through the water column. The particles include faecal pellets (tens to a few hundred micrometres in size), together with larger, less well-defined aggregates that are collectively dubbed 'marine snow' (or 'fluff', see Figure 4.11). In terms of our two-box ocean model, these sinking particles represent a net and *direct* transfer of carbon from the upper box to the lower one. *Enter this flux on Figure 4.7, i.e. insert an arrow (and the number 4) from the box 'marine biomass' to the box 'deep ocean', and label it* '**biological pump**'.

Now think about the consequences of this biological pump working away year after year. *By itself*, this would represent a steady drain on the supply of DIC in the surface ocean. In turn, that would be expected to draw a *net* flux of CO_2 into solution (point 2 in Box 4.2), and hence gradually deplete the atmospheric reservoir. But during the 800 or so years that preceded the industrial age the atmospheric concentration of CO_2 was more or less constant (Question 4.3). Is there, then, some *other* mechanism whereby the reservoir of DIC in the upper ocean is kept 'topped up', as it were? Indeed there is; this is where the exchange of water between the two boxes

Figure 4.11 Examples of marine snow. (a) Loosely associated aggregate of living, chain-forming diatoms (zooplankton, scale bar = 1 cm). (b) Typical comet-shaped aggregate (scale bar = 1 mm).

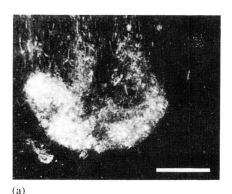

(a)

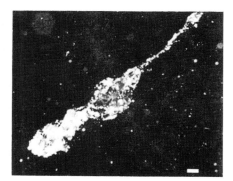

(b)

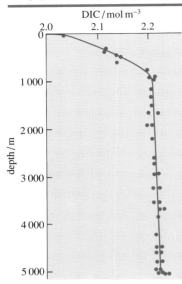

Figure 4.12 Variation with depth of total dissolved inorganic carbon (DIC), sampled in the North Atlantic (36° N, 68° W).

in Figure 4.7 comes in. Analysis of samples of seawater drawn from different depths in the ocean reveals that the *concentration* of DIC is significantly higher in all the waters that comprise our lower box than in the surface layer; Figure 4.12 is a typical profile for the North Atlantic. Why is this?

One contribution comes from the sinking particles. On average, little of the organic matter in these particles survives the journey to the sea-bed. The rest provides food for successive populations of filter feeders and other animals, and the ubiquitous decomposers. Ultimately, the carbon is released as CO_2 via heterotropic respiration; in the cold depths of the ocean, the CO_2 goes into solution. Another contribution was foreshadowed in your answer to Question 4.3; at high latitudes in winter, the formation of deep-water masses carries the net flux of atmospheric CO_2 into the cold surface layer directly down to the depths.

The following activity gives you an opportunity to get a rough estimate of the *net upward* flux of 'dissolved' carbon that, *in an unperturbed world*, balances the direct downward transfer driven by the biological pump.

Activity 4.1

If the profile in Figure 4.12 is assumed to be fairly typical of the whole ocean, this suggests that the upper and lower oceanic reservoirs in Figure 4.7 contain DIC at concentrations of around $2.0 \, mol \, m^{-3}$ and $2.2 \, mol \, m^{-3}$, respectively.

(a) Now concentrate on Figure 4.7. Recent estimates put the annual exchange of *water* between the surface ocean and the deep ocean close to $2 \times 10^{15} \, m^3 \, yr^{-1}$, i.e. the arrows labelled 'upward transport of water' and 'downward transport of water' each represent $2 \times 10^{15} \, m^3$ of seawater. Assuming that water transported down has a DIC concentration of $2.0 \, mol \, m^{-3}$, whereas water transported up contains $2.2 \, mol \, m^{-3}$, work out the *mass* of carbon transferred in each direction each year. (Remember, from Box 4.2, that 1 mol of DIC is equivalent to 12 g of carbon.) What is the *net* annual upward flux of carbon?

(b) What do your figures suggest for the residence time of carbon in the deep ocean? Is this the order of magnitude you would expect?

4.2.3 Perturbing the natural cycles: human activities

Based on several careful analyses of historical patterns of fossil fuel usage, the IPCC estimated that CO_2 equivalent to 195 ± 20 petagrams (Pg) of carbon was added to the atmosphere between 1850 and 1986. The current annual flux is around 5–6 PgC. But this is only part of the story. Other human activities also interfere with the natural carbon cycle.

Today, the media carry frequent and compelling images of tropical forest being hacked down and burnt (Plate 4.1). The scale of destruction *is* staggering: some estimates put the current annual loss at close to 15 million hectares ($15 \times 10^6 \, ha = 15 \times 10^{10} \, m^2$). However, the practice of clearing forests, burning their wood, and turning vast tracts of virgin land over to agricultural use was already widespread before the 19th century. At temperate latitudes (e.g. in North America and parts of Europe and Australasia), it reached a peak during the late 19th and early 20th centuries. To understand the impact of these past and ongoing changes to terrestrial ecosystems, a brief digression is in order.

Early in its history, a forest (or area of woodland) acts as a net (if local) *sink* for atmospheric CO_2. Rapid growth stores a significant fraction of annual NPP in the living tissues of its trees and other woody plants. As the forest matures, however, the rate of accumulation falls off. Eventually trees begin to die. If the forest is left unmanaged, dead trees are replaced naturally — and large areas approach the steady state described in Box 4.1 and captured in Figures 4.5 and 4.6; uptake of CO_2 is balanced by its release, as organic matter is broken down by the decomposers. Human intervention strikes at this delicate balance. Felling trees depletes the stock of carbon stored in plant biomass. Burning the wood or allowing it to decay — either on site (stumps, branches, roots, etc.) or in wood products (paper, timber and so on) removed from the site — sooner or later returns this carbon to the atmosphere as CO_2. Moreover, ploughing cleared (or any virgin) land aerates the soil, and this speeds up the decay of organic matter, thus depleting the second terrestrial reservoir as well. In short, the cleared area becomes a net *source* of atmospheric CO_2, albeit temporarily.

Given studies of the way different ecosystems and their soils respond to disturbance, historical records of the changing pattern of land use around the world provide a means of 'bookkeeping' the carbon content of both terrestrial reservoirs as a function of time — and hence assessing the impact *at the global level* over a specified period. Or at least, they do in principle. In practice, many of the processes involved remain poorly characterized — the actual *rate* at which carbon is released during and after forest clearance, for example, or is stored when cultivated land or pasture is abandoned, and then either recolonized naturally or deliberately reforested, and so on. Moreover, tracking the ebb-and-flow of forests and other ecosystems is far from straightforward — even now, with widespread satellite surveillance (Plate 4.2). Not surprisingly, then, these historical assessments are difficult and uncertain, as suggested by the differences between the plots in Figure 4.13; the IPCC report quotes a figure of $117 \pm 35 \, PgC$ for the cumulative input of CO_2 from this source between 1850 and 1986. The present annual flux (virtually all of which is from the tropics) is estimated to be $1.6 \pm 1.0 \, PgC \, yr^{-1}$, roughly a third of that from the combustion of fossil fuels.

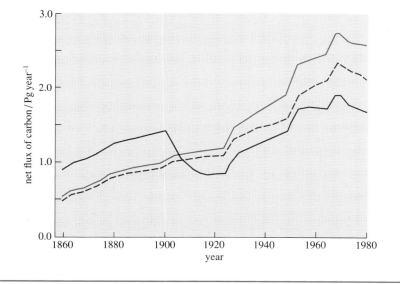

Figure 4.13 Global annual emissions of carbon to the atmosphere due to deforestation and changing land use, estimated by three different procedures. Without pursuing the details of these procedures, the important point is that they produce different estimates of the time-evolving input of CO_2 from this source.

Activity 4.2

Between 1850 and 1986, the atmospheric concentration of CO_2 increased from around 288 p.p.m. to 348 p.p.m.

(a) Taking 1 p.p.m. of CO_2 to be equivalent to 2.12 PgC, what was the increase in the mass of carbon carried in atmospheric CO_2 over this period?

(b) What proportion of the estimated cumulative input from fossil fuel burning and changing land use does this represent — expressed as a percentage?

(c) What conclusions can be drawn from your answer?

Your analysis highlights a crucial issue; a significant proportion (some 60%) of the historical input of 'anthropogenic' CO_2 has been locked away, or 'sequestered', again. But where exactly? And can we rely on this natural sink (*or sinks?*) to go on sequestering such a large fraction of the CO_2 released by human activities?

4.2.4 Modelling the 'redistribution' of anthropogenic carbon dioxide

Until recently, it was widely assumed that the oceans provide the sink for most, if not all, of the 'missing' anthropogenic CO_2. Now refer to Figure 4.14. Part (a) is a repeat of our 'balanced' two-box ocean model (from Figure 4.7), but with everything bar the fluxes of carbon omitted. The figures against the 'downward' and 'upward' arrows (they come from the IPCC report) are somewhat different from the rough estimates you came up with in part (a) of Activity 4.1. No matter. The important point is that in this 'unperturbed' situation the *difference* between them — the net upward flux of DIC — matches that transferred into the depths by the biological pump.

But what of the 'perturbed' world in which we now live, with atmospheric CO_2 steadily increasing? This situation is illustrated schematically in Figure 4.14b. First, point 3 in Box 4.2 implies a *net* uptake of CO_2 by surface waters, thereby increasing the concentration of DIC in our upper oceanic reservoir — and hence, in turn, increasing the flux of dissolved carbon into the deep ocean. (Recall the calculation in Activity 4.1.) These changes are indicated in general terms in Figure 4.14b.

▷ Why, then, is there no change to the figure against the 'upward' arrow? (Think about your answer to part (b) of Activity 4.1.)

▶ The heart of the matter is the long residence time of carbon in the deep ocean. Once 'excess' CO_2 is moved from the atmosphere into the deep ocean, it should be centuries — on average — before DIC-enriched water returns to the surface ocean.

Until it does, something like the situation depicted in Figure 4.14b should prevail — with the *net* upward flux of *dissolved* carbon (i.e. $37 - (33 + y) = 4 - y$) now *less than* the direct downward transfer by the biological pump (4). Of course, this presupposes that the latter does not itself respond in some way to enhanced levels of atmospheric CO_2 — neither 'strengthening' nor 'weakening', as it were: more on that assumption shortly. For now, the point to note is that carbonate chemistry (Box 4.2), together

Figure 4.14 Schematic representations of the ocean–atmosphere carbon system in (a) an 'unperturbed' world (cf. Figure 4.7), and (b) a world perturbed by human actions which are adding CO_2 to the atmosphere. The workings of this 'physico-chemical' oceanic sink for *excess* CO_2 are described in the text. Fluxes are in $PgC\,yr^{-1}$, as before.

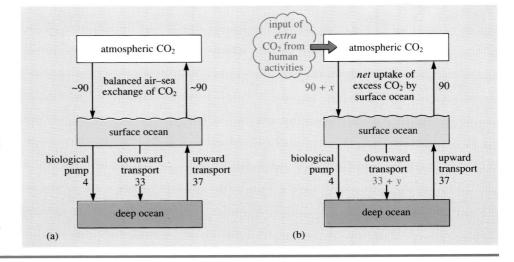

with the physical processes that govern the vertical mixing of the oceans (Section 2.3.3) provides a mechanism for sequestering 'anthropogenic' CO_2 in the deep ocean.

To date, most of the computer models used to estimate the historical uptake of CO_2 have been based on a mathematical description of this essentially physico-chemical mechanism. Such assessments use what amounts to a 'box model' of the ocean. The only major refinement over our simple picture is that the upper box in Figure 4.14 is a little shallower and the lower box is not treated as a single well-mixed reservoir, with a uniform concentration of DIC. Rather, it is itself divided into a series of layers (Figure 4.15a). In some versions, these deeper layers reach part of the surface of the model ocean in a sort of 'polar outcrop' (Figure 4.15b) — thus taking some account of the direct flux of CO_2 into deep water at high latitudes mentioned earlier (Section 4.2.2).

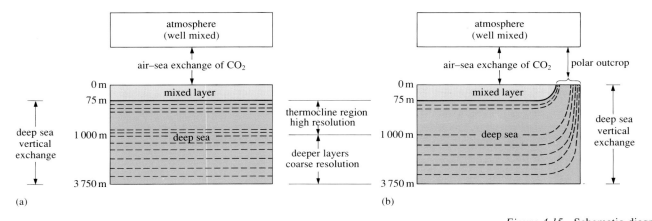

Within this highly simplified framework, there are well established techniques for treating the rate at which water masses (carrying their load of dissolved carbon) are exchanged between the various model layers. There are also well established equations to describe the chemistry of the aqueous carbonate system, and the exchange of CO_2 between air and sea. Thus, the 'model' essentially comprises a set of equations. These are the rules that a computer follows so as to simulate the behaviour of the real system in response to a given perturbation. In simulations of the past rise in CO_2, the perturbation is an estimate of the emissions due to human activities over the period selected for study. In such studies, it has generally been found that the model simulated increase in atmospheric CO_2 is *larger* than that actually observed. Some typical figures for the decade 1980–89 are collected in Table 4.2.

Figure 4.15 Schematic diagrams to show the basic features of the elaborated ocean box models frequently used to estimate the oceanic uptake of anthropogenic CO_2. See text for details about parts (a) and (b).

Table 4.2 The budget of atmospheric CO_2 for the decade 1980–1989, based on estimated anthropogenic emissions, the observed increase in the atmospheric concentration, and the modelled uptake by the ocean.

	PgC yr^{-1}
emissions from fossil fuel combustion	5.4 ± 0.5
emissions from deforestation and changing land use	1.6 ± 1.0
total emissions	7.0 ± 1.1
observed atmospheric accumulation	3.4 ± 0.2
modelled oceanic uptake (by physico-chemical mechanism)	2.0 ± 0.8
net imbalance	$1.6 \pm 1.4^*$

* Remember that the errors cannot be summed in the same way as the figure for the net imbalance.

Activity 4.3

Suppose it were claimed, on the *sole* basis of figures like those in Table 4.2, that there *must* be another significant sink for anthropogenic CO_2 — presumably somewhere on land. What reservations would you have about such a categorical statement?

The problem of balancing the 'excess' carbon budget brings into sharp focus just how important are the research projects being coordinated through the IGBP. We outline here two key areas of uncertainty.

A terrestrial sink?

In reality, there are small differences (a few p.p.m.) in the levels of CO_2 recorded by the monitoring stations now scattered around the globe. In the late 1980s, modelling studies (but of the *atmospheric circulation* this time — of which more in Chapter 5) used to analyse these small differences began to point to an unexpectedly large sink for CO_2, somewhere on land in the Northern Hemisphere. We cannot go into details of the analysis. Suffice it to say that there has been much speculation as to the nature of such a sink. Here we note one regional possibility, and two more general ones:

1   Managed forests go through a cycle of harvest and regrowth. Several studies have suggested that, on average, such forests in northern mid-latitudes are currently in a period of net regrowth — and may be accumulating carbon at an annual rate of around $1-2 \, \text{PgC yr}^{-1}$.

2   A CO_2-rich environment could be stimulating plant growth — the so-called '**carbon dioxide fertilization effect**'. Glasshouse experiments indicate that many plants do indeed respond in this way. However, the net effect on carbon *storage* is obscured by complex interactions with other environmental factors, such as nutrient levels, soil moisture, ambient temperature, and so on. These are issues we shall explore further in Chapter 8.

3   Plant growth may be enhanced through the increased availability of nutrients derived from artificial fertilizers, now widely used in both agriculture and forestry. Moreover, burning fossil fuels itself produces nitrogen oxides (see Section 4.3.2), another source of 'fixed' nitrogen for terrestrial ecosystems.

To date, there have been few of the field trials — or studies of natural ecosystems — needed to assess whether or not these (or other) responses of the terrestrial biosphere are, in fact, sequestering excess CO_2 on land.

A more 'efficient' oceanic sink?

To pick up a point noted in the answer to Activity 4.3: ocean–atmosphere 'box models' (like those depicted schematically in Figure 4.15) are actually highly simplified. For a start, the analysis embedded within them amounts to a 'globally averaged' representation of the physical and chemical controls over the ocean–atmosphere carbon cycle — albeit with some account being taken of the vital part played by formation of deep-water masses at high latitudes (Figure 4.15b). Recently, several groups have begun to develop models that incorporate a more complete description of the full three-dimensional circulation of the world's oceans — and the influence that has on the geographical distribution of CO_2 fluxes across the air–sea boundary (evident in Figure 4.16), and the vertical movement of dissolved carbon within the oceans. This is a formidable task — one we shall return to in the next chapter. For now, suffice it to say that early studies with such models indicate a simulated oceanic uptake of anthropogenic CO_2 within the range quoted in Table 4.2. It seems unlikely, therefore, that the net imbalance noted there can be wholly ascribed to an inadequate representation of the *physical* processes that move excess CO_2 into the deep ocean.

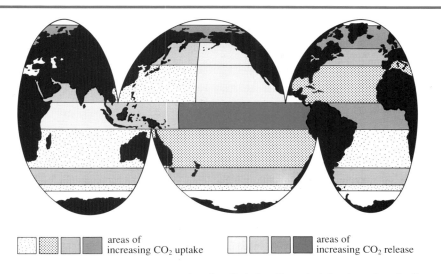

areas of
increasing CO_2 uptake   areas of
increasing CO_2 release

Figure 4.16 The broad outline of the observed geographical distribution of the exchange of CO_2 across the air–sea boundary. Averaged over a year, there is a net uptake of CO_2 mostly in temperate and sub-polar regions (especially the North Atlantic), coupled with a net release of CO_2 mostly in equatorial regions (particularly the Pacific) — roughly the situation touched on in Question 4.3. These large-scale features closely match the global pattern of ocean circulation — with surface water cooling and sinking in the temperate and sub-polar regions, and deep water upwelling and warming in the equatorial regions. Lateral movements of upper and near-bottom water — in opposite directions across most ocean basins — complete the physical 'ocean conveyor belt' (recall Figure 2.32) for the transport of dissolved carbon around the world.

But what of the fundamental assumption implicit in all such 'physico-chemical' models — effectively that the marine biosphere plays no part in sequestering *extra* CO_2? This assumption is usually justified on the grounds that the growth of phytoplankton (unlike that of land plants) does not respond directly to enhanced levels of atmospheric CO_2. Rather it is controlled by other factors: light, temperature and the supply of so-called *limiting nutrients* (usually nitrogen, phosphorus and silicon). However, the interplay among these various factors is, in turn, shaped by the ocean circulation. This produces a pattern of phytoplankton productivity that varies markedly with the seasons, and from place-to-place in the great ocean basins (Plate 4.3). And so too does the fate of the carbon fixed via photosynthesis. In other words, the biological pump is actually a far more subtle machine than the globally-averaged picture outlined in Section 4.2.2 might suggest.

In broad terms, ocean waters at temperate and near-polar latitudes mix to greater depths during the winter months. Like carbon, the nutrients mentioned above are also more abundant in the deep ocean, so this seasonal mixing enriches the surface layers. With the arrival of spring, light levels increase and the surface waters warm and stabilize: successive 'blooms' of phytoplankton sweep across these oceans (Figure 4.17, *overleaf*). This seasonal burst of activity sends a pulse of debris into deeper waters (Plate 4.4) and draws atmospheric CO_2 into solution to compensate for that 'consumed' by photosynthesis (point 2 in Box 4.2). By contrast, the warmer waters typical of lower latitudes are, in general, more stably stratified throughout the year. Such conditions favour the very efficient recycling of carbon (and other nutrients) in the upper ocean, thus maintaining a more constant (if lower, on average) level of marine productivity — and sending relatively little organic carbon down through the water column.

In reality, there is much fine detail within this broad picture. The important general point is that there remain significant uncertainties as to how the shifting and diverse pattern of biological activity in the oceans controls the workings of the biological pump — and the influence that, in turn, has on the *detailed* geographical distribution of CO_2 fluxes across the air–sea boundary, and any seasonal variations therein.

On a different note, the oceans also contain dissolved 'organic' carbon (DOC) — organic compounds, mostly produced as metabolic by-products by the phytoplankton — together with 'particulate' organic matter (including free-living bacteria) too small to sink through the water column. Biological activity results in a continual exchange of material between these two 'pools' of organic carbon, but the role they play in the overall oceanic carbon cycle is poorly understood as yet. This *could* be important — not least because a new analytical technique for measuring the DOC in seawater

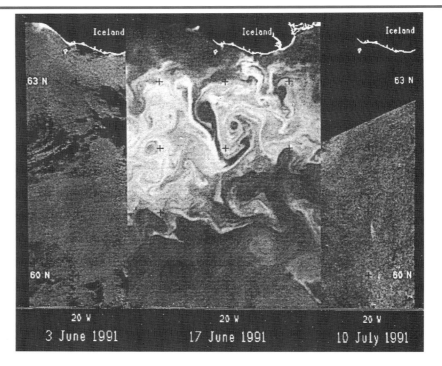

Figure 4.17 Three images of the same region of the North Atlantic (off Iceland) recorded by a satellite-borne 'radiometer' (an instrument that measures radiation — here in the visible band) during early summer 1991. The left image (3 June 1991) was obtained prior to the appearance of the high reflectance phytoplankton bloom, observed on the middle image (17 June) and sampled by RRS *Charles Darwin*. A later image (on the right), obtained on 10 July shows little evidence of the bloom in surface waters.

suggests there may be far more of it than the modest amounts (some 1000 PgC in total, compared with about 38 000 PgC for DIC, Figure 4.7) previously supposed.

Question 4.4 How could increased use of artificial fertilizers on *land* affect marine productivity? Where would you look first for evidence of such an effect?

The **Joint Global Ocean Flux Study (JGOFS)**, a core project of the IGBP, is attempting to address these crucial issues in a systematic way. Over a period of 10 years (starting in 1989), teams of oceanographers, marine chemists and marine biologists are taking to the seas. By combining 'ocean-going' experiments with data collected by satellites or aircraft (see Figure 4.18, for example), this international project aims to build up an extensive body of data on the way 'carbon' behaves in selected ocean regions — closely correlated with the local pattern of biological activity, the physics and chemistry of the water column, etc. — and any changes over time. Similar intensive studies will be devoted to selected coastal and shelf waters.

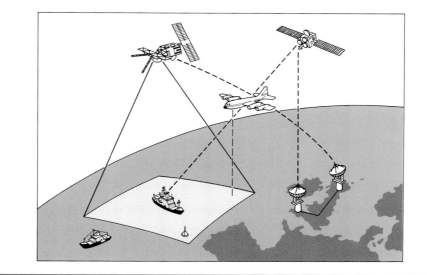

Figure 4.18 'Platform' deployment during the 'North Atlantic Bloom Experiment' in 1989 — the first stage of the JGOFS North Atlantic programme. Results from 1989 and 1990 have shown that in this region, CO_2 exchanges across the air–sea boundary in spring and summer are dominated by the patterns of biological activity in the upper ocean, controlled in turn by circulation features within the ocean.

A parallel task will be the critical analysis of these observational data. This is a crucial step in the whole modelling process. In the present context, the aim is to identify the *key* biological controls over the movement of carbon into and through the ocean, i.e. the processes involved and the variables they depend on. The next step is to formulate these controls as a set of rules that can be incorporated into existing, essentially physico-chemical, ocean models. A model of the ocean–atmosphere carbon system that includes biological factors will increase the level of confidence in assessments of the ocean's role in sequestering excess CO_2.

▷ But would such a model truly capture *all* the essential features of the 'real world' system if the ultimate aim is to simulate the response of the global carbon cycle to rapidly increasing levels of atmospheric CO_2?

▸ No. Given the possibility that 'excess' CO_2 is being sequestered by terrestrial ecosystems, a 'full' model should ideally incorporate some mathematical representation of the land-based carbon cycle as well.

This is where another core project of the IGBP, the **International Global Atmospheric Chemistry Programme (IGAC)**, comes into play. Once again, it envisages a vital symbiosis between observations, data analysis and modelling studies. One central aim is to document *and account for* (in terms of the processes involved, the type of ecosystem, the influence of human intervention, and so on), spatial and temporal patterns in the fluxes of CO_2 over *land* surfaces in tropical, polar and mid-latitude regions — as well as over the oceans (a goal it shares with JGOFS). However, the programme also takes in the other greenhouse gases. That's where the 'chemistry' comes into the title.

Activity 4.4   *You should spend up to 15 minutes on this activity.*

Figure 4.19 (*overleaf*) is a schematic representation of the current 'status' of the global ocean–atmosphere–terrestrial carbon system, as summarized in the IPCC report. Most of the numbers collected here were included in various figures scattered through Section 4.2 (i.e. Figures 4.6, 4.7 and 4.14): the important difference is that it now incorporates estimates of current anthropogenic emissions of CO_2 (from Section 4.2.3) and the resulting *imbalances* in the overall system.

To check your understanding of key points developed in Section 4.2, try to do parts (a) and (b) without referring back.

(a)   Describe *briefly* the processes represented by each of the arrows labelled (i)–(v).

(b)   Now repeat the exercise for the arrows labelled (vi)–(x).

(c)   According to Figure 4.19, what is the annual *net* uptake of atmospheric CO_2 (in PgC) by the surface ocean and the *net* transfer of carbon into the deep ocean? Jot down any reservations you have about these estimates.

(d)   According to Figure 4.19, on a *globally-averaged* basis, is the land-based carbon cycle in a state of balance at present? Can you now spot the assumption that has been incorporated into this schematic representation? Again, jot down any reservations you have.

One final and more general point warrants a brief reminder. Figure 4.19 (like Figure 4.6 before it) incorporates the 'slow leaks' from the 'active' carbon reservoirs we have focused on throughout Section 4.2. None of these are quantified, the implicit assumption being that these transfers have no *net* effect on atmospheric CO_2 on the decade–

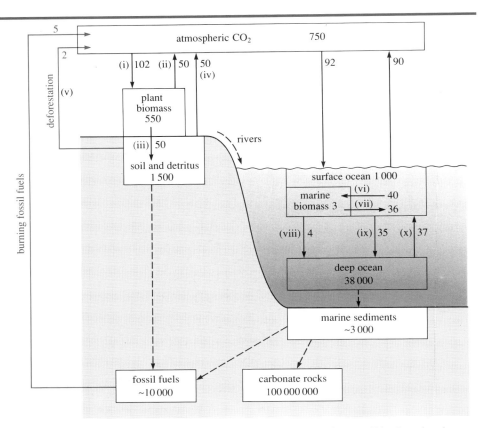

Figure 4.19 Global carbon reservoirs and fluxes (in PgC and PgC yr^{-1}, respectively). The numbers apply for the *present-day* situation and represent typical literature values. *Important*: Unlike earlier versions in this chapter, this figure incorporates estimates of current anthropogenic emissions of CO_2 (in blue) and the resulting *imbalances* in the overall system.

century time-scale, as noted at the outset (Section 4.2.1). It is *possible* that the data being collected under the JGOFS umbrella may challenge that assumption — especially as regards the supposed balance between the dissolved carbon transported to the world's oceans by rivers, and that ultimately 'dumped' on the sea-bed. If it does, then modelling studies will need to incorporate these transfers as well!

4.3 Other greenhouse gases: natural and unnatural

The other greenhouse gases considered here differ from CO_2 in one important respect: once released, the fate of all of them is bound up with atmospheric chemistry. Or to spell it out a little, each of them is 'destroyed', i.e. broken up or otherwise converted into something else, via chemical or photochemical reactions *within* the atmosphere (recall Box 2.2 in Section 2.2.3). As you will see, this adds further strands to our unfolding story of the interconnectedness of the planetary system.

4.3.1 Methane

The atmospheric concentration of methane (CH_4) is now (at 1.72 p.p.m.) more than double the estimated 'pre-industrial' value (0.8 p.p.m.) recorded in Table 4.1, and is currently increasing roughly twice as fast as that of CO_2. Furthermore (and like the CFCs), on a molecule-for-molecule basis, methane is a more potent greenhouse gas than CO_2 (see Table 4.4 in Section 4.3.3).

In an oxygen-rich environment, dead organic matter is ultimately oxidized to CO_2, whether chemically or via biological activity. All of the natural sources of atmospheric methane can be traced back to the breakdown of organic matter by bacteria under *anaerobic* (i.e. oxygen-free) conditions — principally, in the intestines of ruminant animals and in waterlogged soils (hence methane's common name of 'marsh gas'). Rice

Figure 4.20 Rice is a staple food for a large proportion of the world's population. According to current estimates (Table 4.3, *over-leaf*), the methane released by microbial activity in paddy fields is the major anthropogenic source of this greenhouse gas.

paddies, which in that respect are artificial marshes, are major sources of methane (Figure 4.20), and so are herds of cattle and flocks of sheep. Such sources are undoubtedly biogenic. But they also clearly have an anthropogenic element, as demonstrated in Figure 4.21; the accumulation of atmospheric methane over the last 300 years shows a good correlation with the growth of world population, suggesting that the rise in concentration of the gas is indeed related to human activities — agricultural production, in this case. More obviously, anthropogenic sources include the rotting of organic matter in landfill sites, as well as the fuel extraction operations mentioned in Section 4.1. Burning biomass — depending on the type of vegetation and the way it burns (i.e. smouldering as against flaming) — adds further to the atmospheric burden of CH_4.

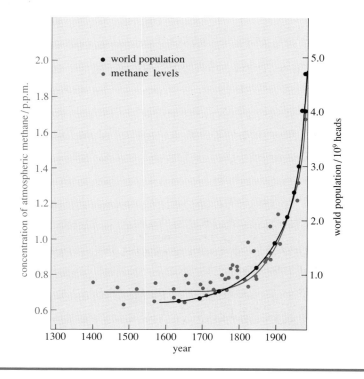

Figure 4.21 Correlation of the increase in the atmospheric concentration of methane (blue) with the growth of world population (black), from 1400 to the present day.

The identified sources of CH_4 are listed in Table 4.3 — together with current 'best estimates' of the annual contribution each makes, and the range of recent (up to 1990) literature values.

Table 4.3 Estimated sources and sinks for methane (data from IPCC).

	'Best estimate' of annual flux*/Tg CH_4 yr^{-1}	Range/ Tg CH_4 yr^{-1}
Sources		
natural wetlands (bogs, swamps, tundra, etc.)	115	100–200
rice paddies	110	25–170
ruminants	80	65–100
gas drilling, transmission, etc., and coal mining	80	44–100
landfill sites	40	20–70
biomass burning	40	20–80
termites	40	10–100
others	20	6–145
Sinks		
removal by soils	30	15–45
chemical destruction within the atmosphere	500	400–600
Observed atmospheric increase	44	40–48

* One teragram (1 Tg) = 10^{12} g.

Activity 4.5

(a) According to the 'best estimates' recorded in Table 4.3, does present understanding of the sources and sinks of CH_4 balance the methane budget?

(b) Is the information collected in Table 4.3 sufficient to attach 'uncertainty limits' to the 'best estimate' of the total present annual input of CH_4 to the atmosphere — or, indeed, to explain how the individual entries under 'sources' were arrived at?

Evidently, there are significant (if presently unquantifiable) uncertainties here — as there are in attempts to track the way the various factors have contributed to the observed build up in atmospheric CH_4 since pre-industrial times. One or two examples of the inherent difficulties must suffice. The flux of CH_4 from rice paddies is known to depend on a whole complex of factors — temperature, soil type, water management, the cropping system, the type of manure or artificial fertilizer applied, and so on. However, some 60% of the world's rice paddies are in China and India from where no detailed data are yet available. Is it legitimate to assume that CH_4 emissions have mirrored recorded increases in rice production? The rearing of 'domestic' ruminants has increased markedly over the past century, but to what extent has this been offset by the dramatic decline in certain populations of wild animals — elephants and North American bison, for example?

These difficulties are further compounded by the possibility that the strength of the major sink for atmospheric CH_4 is also changing. Unlike CO_2, methane is not taken up by the oceans and biosphere (except perhaps to a minor extent by soils, Table 4.3). Rather, it is oxidized *within* the atmosphere in a complex *sequence* of transformations that leads to carbon monoxide (CO), and then on, via a further round of reactions, to CO_2 as the end product. The whole process is triggered off (the technical term is 'initiated') by reaction with the atmosphere's paramount molecular scavenger — the **hydroxyl radical, OH•**.

$$CH_4 + OH• \rightarrow CH_3• + H_2O \tag{4.5}$$

The best way to think of OH• is as a water molecule with a hydrogen atom, *complete with its single electron*, stripped away (Figure 4.22). This leaves a molecular fragment which itself contains an *unpaired* electron. (Think of it as the electron originally paired up with the one on the lost hydrogen atom if this helps — although electrons cannot actually be 'identified' in this way.) All **free radicals** — or **radicals**, for short — share this characteristic feature. As a consequence, they are all highly reactive. Their attack on 'intact' molecules (like CH_4) invariably generates further radicals (the methyl radical, CH_3•, in Equation 4.5, for example) which are themselves highly reactive, and so on. The chemistry of the atmosphere is dominated by complex chains and networks of interacting and often competing chemical and photochemical reactions that involve a huge variety of radical species.

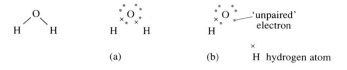

(a)   (b)   × H hydrogen atom

Figure 4.22 Lewis structures of (a) the water (H_2O) molecule, showing pairs of electrons shared between the oxygen and hydrogen atoms, and (b) the OH• radical, showing an 'unpaired' electron.

Returning to the methane sink, estimates of its present strength draw on laboratory studies of the rate of the reaction in Equation 4.5 — and how this depends on the concentrations of CH_4 and OH•, and on other factors, notably temperature. The end result is an equation that effectively summarizes all this information. Married to data on the global distribution of hydroxyl radicals (and there are ingenious indirect ways of making such assessments), this, in turn, provides a characteristic **atmospheric lifetime** for methane. The 'lifetime' (as used by the atmospheric chemist) is essentially equivalent to the 'residence time' (as used by the geochemist and ecologist), save that the former is invariably defined, as here, through the chemical mechanisms that *remove* the gas from the atmosphere. The distinction becomes important in a changing world, where sources and sinks are no longer in balance. Thus, the 'annual sink' entered in Table 4.3 (i.e. 500 Tg CH_4 yr^{-1}) was calculated as:

$$\text{rate of loss} = \frac{\text{atmospheric concentration of methane}}{\text{lifetime}} \qquad (4.6)$$

based on the current estimate of 10 ± 2 yr for the average lifetime of methane. For our present purposes, the crucial point is that this figure depends on the atmospheric burden of OH• radicals. A general *decrease* in the concentration of hydroxyl radicals would lengthen the lifetime of CH_4, thereby weakening its major sink and contributing to the build up of the gas in the atmosphere. In short, the factors that control the life cycle of the hydroxyl radical (it has a lifetime of only a second or so!) become important to the methane budget.

Any attempt to explore these factors in detail would immediately draw us in to the full (and fascinating) drama of tropospheric chemistry. Sadly, space does not permit us such a lengthy digression. Instead, the essential features are summarized in Box 4.3. Read this now.

Box 4.3   *The troposphere's 'cleaning agent' — the hydroxyl radical*   4.3

Hydroxyl radicals are constantly being created and destroyed in the troposphere. The concentration and global distribution of OH• radicals is the result of a complex balancing act between the rates of many competing reactions. However, a few key points can be identified.

1   The primary driving force for OH• radical production is the *photolysis of ozone* (recall

Figure 2.13 in Box 2.2). Put simply, oxygen atoms generated in this way can strip off hydrogen atoms from water molecules:

$$O + H_2O \rightarrow OH• + OH• \qquad (4.7)$$

2   Hydroxyl radicals are destroyed in reactions (analogous to that in Equation 4.5) whereby they initiate the oxidation, not only

of CH_4, but also of CO and other hydrocarbons (often collectively dubbed 'non-methane' hydrocarbons, NMHC) present in trace amounts in the atmosphere. Atmospheric CO includes that generated *in situ* (via the oxidation of CH_4) and that released directly (via the incomplete combustion of fossil fuels and biomass). The oceans and plants are major natural sources of NMHC: anthropogenic sources include the evaporation of solvents and liquid fuels.

3   In reality, the OH• radical plays a yet more pivotal role in tropospheric chemistry than is suggested here. It also triggers off the oxidation of trace gases containing sulphur (e.g. SO_2) and nitrogen and many halocarbons (of which more in Section 4.3.3). *However, present estimates suggest that reaction with CH_4 and CO together accounts for about 97% of the total tropospheric destruction of OH•.* ■

To summarize:

o   There is a long-term upward trend in the atmospheric burden of methane, but present understanding of the methane budget reveals a deficit (Activity 4.5). Whether this stems from an underestimate of methane emissions (possibly a missing source?) or an overestimate of the atmospheric sink remains unclear.

o   *Future* concentrations of methane will be affected by a range of human activities, either *directly* (by changing emissions) or *indirectly* (by changing the atmospheric abundance of OH• radicals).

The central message to take from Box 4.3 is that this final point effectively draws in to the methane budget a number of other trace constituents in the atmosphere. The key ingredients to register are water vapour and *tropospheric* ozone (which are crucial for generating OH• radicals), and a whole range of other gases (notably carbon monoxide) that effectively 'compete' with CH_4 in destroying them again. The water vapour story is taken up in Chapter 5, and we shall not dwell further on carbon monoxide — other than to note that there is some (albeit rather inconclusive) evidence that its atmospheric concentration *is* increasing. But what about ozone, which is an important greenhouse gas — quite apart from the link with OH• radical production?

4.3.2 Tropospheric ozone

As you saw in Section 2.2.3, the Earth's paramount ozone factory is in the stratosphere. Transport down from there, via a slow exchange of air across the tropopause, is the major natural source of the 'normal' background concentration of ozone in the lower atmosphere (Figure 2.12) — some 0.01–0.1 p.p.m. However, there is now good evidence that human activities can — and do — lead to ozone being generated at or near ground level as well. This is always bad news. At concentrations little higher than the normal background level, ozone irritates the respiratory system and can cause severe damage to human health. Plant growth may also be impaired.

The chemistry and photochemistry that produces enhanced levels of tropospheric ozone is complicated, and we shall not attempt to grapple with the details. Put simply, it comes down to the action of sunlight on the mix of gaseous pollutants that typically goes along with the ubiquitous burning of fossil fuels and biomass (see Plate 4.5). The products of 'incomplete' combustion — in vehicle exhausts, power station emissions and so on are a necessary part of the 'brew'. But the crucial ingredients are 'reactive' nitrogen oxides — known collectively as NO_x: combustion in air at high temperatures inevitably produces some NO_x, through reaction between the atmosphere's major constituents (N_2 and O_2).

Atmospheric NO_x — a shorthand for **nitric oxide (NO)** and **nitrogen dioxide (NO_2)** — is part of the natural 'nitrogen cycle'. For example, microbial processes in soils are a major source of the background concentrations of NO_x in 'unpolluted' air (a few p.p.t.

at most): emissions are known to be stimulated by agricultural activities, such as the application of fertilizers, manures, etc. But the main anthropogenic sources stem from the high-temperature combustion of living or 'fossil' carbon. If this pushes the atmospheric concentration of NO_x above a certain threshold value — current estimates suggest some 5–30 p.p.t. — ozone can begin to build up at or near ground level. (For the curious, some brief notes about the chemistry involved are collected in Box 4.4.) There is good evidence that this happens on a local, or even regional scale (during the burning that accompanies tropical deforestation, for example). Indeed, in the UK we now get warnings about 'high ozone' episodes along with the weather forecast. However, it is a far more difficult task to assess whether — and to what extent — human activities may be affecting tropospheric ozone on a *long-term and global* scale.

We shall not dwell on those difficulties here. Suffice it to say that existing data (mainly dating back to the late 1960s) do suggest an increase in the ozone concentration of around 1% a year in the lower troposphere of the Northern Hemisphere, especially over the heavily industrialized regions of north Europe and Japan. Overall, however, the IPCC report concluded that truly global trends are as yet too ill-defined to permit a quantitative assessment of their possible contribution to the *enhanced* greenhouse effect (more on which in later chapters).

Box 4.4 'Anthropogenic ozone'

1 The heart of the matter is that it takes a supply of oxygen *atoms* (O) to make ozone. But the short uv wavelengths in the incoming solar radiation needed to break up molecular oxygen are effectively filtered out by that process occurring in the *stratosphere* — recall the discussion in Section 2.2.3.

2 The only known *tropospheric* source of O atoms is quite different — photolysis of the much weaker N–O bond in NO_2 (Figure 4.23a), by longer uv and visible wavelengths that *do* penetrate to ground level.

3 In the unpolluted atmosphere, this photolysis triggers off a cycle of reactions

(captured in Figure 4.23b) — whereby the O atom is effectively shuffled back and forth between NO_2 and O_2, with NO as the vital intermediary. As a result, ozone is continually created and destroyed: its concentration does not build up.

4 When concentrations of NO_x get above the critical threshold, however, chemical reactions come into play — they involve a whole range of hydrocarbons and other partial combustion products — the crucial effect of which is to convert NO into NO_2, *without at the same time consuming ozone*. Tropospheric ozone can then accumulate. ■

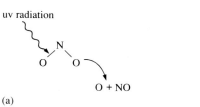
(a)

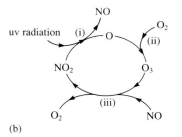
(b)

Figure 4.23 (a) Photolysis of one of the O–N–O bonds in nitrogen dioxide (NO_2) yields oxygen atoms and nitric oxide, NO. (b) O atoms (produced by the photolysis of NO_2 (i)), react with molecular oxygen to form ozone (ii). But ozone is destroyed by reaction with nitric oxide, reforming molecular oxygen and nitrogen dioxide (iii). Given constant conditions, a steady state is set up, with the concentration of ozone maintained at its 'normal' background value (around 100 p.p.b. at ground level).

4.3.3 Halocarbons: CFCs and their substitutes

We shall not attempt an exhaustive survey of the industrially produced halocarbons here. Rather, we concentrate on a representative selection: information pertinent to their role as greenhouse gases in the troposphere (and, indeed, as destroyers of *stratospheric* ozone) is collected in Table 4.4. Concentrate for now on the three CFCs. Think of these as derived from either methane (CFCs-11 and -12), or ethane (CFC-113), but with *all* their hydrogen atoms replaced by varying combinations of fluorines and chlorines.

Table 4.4 Tropospheric concentrations (1990) and atmospheric lifetimes of artificial halocarbons (together with CO_2, CH_4 and N_2O for comparison), and their 'effectiveness' as greenhouse gases.

Compound	Concentration*	Lifetime/ yr	'Effectiveness' as greenhouse gas relative to CO_2[†]
CO_2	353 p.p.m.	~50–200[‡]	1
CH_4	1.72 p.p.m.	10	21
N_2O	310 p.p.b.	150	206
CFC-11 ($CFCl_3$)	280 p.p.t. (~3%)	65	12 400
CFC-12 (CF_2Cl_2)	484 p.p.t. (~4%)	130	15 800
CFC-113 ($C_2F_3Cl_3$)	57 p.p.t. (~10%)	90	15 800
carbon tetrachloride (CCl_4)	107 p.p.t.	50	5 720
methyl chloroform (CH_3CCl_3)	160 p.p.t. (~4%)	6	2 730
HCFC-22(CHF_2Cl)	103 p.p.t.	15	10 700

* The figures in brackets are the current annual rate of accumulation of each gas, as a percentage of the present concentration.

[†] For each compound, the figure quoted in this column is on a molecule-for-molecule basis, relative to CO_2. In effect, it measures the radiation 'trapping', relative to CO_2, induced by adding to the atmosphere the same number of molecules of each gas.

[‡] See Section 4.4 for a brief discussion of this estimate.

As far as the CFCs are concerned, the immediately striking feature is their efficiency as greenhouse gases and their very long atmospheric lifetimes. The latter stems from the very characteristics that made CFCs seem so ideal (Figure 4.24!), and saw their rapid expansion into the now familiar sectors — as refrigerants, as propellants in aerosol spray cans, as blowing agents (to put the bubbles into all manner of 'foamed' plastics), and as solvents and cleaning fluids in many speciality areas (notably, the electronics industry). They not only have physical properties well suited to all these applications and are cheap to produce, they are also stable, non-toxic, non-flammable — in short, effectively completely inert in the lower atmosphere. Despite prodigious research efforts, no evidence has emerged for any significant tropospheric sink for CFCs (although tiny amounts are taken up by the oceans).

Indeed, the inertness of the CFCs was the driving force behind the first measurements of their atmospheric concentrations, using the exquisitely sensitive analytical technique still used to monitor the build up of these gases (recall they have concentrations measured in parts per trillion). The aim was to use CFCs as passive 'tracers' of the general atmospheric circulation: they are still used in this way (as, indeed, they are to track how different water masses move through the oceans). However, their eventual fate is sealed once they are carried across the tropopause into the stratosphere. Mostly this happens over the tropics — a region of rapidly rising air currents, often driven by violent storms.

Once in the stratosphere, the compounds encounter an environment that is both calmer and more 'hostile'. It is calmer, because there is little of the turbulent motion characteristic of the lower atmosphere. The temperature inversion at the tropopause (Figure 2.11) produces a more stably stratified structure (hence the name of this region). Layers of air sliding over one another produces vertical mixing, but it is generally much slower than that in the troposphere. The 'hostility' comes from the increasing intensity, with altitude, of the short uv wavelengths in the *incoming* solar radiation that are energetic enough to break up molecules of the CFCs — in the range 190–210 nm for CFCs-11 and -12. Photolysis releases one chlorine atom immediately, (see Figure 4.25 (*overleaf*), for example), and the remainder as radical fragments engage in further chemical and photochemical reactions.

Figure 4.24 A 'hard sell' on the new 'miracle' aerosol propellants: Freon was the trade name for the CFCs. From *Soap and Sanitary Chemicals*, January 1950.

For our present purposes, the crucial point is that CFC molecules are not effectively removed from the atmosphere until they reach altitudes where the rate of photolysis can 'keep up' with the rate at which they are arriving — some 20–25 km for CFC-11, for example. On average, it takes molecules released at the surface several years to get to this height. This time-scale, combined with the small fraction of the total pool of CFC molecules actually at these altitudes at any given instant (a few per cent), produces a slow overall rate of removal — and hence the long lifetimes recorded in Table 4.4.

Photolysis of CFC molecules adds to the burden of stratospheric chlorine. The long debate about the threat thereby posed to the ozone layer is taken up in Chapter 6. Suffice it to say here that the threat is no longer in doubt, now that depletion of

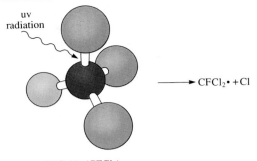

CFC-11 (CFCl₃)

Figure 4.25 A schematic representation of the photolysis of CFC-11, breaking one of the carbon–chlorine bonds and so releasing a chlorine atom.

stratospheric ozone is manifestly evident — most dramatically over Antarctica each southern spring (the so-called 'ozone hole'), but also elsewhere. Concern about it is embodied in the terms of the 'Montreal Protocol on Substances that Deplete the Ozone Layer'. The original Protocol (agreed in 1987) provides for a periodic review of its control measures 'on the basis of available scientific, environmental, technical and economic information'. At the time of writing, two such reviews had taken place — in 1990 and 1992. These produced agreement to a strengthened set of controls that effectively cover *all* long-lived *fully-halogenated* halocarbons, i.e. all CFCs, *and* carbon tetrachloride (also included in Table 4.4). In 1992, signatories to the Protocol pledged to phase out production of all of these compounds before the end of the century, with a staged reduction in production and consumption before that.

Given world-wide compliance with these stringent regulations (and the mechanisms for achieving that are not clear as yet), future *emissions* of these gases should be significantly lower than today's: eventually emissions should be virtually eliminated. Bear in mind, however, that stopping the release of a long-lived gas simply initiates the slow process whereby its atmospheric concentration gradually 'decays' away. The word in quotes is chosen with care. Once emissions cease (*but only then* cf. Equation 4.1 in Section 4.1) the equation that governs the rate of change of the atmospheric concentration of a halocarbon becomes formally identical with that describing the time course of radioactive decay. Insight into the time-scale hinted at above is then obtained by defining a corresponding **half-life** (τ): we ask you to accept that this is related to the lifetimes recorded in Table 4.4 as follows:

$$\tau = 0.69 \times \text{lifetime} \tag{4.8}$$

Question 4.5 Given this definition, how long will it take for the atmospheric concentrations of CFC-11 and -12 to be reduced to (a) a half; and (b) one-quarter of the levels they have reached when emissions cease?

Evidently, the atmospheric burden of these long-lived gases will still be significant for much of the next century. Moreover, many of the compounds being considered as potential substitutes for existing CFCs themselves absorb infrared wavelengths within the atmospheric window. Like the CFCs, these are halocarbons — but they are not *fully* halogenated. Rather, the molecules contain one or more hydrogen atoms along with various combinations of chlorine and/or fluorine. They fall into two broad categories: the **hydrochlorofluorocarbons (HCFCs)** and the **hydrofluorocarbons (HFCs)**. A typical example of the first group — known commercially as HCFC-22 (Figure 4.26) — is included in Table 4.4: it is already widely used as a refrigerant. Notice its comparatively short atmospheric lifetime.

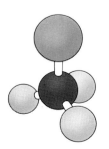

HCFC-22 (CHF₂Cl)

Figure 4.26 The structure of HCFC-22.

Question 4.6 Given the discussion in Section 4.3.1, can you suggest why the presence of hydrogen atoms in *non-fully halogenated* hydrocarbons like HCFC-22 makes them vulnerable to *chemical* attack in the lower atmosphere? Why should this give such compounds shorter atmospheric lifetimes than the CFCs?

On current estimates, the lifetimes of likely substitute compounds range between about 1 and 40 years. It is important to be clear that a lifetime at the lower end of this range does not *prevent* the accumulation of the gas in the troposphere — witness the present, *and rising*, atmospheric concentrations of the two short-lived compounds included in Table 4.4, i.e. HCFC-22 and methyl chloroform (strictly 1,1,1-trichloro-ethane, a widely-used solvent and cleaning fluid). This reflects emission rates for the two gases that continue to outstrip their loss rates.

Methyl chloroform was included in the revised (1990) Montreal Protocol: its use should be phased out by 2005. HCFC-22 was not, and neither were any of the other likely successors to the CFCs. Whether these short-lived halocarbons are allowed to accumulate in the atmosphere to levels where they too become important in trapping outgoing longwave radiation depends on a complex set of essentially economic, technological and political factors. In short:

o   the extent to which they capture the former market for CFCs;

o   the scope and timing of control measures aimed at them in future revisions to the Protocol;

o   the adoption of 'containment' strategies by all sectors of the industry, whereby the compounds are captured and recycled, or safely destroyed — thus limiting emissions to the atmosphere.

4.3.4 Nitrous oxide

Turning now to the last of the natural greenhouse gases, we find a familiar mix of biogenic and anthropogenic forces at work. For a start, the major identified sources of N_2O are biogenic (i.e. like NO_x, N_2O is also part of the nitrogen cycle), stemming from microbial processes in soils and in the oceans. Fluxes of N_2O from soils are strongly dependent on the type of ecosystem, and other environmental factors. For agricultural land, detailed farming practices also become important — the type of fertilizer applied, patterns of ploughing and irrigation, and so on. Clearly there is scope here for an anthropogenic component to help explain the observed buildup in atmospheric N_2O (Figure 4.1d), but it is difficult to quantify. As indeed, is the contribution made by burning biomass and fossil fuels — practices that produce a small proportion of N_2O, along with the other oxides of nitrogen (i.e. NO_x). In short, there are significant uncertainties in attempts to quantify the strength and geographical distribution of the various natural and anthropogenic sources of nitrous oxide.

Nevertheless, the coming of the industrial age clearly triggered an imbalance between the sources and sinks of N_2O: as of 1990, global emissions of the gas exceed its sinks by some 30%. And the legacy of this imbalance will persist. Like the CFCs — and *unlike* NO_x — nitrous oxide is resistant to chemical attack in the troposphere. Its major sink is photochemical decomposition in the stratosphere, a relatively well characterized process that gives it an atmospheric lifetime of around 150 years (Table 4.4). As a result, the atmospheric concentration of N_2O would respond only slowly to any attempts to curtail emissions of the gas.

Activity 4.6 *You should spend up to 15 minutes on this activity.*

(a)   List the main anthropogenic sources of (i) the greenhouse gases discussed in this chapter, and (ii) other trace gases that can influence their atmospheric concentrations. Briefly explain your answer to part (ii).

(b)   Reflect on your list for a moment. Drawing on your own general knowledge of the world, jot down any factors you feel could influence *future* anthropogenic emissions of the key trace gases. *Don't spend long on this* — say, 5 minutes at most. Now, given your list, do you think that *forecasting* such emissions is primarily a task for scientists?

4.4 Drawing the threads together: what of the future?

The main focus of this chapter has been the link between human activities and the observed buildup in the atmosphere of various greenhouse gases. Having examined that link for each of the gases in turn, some common themes begin to emerge. They bear sharply on the problem of forecasting how the composition of the atmosphere will evolve into the future.

Reference to the list you drew up for part (a) of Activity 4.6 suggests that anthropogenic sources of *all* the important trace gases fall into three broad categories. First, there are the uses of entirely synthetic compounds (i.e. the halocarbons). Second, there is the extraction, processing and combustion of fossil fuels. Both of these categories are broadly linked with the level of economic development, industrialization, etc. Third, there are human activities that either interfere with natural control mechanisms, or effectively enhance natural sources (rearing cows and other domestic ruminants, for example). Deforestation, and the associated burning of biomass and changing land use, together with agricultural activities in general, fall into this category.

Although the major anthropogenic sources of the various gases have probably been identified, aspects of many of them have not yet been adequately quantified — either because the observational data are lacking, or because the underlying processes are not fully understood, or more often, both. As a result, there are significant uncertainties in estimates of *current* (and past) emission rates, especially for CH_4 and N_2O, and also for NO_x, the key 'precursor' to enhanced levels of tropospheric ozone. Once attention turns to the *future*, however, the issue of emission rates is further compounded by uncertainties of a quite different kind. Have your thoughts on Activity 4.6b to hand at this point.

To focus the discussion, take CO_2 as an illustrative example: forecasting its emission rate is essentially a problem for social scientists. In outline, it requires predictions of population trends, economic growth, the relationship between economic development and energy consumption, and the proportion of those energy demands that will be met by burning fossil fuels. Fossil fuel usage will also depend on factors such as the price of oil, the availability and cost effectiveness of alternative energy sources, energy conservation measures, and so on, which may, in turn, depend on scientific and technological developments. Social and political pressures for measures to counter anthropogenic greenhouse warming will probably also come into the equation in the coming decades — as, indeed, could future wars, or other periods of international tension.

Depending on your background, you may well have identified other factors. The important general point is that there are very large uncertainties associated with any projection of global energy requirements and fossil fuel consumption — even in the short term (a decade, say). These uncertainties are different in kind from those which scientists attach to experimentally measured quantities, or even to the predictions of their own (albeit flawed) mathematical models. In particular, demographic and economic factors are not amenable to modelling in quite the same way as quantities governed by natural laws, and economic factors are further complicated by political decisions. In short,

> ... any particular trajectory [of CO_2 emissions] implies some combination of political, technological and social developments that cannot be predicted.[*]

Fossil fuel usage also releases all the other key trace gases (except the halocarbons, of course), and forecasting trends in the rate of deforestation, and in the range of agricultural activities that release methane and oxides of nitrogen, is subject to similar constraints. Faced with the impossibility of quantifying all the factors involved, researchers adopt a different strategy. They construct **emission scenarios** — essentially the emission rates to expect, given certain basic assumptions about future developments. A scenario is not an image of a definite future; it is an image of what *could* happen if a particular set of conditions is fulfilled. We look at typical emission scenarios in Chapter 7.

For now, we focus on the task of 'translating' emission scenarios into forecasts of atmospheric concentrations — a problem that *is* amenable to scientific modelling, of the kind outlined for CO_2 and the carbon cycle in Section 4.2.4. Indeed, set in the present context, computer experiments designed to simulate the *past* rise in CO_2 can be seen as a crucial test of the **carbon cycle models** used to predict *future* levels of the gas, given a particular emission scenario. That test reveals deficiencies in existing models. Undoubtedly, they are over simplified and incomplete. For example, they do not yet include biological controls over the ocean–atmosphere carbon cycle. Probably, they should be expanded to incorporate elements of the terrestrial cycle as well (a thought crystallized at the end of Section 4.2.4).

However, simulations with existing ocean–atmosphere carbon-cycle models do highlight a crucial distinction that we did not stress earlier. In Question 4.2 (Section 4.2.1) you estimated that CO_2 has a *residence time* in the atmosphere of around 4 years. This figure is a measure of the 'turnover' time for atmospheric CO_2 — of how long it takes, on average, for a molecule of CO_2 in the atmosphere to be taken up by plants or dissolved in the ocean. It is quite different from the very much longer time-scale over which the atmospheric concentration of CO_2 might be expected to respond to attempts to curtail anthropogenic emissions.

Because CO_2 is not destroyed within the atmosphere, it is not possible to define an atmospheric 'lifetime' (and hence half-life, Equation 4.8) that is strictly analogous to the figures quoted earlier (Table 4.4) for the other greenhouse gases. But on a roughly comparable basis, model simulations suggest a figure of the order of 50–200 years —

---

[*] Keepin, W., Mintzer, I. and Kristoferson, L. (1986) Emissions of CO_2 into the atmosphere: the rate of release of CO_2 as a function of future energy developments, Chapter 2 in B. Bolin *et al.* (eds) *The Greenhouse Effect, Climatic Change and Ecosystems*, John Wiley. This report (often known as SCOPE 29) was put together under the auspices of the United Nations Environment Programme (UNEP), the World Meteorological Organization (WMO) and the International Council of Scientific Unions (ICSU). Its conclusions played an important part in establishing the global warming issue on the international political agenda.

determined mainly by the slow exchange of carbon between surface waters and the deep ocean. The important general point is that this time-scale puts atmospheric CO_2 in the same 'long-lived' category as N_2O and the CFCs.

For the other greenhouse gases, achieving a quantitative understanding of the relationship between emission scenarios and future atmospheric concentrations again involves modelling studies. Take methane as a specific example. Here, the kind of model required needs to incorporate a mathematical description of the life cycle of the hydroxyl radical — a network of coupled, interacting and often competing chemical and photochemical reactions (far more complex in reality than the brief outline in Box 4.3 might suggest). In practice, that means a set of equations which summarize the results of experiments on the *rates* of all these processes — and how those rates depend on the concentrations of the chemical species involved, and other factors (such as temperature, or the intensity of certain wavelengths in sunlight).

But this captures only part of the problem. In the real atmosphere, the balance struck by all these processes — and hence the concentration of OH• radicals — depends not only on relatively local atmospheric conditions (temperature, intensity of solar radiation, and hence cloudiness, season of the year and so on), but also on the *supply* of the various ingredients in the atmospheric chemistry 'brew'. That supply is bound up with the *dynamics* of the atmosphere: ultimately, it is driven by the large-scale atmospheric circulation outlined in Section 2.3.2.

In short, in the real world, the concentration and global distribution of OH• radicals is shaped by an all-pervasive interplay between chemistry and atmospheric dynamics. You will be in a better position to appreciate just how difficult it is to construct a model capable of simulating that interplay after studying Chapter 5. Suffice it to say that existing **'chemistry' models** have echoes of their carbon-cycle counterparts, in that they usually incorporate a much simplified treatment of atmospheric dynamics. On the other hand, they include quite detailed chemistry. Overall, however, the simplifying assumptions and approximations built into such models raise questions about the reliability of their forecasts of future OH• radical concentrations. In other words, future trends in the atmosphere's power to 'dispose of' potent greenhouse gases like methane and the CFC substitutes remain uncertain.

The important general point is that model deficiencies, whatever their precise nature, introduce further inherent uncertainties into projections of the atmospheric burden of the various greenhouse gases — further, that is, to the fundamental uncertainty about future cultural evolution embedded in the emission scenarios themselves. All of which creates a potential problem for climate modellers. In essence, their task is to 'translate' the build up in greenhouse gases into an assessment of the likely scale and *rate* of climatic change — in response to the enhanced radiation 'trapping' (recall Section 2.2.2) associated with that build up. The strategy currently adopted to tackle that problem is the subject of the next chapter.

Summary of Chapter 4

1   Over the past 200 years or so, a whole range of human activities (collected in the answer to Activity 4.6) have increased the atmospheric burden of greenhouse gases, both natural (i.e. CO_2, CH_4, N_2O, and possibly tropospheric ozone) and unnatural (i.e. various halocarbons, particularly the CFCs). For each gas, this buildup implies an imbalance between its sources and sinks.

2   Unlike the other greenhouse gases, CO_2 is not destroyed via chemical or photochemical processes within the atmosphere. Rather it is circulated between various carbon reservoirs: on the decade-to-century time-scale, the 'active' reservoirs

are the atmosphere, oceans and terrestrial ecosystems. At present, slow transfer into the deep ocean is believed to be the principal sink for anthropogenic CO_2, but existing ocean–atmosphere carbon-cycle models do not balance the 'excess-CO_2' budget. As yet, such models do not incorporate any biological factors (in particular, the workings of the biological pump). Neither do they permit estimates to be made of any possible uptake by terrestrial ecosystems.

Important: You should be able to interpret a diagrammatic representation of the global carbon cycle (like the one in Figure 4.19, say), and explain briefly the physical, chemical and/or biological controls over the various carbon fluxes, and the way human activities can interfere with these controls (as summarized in Activity 4.4).

3 Current understanding of the methane budget reveals a deficit (Activity 4.5), but whether this stems from an underestimate of methane emissions, or an overestimate of the atmospheric sink (through reaction with the OH• radical) is unclear.

Important: You should be aware of the range of human activities that can affect the atmospheric concentration of CH_4, either *directly* (by increasing sources of CH_4), or *indirectly* (by changing the atmospheric abundance of OH• radicals). Part (a) of Activity 4.6 is a good guide to the basic level of understanding required.

4 There is good evidence that anthropogenic sources of the key 'precursor' gases (i.e. partial combustion products in the presence of elevated levels of NO_x) can produce a build up in tropospheric ozone on a local or regional scale. But truly global long-term trends are ill-defined as yet.

5 Industrially produced halocarbons may have chemical sinks in the lower atmosphere (if they contain H atoms), or photochemical ones in the stratosphere (if they do not, like the CFCs). The latter compounds have long atmospheric lifetimes.

6 Projecting future anthropogenic emissions of the various greenhouse gases (or its precursors, in the case of tropospheric ozone) is essentially a problem for social scientists: they tackle it by constructing emission scenarios (more on which in Chapter 7). The atmospheric concentrations of those gases with long atmospheric lifetimes (not only the CFCs and N_2O, but also the 'special' case of CO_2) will respond only slowly to attempts to curtail emissions.

Afterword

But there is also a more general message to take from this chapter. The life cycles of the various greenhouse gases are eloquent testimony to the web of interactions that binds together the 'total Earth system', with threads that reach down into the deepest ocean, and extend up into the stratosphere as well. Traditionally, scientists have carved up the study of this complex, interconnected system into their various disciplines. There are good reasons for this: different techniques and methodologies are appropriate for the study of different types of problem. But Nature herself is cavalier about such distinctions. A better understanding of the planetary system, and its response to human activities, is a truly interdisciplinary endeavour — a view captured in the description of the IGBP quoted in Section 4.1.

Research during the 1990s, coordinated through major international programmes like this, should address important areas of uncertainty. For example, the many uncertainties surrounding the detailed workings of the ocean–atmosphere–terrestrial carbon cycle are being tackled through collaborations between *three* core projects of the IGBP — not just JGOFS and IGAC (touched on at the end of Section 4.2.4), but also the **'Global Change and Terrestrial Ecosystems'** project (GCTE). Parallel collaborations between IGAC and GCTE should provide much needed information about the strength and geographical distribution of the sources — both natural and anthropogenic — of the other key trace gases as well. For example, initial targets include wetland sources of methane, trace gas fluxes from natural ecosystems such as forest, grasslands, etc., and the impact of human intervention thereon (be it through deforestation, biomass burning or other changes in land use), and so on.

The long-term aim of these collaborative research programmes is to:

> *... develop models that integrate relevant biospheric and atmospheric processes for a wide suite of reactive gases, contributing to a predictive capability for the atmospheric and Earth systems as a whole under conditions of global change.*

> *(IGBP (1992)* Global Change: Reducing Uncertainties*)*

This quote brings to the fore another theme running through this chapter: the vital link between observational data — whether collected in the laboratory or in the field, by ground-based monitoring stations, ships or satellite-borne remote sensors — and modelling studies. However flawed, incomplete and oversimplified they may be, computer models are the only tools capable of simulating the workings of the planetary system. Such models are central to the discussion in the next chapter.

5 Simulating climatic change

5.1 Introduction

It is important to be clear that there is no dispute about the nature of the greenhouse effect, and the critical role it plays in the Earth's climate system. However, there *is* still controversy surrounding assessments of the possible extent of anthropogenic contributions to the greenhouse effect, in particular:

1 the amount by which the Earth's surface temperature may rise as a consequence of the increased atmospheric burden of greenhouse gases;

2 the geographical distribution of any such temperature increase, and of changes to other important climate parameters, such as rainfall, cloudiness, snow cover, storms, etc; and

3 the likely time-scale of such changes.

The previous chapter (and Section 4.4 in particular) stressed one fundamental source of uncertainty in all assessments of climatic change — the likely *future* levels of greenhouse gases arising from human activities. For now, we uncouple that source of uncertainty, and focus instead on current assessments of climatic change in response to a *prescribed* increase in greenhouse gases — commonly a doubling in the atmospheric concentration of CO_2.

Such studies essentially produce '**global warming scenarios**', but they *do* permit a controlled comparison between the results obtained by different climate modelling groups. This is one of the few ways of achieving some measure of the 'envelope of uncertainty' that necessarily surrounds the output of 'our cloudy crystal balls' — a description of climate models coined by Stephen Schneider (Figure 5.1), an American climatologist who has long been at the forefront of the debates about climatic change.

Concern over global warming has prompted a tremendous and on-going investment of both intellectual and financial resources in the development of climate models. Such models are constantly being updated, not only in response to an evolving understanding of the workings of the Earth's climate system, but also as new generations of ever more powerful supercomputers come on stream. That said, it is important to appreciate that mathematical models can only ever be approximate representations of the 'real world' system — the message implicit in Schneider's image. In this chapter, we aim to convey something of the inherent difficulties involved, and the way they are handled at present. That will serve to highlight the major deficiencies in existing models, and the attendant uncertainties in their predictions of the climatic consequences of enhanced levels of greenhouse gases in the atmosphere. The part those uncertainties have played — and indeed, continue to play — in the public and political debate about climatic change is a theme taken up in the next chapter.

5.2 The 'radiative forcing' of climate

Insight into the problem of predicting the scale of anthropogenic greenhouse warming (i.e. point 1 above) can be obtained by focusing on the Earth's *global-mean* radiation balance — just as we did in Section 2.2 — and then breaking down the process of climatic change into two stages: 'radiative forcing' and 'response'. The strategy is

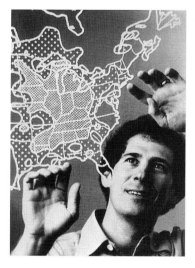

Figure 5.1 Stephen H. Schneider is the head of Interdisciplinary Climate Systems at the National Center for Atmospheric Research (NCAR) in Boulder, Colorado. Incisive and original in his scientific work, Schneider also has a sure grasp of the wide-ranging policy implications of that research. Articulate and sophisticated in the art of communicating the complexities of climatic change to non-specialists, he has a high public profile in the USA — as a witness before countless committees of the state and federal legislatures, in the media, and through the writing of 'popular' scientific articles and a book (*Global Warming*) on the subject.

shown schematically in Figure 5.2 — a doubling in the atmospheric concentration of CO_2 (CO_2-doubling for short) being used as an illustrative example. The essential features are as follows.

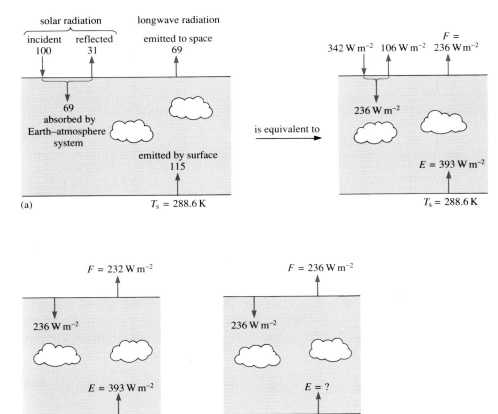

Figure 5.2 The global-mean radiation balance at the top of the atmosphere, and the greenhouse effect. (a) The present situation, with figures expressed as a percentage of the incoming solar flux, on the left (see Figure 2.14), and then translated into energy fluxes, on the right (assuming 100 units is equivalent to $342\,\mathrm{W\,m^{-2}}$). (b) The imbalance induced by an instantaneous CO_2-doubling. (c) The new equilibrium. See text for further details.

1 *The present balance*   Figure 5.2a takes estimates of the present radiation balance at the *top of the atmosphere* from Figure 2.14 (Section 2.2.4) — on the left — and then 'translates' these into radiant energy fluxes — on the right. It also incorporates the flux of longwave radiation emitted by the planetary surface, and the corresponding global-mean surface temperature, T_s, that you calculated from the Stefan–Boltzmann law (i.e. energy flux = σT_s^4) in Activity 2.3. (Refer back to refresh your memory if need be.)

The *difference* between the longwave flux emitted by the surface and that ultimately radiated to space — given the symbols E and F, respectively, in Figure 5.2a — can be interpreted as a 'measure' of the radiation trapping by the atmospheric burden of greenhouse gases and globally-averaged cloudiness. Or in other words, one measure of the global-mean greenhouse effect (G, say) is the difference,

$$G = E - F \tag{5.1}$$

$$= (393 - 236)\,\mathrm{W\,m^{-2}} = 157\,\mathrm{W\,m^{-2}} \text{ (from Figure 5.2a)}$$

Data from satellite-borne instruments (more on which shortly) indicate that the trapping of infrared radiation by clouds contributes some 20% of this global-mean value of G: the remainder is due to the greenhouse gases.

2 *The radiative forcing*   Suppose now that the atmospheric concentration of CO_2 is doubled *instantaneously* — the implication being that all of the other climate parameters which affect the global radiation budget are *fixed* at their present global-

mean values. In practice, this means that the surface temperature (T_s), planetary albedo, and vertical distributions of clouds, water vapour and other greenhouse gases are fixed: only the atmospheric burden of CO_2 is allowed to change.

Under these circumstances, it is a relatively straightforward scientific problem to calculate the ensuing *reduction* in the flux of longwave radiation emitted to space. We cannot pursue the details of these calculations here. Suffice it to say that they are complicated, but well understood: the results indicate that a CO_2-doubling would reduce F by around $4\,W\,m^{-2}$, as shown in Figure 5.2b.

This constitutes a **radiative forcing** (or enhanced radiative heating) of the Earth–atmosphere system, since the latter now absorbs an energy flux that is $4\,W\,m^{-2}$ *greater*, on average, than it emits. At this point, the climate system is no longer in a balanced, or equilibrium, state.

3 *The response* to a radiative forcing is the global warming that then occurs, so as to increase the radiation emitted to space, and thereby restore the balance at the top of the atmosphere. Simulating that response is what climate modelling is all about! From this modelling perspective, the computed increase in global-mean surface temperature (usually written ΔT_s, and spoken 'delta-t-s') needed to restore the Earth's radiation balance is often related to the radiative forcing (i.e. the change in F, ΔF) that induced it through the following simple expression:

$$\Delta T_s = \lambda \Delta F \tag{5.2}$$

where λ is known as the **climate sensitivity parameter**. Think of it as a measure of the 'sensitivity' of the climate system (i.e. its *response*, in terms of an increase in global-mean surface temperature, ΔT_s) to a *particular* radiative forcing — the pertinent example being a CO_2-doubling, with $\Delta F = 4\,W\,m^{-2}$ (from point 2): the larger the value of λ, the greater the ensuing global warming.

Now have another look at Figure 5.2. The situation depicted in part (c) is typical of the response to a CO_2-doubling computed by the simplest type of climate model, known as a 'one-dimensional' (1-D) model — the dimension being altitude. Such models effectively collapse the climate system into a single, globally-averaged surface and atmospheric column. Notice that the response recorded in Figure 5.2c does indeed restore the radiation balance at the top of the atmosphere. In short, the overall effect is to shift the global climatic regime to a *new* equilibrium state, characterized by a *higher* average surface temperature. That is one important point to register. But there is also a second, and less obvious, point to expose.

▷ What is the value of λ according to the 1-D model results recorded in Figure 5.2c?

▶ For a CO_2-doubling

$$\Delta F = 4\,W\,m^{-2}, \text{ so with } \Delta T_s = (289.8 - 288.6)\,K = 1.2\,K,$$

$$\lambda = \frac{\Delta T_s}{\Delta F} = \frac{1.2\,K}{4\,W\,m^{-2}} = 0.3\,K\,m^2\,W^{-1}.$$

This value of λ represents a sort of reference case: it is effectively determined by the assumptions embedded in the kind of 1-D model calculation used to produce the global warming scenario in Figure 5.2c. Put simply, this comes down to allowing the globally-averaged Earth–atmosphere system to warm up, while at the same time holding *all* of the other key factors noted under point 2 above — and in particular, the planetary albedo, cloudiness and atmospheric water vapour — *constant* at their present global-mean values. That amounts to assuming that global warming would not itself produce effects that can, in turn, alter the Earth's radiation balance.

It is widely acknowledged that this assumption cannot hold in the real world. On the contrary, global warming is likely to trigger off numerous interactive **feedback mechanisms**. In general, these could either act to amplify a warming trend (positive feedbacks) or to moderate it (negative feedbacks). Or to put it in terms of Equation 5.2, feedbacks can be interpreted as *changing* the 'reference' value of λ (i.e. $0.3 \, \text{K m}^2 \, \text{W}^{-1}$) — either increasing it (positive feedbacks) or reducing it (negative feedbacks) — and thereby making the climate system either more or less 'sensitive' to a CO_2-doubling than this 'zero climate feedback' assumption would predict.

As you will see time and again in this, and later chapters, feedback processes are a fundamental source of uncertainty in *all* model-based assessments of how the '**greenhouse forcing**' experiment going on in the *real* world might turn out. Below we look briefly at three much discussed examples of such feedbacks.

Question 5.1 What is the *enhanced* greenhouse effect associated with the global warming scenario depicted in Figure 5.2, i.e. how does the value of G for the *new* equilibrium situation (part c) compare with that for the original regime (part a)? (Take the Stefan–Boltzmann constant to be $\sigma = 5.67 \times 10^{-8} \, \text{W m}^{-2} \, \text{K}^{-4}$.)

5.2.1 Radiative feedback mechanisms

The best understood example of a positive feedback loop is one you met in Section 3.3.4 (Figure 3.17a) — **water vapour feedback**. The heart of the matter is that the atmospheric concentration of water vapour depends largely on temperature. The form of this temperature dependence is well-known; it expresses quantitatively the commonly observed fact that as temperature rises, so does the evaporation of liquid water — and so too does the amount of water vapour air can 'hold' before becoming saturated. In the present context, this link implies that global warming, initiated by an increase in one greenhouse gas (CO_2), would be expected to induce an increase in yet another greenhouse gas (water vapour).

The late 1980s saw compelling *observational* evidence for the reality and importance of this feedback loop. It came from a study which combined satellite data (measurements of the outgoing longwave flux F) and observed **sea-surface temperatures, SSTs** (to estimate surface fluxes, from $E = \sigma T_s^4$) to obtain the geographical distribution of the 'clear skies' greenhouse effect G (i.e. data from cloudy areas were filtered out) over the open oceans. Some typical results are shown in Plate 5.1.

Notice the striking correlation between G and SST. A detailed analysis of this G–T_s correlation revealed that it can be explained by the enhanced infrared absorption associated with the increase in atmospheric water vapour as T_s increases. That analysis also provided the first observational measure of the strength of water vapour feedback; in terms of Equation 5.2, it would increase the globally-averaged value of λ from $0.3 \, \text{K m}^2 \, \text{W}^{-1}$ to $0.48 \, \text{K m}^2 \, \text{W}^{-1}$. The crucial point is that for a CO_2-doubling, this would amplify the global-mean surface warming from 1.2 K to 1.9 K — a factor of nearly 60%.

Question 5.2 Assuming that a general increase in surface temperature is likely to reduce snow and ice cover, explain how this could act to amplify a warming trend. Would you expect this amplification to be uniformly distributed around the globe?

This '**snow–ice albedo feedback**' is another well-known example of a positive feedback mechanism. But it is inherently geographical (and seasonal) in nature, and this makes it far harder to characterize than water vapour feedback. Certainly, there seems no obvious way of measuring its likely strength.

The problem is yet sharper for our final example, '**cloud feedback**'. Here, it is difficult to establish even the *direction* of the overall feedback. To see why, recall that clouds not only contribute to the greenhouse warming of the climate system (they absorb and re-emit longwave radiation), they are also highly reflective — thus contributing to the planet's overall albedo, and so reducing the absorption of solar radiation. In short, clouds present a paradox: they both warm and cool the Earth — a point stressed in Section 2.2.4. Satellite data indicate that, at present, the latter effect exceeds the former — the net result being that clouds cool the *global* climate system. However, this overall effect is governed by the complex interplay of many factors — including cloud amount and type, together with their geographical distribution and differing radiative properties (see Figure 5.3). In principle, global warming could

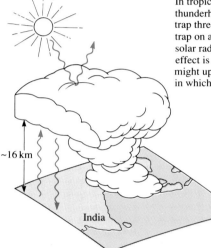

1 CUMULONIMBUS

In tropical storm systems, these thunderheads topped with hugh anvils trap three times as much heat as clouds trap on average, but reflect so much solar radiation back up that the warming effect is cancelled. Global warming might upset this delicate balance, but in which direction?

~16 km

India

2 STRATOCUMULUS

These fluffy clouds lie in vast low layers over oceans in temperate zones. The tops reflect a surprisingly large amount of solar radiation, for a net cooling effect. Global warming could shift them north or south, but would this intensify or moderate the warming?

2–3 km

Britain

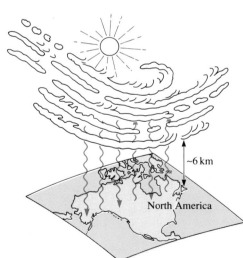

3 CIRRUS

These high wisps were believed to trap much heat below but reflect little back into space. They have recently been found to have an unexpectedly large number of tiny ice crystals. If these reflect more solar radiation than expected, it could counterbalance the heat-trapping effect.

~6 km

North America

Figure 5.3 Over recent years, two major research programmes — the Earth Radiation Budget Experiment (ERBE) and the International Satellite Cloud Climatology Project (ISCCP) — have begun to reveal new (and sometimes surprising) insights into the complex role clouds play in modulating the planet's temperature. The figure summarizes some key points, stressing how various types of clouds affect the Earth's radiation balance differently. The character and radiative effects of clouds also vary with the nature of the underlying surface (whether it is land or sea), and with the time of day and season of the year. Researchers are only beginning to understand how these variations fit together to produce a global cooling effect. How this might be affected by future global warming remains uncertain.

induce changes in any or all of these factors. Cloud feedback is the resulting *change* in the extent to which clouds help to cool the planet; any *diminution* in their net cooling effect would constitute a *positive* feedback, and vice versa.

Contributions to cloud feedback will be determined by possible shifts in the patterns of cloudiness around the world, and in the influence (often delicately poised between heating and cooling) exerted by different types of cloud — the message implicit in Figure 5.3. There is no simple way of assessing what the net effect is likely to be. For a start, cloud feedback — like snow–ice albedo feedback — is inherently geographical in nature. More telling — and this is a crucial point to register — there are also ways in which the feedbacks identified here could, in turn, interact with one another. For example, a general increase in atmospheric moisture might well enhance the number of liquid water droplets (or indeed, ice crystals) in various cloud types. This would be expected to make them 'brighter' — more reflective, that is — a possible negative contribution to cloud feedback. Others have speculated about a compensating positive feedback, induced by concomitant changes to the longwave radiative properties of clouds. And there are reasons to suppose that changes in snow and ice cover could influence cloudiness (and vice versa) as well.

Notice that the feedbacks outlined here are all linked to key elements in the hydrological cycle — atmospheric moisture, clouds and the water 'locked up' as snow and ice. As we sought to stress in Section 2.3.4, that overall cycle — *and* the way it operates on a regional scale — is a powerful manifestation of the interconnectedness of the climate system. The way that system might respond to being forced cannot be adequately explored through simple 1-D models of the kind described in connection with Figure 5.2. That is the important general message. Moreover, concentrating solely on global-mean conditions, and on the shift from one equilibrium climatic regime (Figure 5.2a) to another (Figure 5.2c), *cannot* address questions concerning the likely geographical distribution and pace of climatic change (points 2 and 3 in Section 5.1) — issues that are central to its possible ecological and socio-economic consequences.

To tackle these questions requires models that not only 'resolve' all three dimensions (i.e. latitude and longitude, as well as altitude), but also incorporate a more complete description of the 'real world' climate system. This is where the models to which we now turn come into the picture: they lie at the cutting edge of the modellers' craft.

Activity 5.1

With the assumption of zero climate feedbacks (as depicted in Figure 5.2), the Earth eventually returns to its *original* radiation balance at the top of the atmosphere (Figure 5.2c). Explain *briefly* (in not more than 100 words) why this would not necessarily be so if global warming were to trigger off the kind of feedbacks outlined above.

5.3 Modelling the climate system

The central thrust of the material drawn together in Sections 2.3.4 and 2.4 can be stated quite simply: the climatic conditions experienced around the world result from the combined influence of, *and interactions between*, the atmosphere, oceans, cryosphere and land surface. That message was crystallized in the schematic representation of the Earth's climate system shown in Figure 2.35 — repeated and added to here as Figure 5.4. At that stage, the inclusion of terrestrial vegetation recognized its role in the regional hydrological cycle and surface energy balance (recall Figure 2.34) — and hence in shaping climate on this scale. Since then, you have seen how the wider 'biosphere', i.e. not just plants and not just on land, is woven into the controls over the Earth's climate in a far more fundamental way than this. In reality, the life cycles of the natural greenhouse gases are intimately bound up with the biosphere. That was a strong theme running through Chapter 4, as was the importance of atmospheric chemistry in determining the fate of these gases once released (with the sole exception of CO_2).

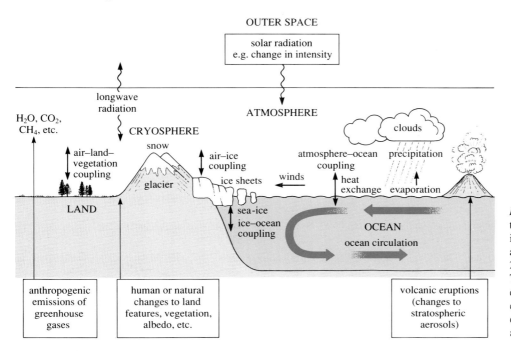

Figure 5.4 Schematic representation of the various components and interactions in the climate system, as outlined in Sections 2.3.4 and 2.4 (compare with Figure 2.35). The boxes around the outside indicate various possible causes of climatic change — both natural (as discussed in Chapter 3) and anthropogenic (Chapter 4).

Figure 5.4 does not incorporate these extra 'dimensions' to the interconnectedness of the *total* planetary system — and neither (as yet) do even the most sophisticated climate models. The important implications of these omissions will be taken up in Chapter 7. For now, it is sufficient to note that existing models are based on a more restricted, essentially 'physicists' view' of the climate system — effectively that depicted in Figure 5.4. Indeed, set in the present context, this figure captures the underlying structure of these models quite well. In short, the total system is carved up into a series of subsystems: the atmosphere, oceans, cryosphere and land surface. But at the same time, these subsystems are allowed to 'communicate' with one another (in a more or less sophisticated way), essentially via mathematical descriptions of the *physical* processes that link (couple) them together. As discussed in Sections 2.3.4 and 2.4 (and it might be a good plan to refresh your memory with a quick re-read), this comes down to the exchange of heat, moisture and momentum across the surface–air boundary. Further insight into how this is achieved in practice is best obtained by turning now to a concrete example.

5.3.1 General circulation models (GCMs)

The history of science is rich with serendipity and coincidence. As the (now routine) monitoring of atmospheric CO_2 was getting under way — with the inception of the International Geophysical Year in 1957 (Figure 4.1) — so too was another key development. 1956 saw the first attempt to represent atmospheric behaviour on computer — the beginnings of numerical weather forecasting, from which climate 'forecasting' has evolved. The first global climate model, now usually known as a

general circulation model or **GCM**, was developed during the 1960s at the Geophysical Fluid Dynamics Laboratory (GFDL). Set up on the campus of Princeton University in 1963, this centre was devoted to the mathematical modelling of the atmosphere using the largest and fastest digital computers available. Since then, other modelling groups have been established — both in the United States (leading examples being at NCAR (Figure 5.1) and at NASA's Goddard Institute for Space Studies (GISS) in New York), and elsewhere (at the Meteorological Office in the UK, for example). The GCMs developed by these, and other groups, remain similar in principle to the models used for numerical weather forecasting. Specifically, the *central* element of a GCM is a detailed, three-dimensional, time-evolving model of the atmosphere — usually represented as an array of 'grid boxes', as shown schematically in Figure 5.5. Beyond this, there is a set of '*boundary conditions*' at the top and bottom of the model atmosphere. At the top of the atmosphere, this is the input of solar radiation to each vertical column — and the way the computer is instructed to vary this during the model year (Figure 5.5).

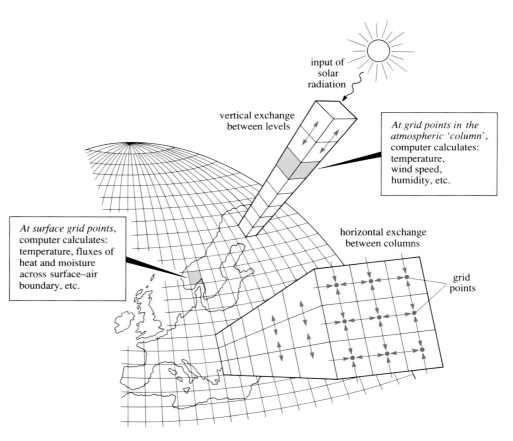

input of solar radiation

vertical exchange between levels

At grid points in the atmospheric 'column', computer calculates: temperature, wind speed, humidity, etc.

At surface grid points, computer calculates: temperature, fluxes of heat and moisture across surface–air boundary, etc.

horizontal exchange between columns

grid points

Figure 5.5 Schematic representation of the basic structure of a general circulation model — a grid of interacting columns spread over the surface of the globe.

The boundary conditions at the bottom of the atmosphere include a specification of the physical character of the surface underneath each atmospheric column — whether it is land or sea, for example, and if the former, the type of terrain involved. But they also take in the **boundary fluxes**, i.e. the exchange of heat, moisture and momentum across this lower boundary, as indicated in Figure 5.5. Since this is how the atmosphere interacts with the other components of the climate system, this is clearly a crucial issue for climate modellers. It is handled by linking the atmosphere model to an array of other models at the planetary surface. For example, an ocean model fed with information from the atmosphere model calculates SSTs, which in turn feeds information back to the atmosphere model (a change in the heat or moisture flux, say) and so on. There are other models for sea-ice and a variety of important land-surface processes; more on this later. For now, we return to the atmosphere model that lies at the heart of a GCM.

The mathematical formulation of the model involves a set of time-dependent 'governing' equations, which together describe the dynamics of the atmosphere, and the ensuing transport of heat and water vapour by atmospheric winds. It is worth emphasizing that these equations are based on well-established physical laws — the conservation of momentum (otherwise known as Newton's second law of motion), energy and mass — as they apply to a fluid (the atmosphere) on a rotating planet, under the influence of a differential heating (the temperature contrast between low and high latitudes) caused by an external heat source (the Sun). These governing equations include terms for the boundary fluxes at the planetary surface. In addition, water vapour is conserved through evaporation sources at the surface and sinks through rainfall (or snowfall, if the computed temperature is low enough).

The governing equations are the core of the atmosphere model. Between them, they describe the variation — in both space and time — of five basic variables: north–south and east–west components of winds, atmospheric pressure, temperature and humidity. Given some specified set of initial conditions (appropriate to a particular time of year, say), values of these variables at each of the grid points (indicated in Figure 5.5) are computed by solving a pretty formidable set of simultaneous equations. The computer then 'steps' forward in time, through a pre-set interval (commonly 10–30 minutes) and repeats the whole set of calculations — thereby building up a picture of how each of these variables, and the pattern of moving weather systems they represent, changes through the model year.

Based as they are on sound physical principles, GCMs formulated as outlined here could, in principle, come very close to simulating the behaviour of the real atmosphere. In practice, there are serious practical and theoretical limitations. Practical constraints come down to the enormous amount of computation required to produce simultaneous solutions to all of the equations. (Something like a hundred thousand numbers have to be stored, retrieved, recalculated and re-stored at each time step in order to calculate *each* of the basic atmospheric variables at *each* grid point!) The better the 'spatial resolution' of the model (i.e. the finer the grid), the greater the requirement for high computer capacity and speed. At the time of writing, this constraint is such that typical GCMs have around a dozen vertical levels in the atmosphere, together with a horizontal resolution of a few *hundred* kilometres. So the model world actually looks something like the map in Figure 5.6. (Notice how the UK has finally joined Europe!)

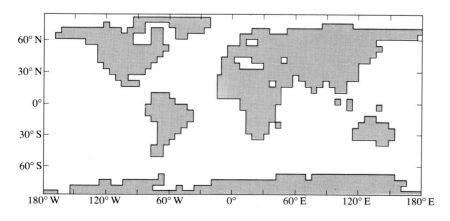

Figure 5.6 The 'map' of the world, as represented in a typical GCM.

This limited spatial resolution, in turn, creates problems of a more theoretical kind. In particular, it means that GCMs cannot *directly* simulate several small-scale atmospheric processes of critical importance to climate in the real world. Examples include cloud formation, precipitation and a variety of small-scale convective and turbulent mixing processes (especially close to the planetary surface). These so-called 'sub-grid scale' processes are brought into GCMs in an average or approximate way through a technique known as **parameterization** (short for 'parametric representation'). Basically, this involves devising a scheme (i.e. a set of mathematical rules for the computer to follow) whereby the phenomenon in question is related to the large-scale grid box variables that are computed directly. In general, such schemes are based on a combination of empirical (i.e. drawn from observations) correlations and theoretical studies (perhaps a more detailed model of the physical processes involved).

To give you a feel for such schemes, we focus on just one example; *cloud parameterization schemes* are clearly central to the issue of assessing the strength and direction of cloud feedback raised earlier. In principle, the scheme used should incorporate all the radiatively important cloud properties touched on in Figure 5.3 (type and coverage, height, liquid water or ice content and so on), with a sufficiently strong theoretical basis that their *change* with climatic change can be adequately simulated. A fundamental difficulty here is that the relationship between these sub-grid scale properties and the large scale meteorological processes resolved by GCMs is only poorly understood.

On-going research programmes, such as those noted in the caption to Figure 5.3, are beginning to provide much needed information about the details of how different types of clouds form, maintain themselves and dissipate, and so on. At present, however, most existing models employ very simple parameterization schemes. For example, by analyzing observational data, the *average* cloudiness over the large areas defined by the model grid (Figure 5.5) can be related — through a parameter or proportionality constant in an equation, say — to the average temperature and humidity over the same area. This parameterization then allows the average cloudiness in a given grid box to be predicted from the computed temperature and humidity, even though it cannot predict the formation of individual clouds. Analogous techniques are used to predict the onset and vertical penetration of sub-grid scale 'cumulus convection' in a given column of the model atmosphere. As yet, few schemes incorporate the water or ice content of clouds in an explicit way. Whatever the details, however — and these vary significantly from one model to another — it is generally acknowledged that existing schemes are extremely crude, and that this, in turn, is a major source of uncertainty in current estimates of climate sensitivity: more on this in Section 5.5.

5.3.2 Model deficiencies

Apart from the parameterization schemes embedded in the atmosphere model itself, other major deficiencies in existing GCMs come down to the much cruder models used to represent the other components of the climate system. We consider these under two broad headings.

The oceans and sea-ice

In numerical weather forecasting, boundary fluxes over ocean areas are constrained by prescribing SSTs to be the observed values: these are 'updated' as the simulation proceeds. In GCM studies of climatic change, SSTs have to be *calculated* by an ocean model. In reality, the ocean is certainly as complex a dynamic system as the atmosphere. Yet, to date, most GCM studies have used a simple '**mixed-layer ocean' model**. This effectively characterizes the ocean as a heat and water reservoir — a slab of seawater with a fixed depth (typically 70–100 m) and uniformly mixed in the vertical dimension. Various parameterized formulations allow the model ocean to store heat absorbed in summer, and release it in winter, thus capturing the seasonal cycle of

SSTs (evident in Figure 2.16). *Horizontal heat transport within the ocean is not modelled explicitly*; it is either neglected entirely, or in more recent versions, it is parameterized in some way to match the best existing estimates of present-day values. At best, then, such models effectively *prescribe* the redistribution of heat by ocean currents — and in particular, the important contribution that makes to the net transport of heat from low to high latitudes.

▷ What feature of oceanic heat 'storage' and transport in the real world is completely missing from these simple ocean models?

▶ The *vertical* exchange of heat between the upper mixed layer (the only part of the real ocean which *is* modelled) and the deep ocean — through the workings of the thermohaline circulation.

Ocean models formulated as outlined here have important shortcomings when it comes to simulating the climatic response to a 'greenhouse radiative forcing'. Specifically, they cannot simulate any possible *changes* in ocean circulation, nor the effect that might have, in turn, on the horizontal and/or vertical transfer of heat within the oceans. This issue is being addressed by the ocean modelling community. As we said in Chapter 4, dynamic ocean models (usually designated **OGCMs** to distinguish them from their atmospheric cousins, or **AGCMs**) are being developed; more on this in Section 5.6. For now, we simply note that deficiencies in existing ocean models also have knock-on effects for the modelling of other key elements of the climate system — notably the extent of polar sea-ice, and its seasonal variation. As yet, this is also handled in a fairly crude way. For example, sea-ice forms if the computed SSTs fall below the approximate freezing point for seawater (−1.9 °C). The growth and melting of sea-ice are commonly assumed to depend on both the calculated energy balance at its surface and the heat conduction through it (from the underlying ocean), following some parameterization scheme.

Land-surface processes

There are two major, but interrelated, elements in modelling the 'land-based' components of the climate system. First, important characteristics of the terrain have to be specified — its topography and surface 'roughness', the presence of ice sheets and mountain glaciers, the type of vegetation and soil, and their albedos, together with some measure of the water-holding capacity of the soil. These surface properties, in turn, affect the processes assembled in Figure 5.7, which must be simulated in order to compute boundary fluxes to the atmosphere model, as well as two key 'surface climate' parameters — temperature and '**soil moisture**'. In the real world, the balance between precipitation, evaporation, snow melt (where relevant), storage of water in the ground, and surface runoff is critical to local climate, to plant growth (whether natural or cultivated), and indeed to freshwater resources in general. Thus, successful simulation of the local water budget or '**land surface hydrology**' — and this includes precipitation — is crucial if model forecasts are to provide a guide to how any or all of these factors may change in a warmer world.

Once again, the limited spatial resolution of existing GCMs imposes inherent constraints. Even where remote satellite-borne sensors are now providing global data sets on some land-surface properties — vegetation type, for instance — there remains the problem of 'translating' these data into the areal averages required as input to a GCM. Figure 5.8 is a compelling example of the crude ecological classification which ensues: compare it with the global distribution of biomes that you met in Chapter 2 (Figure 2.1)! For other properties, there is simply a dearth of global-scale information (for example, field-based hydrological studies commonly relate to sub-grid scale river

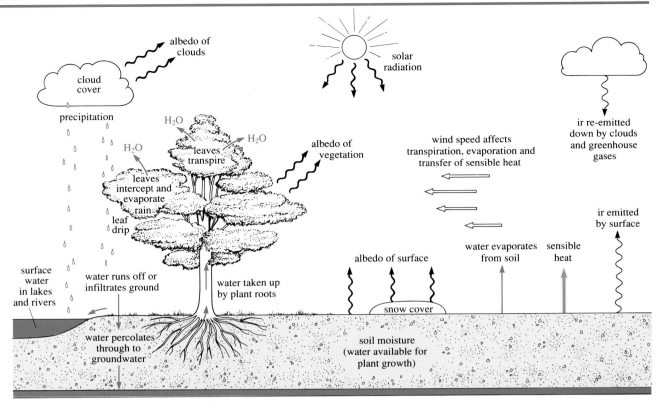

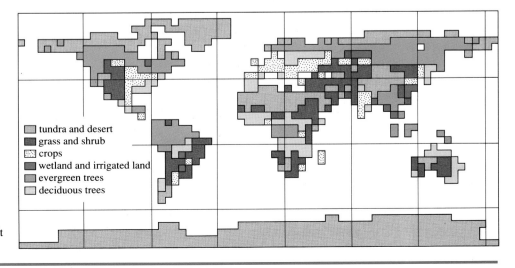

Figure 5.7 A schematic representation of the processes and features relevant to the energy balance at the land surface and land surface hydrology (as defined in the text). This is a slightly more detailed version of Figure 2.34 in Section 2.3.4.

basins). Finally, the difficulty of modelling the all-important involvement of vegetation in the surface water budget is further compounded by the requirement that parameterization schemes be appropriate to typical GCM grid squares.

To date, most such schemes have been highly simplified. The 'bucket model' for surface hydrology outlined in Figure 5.9 is a typical example. Notice the total lack of vegetation — when, in nature, less than half of the moisture lost to the air from the ground is due to simple evaporation; the rest flows through plants. More recent schemes do attempt to incorporate evapotranspiration by plants, along with their involvement in the other processes depicted in Figure 5.7. But there is an urgent need for observational data to 'validate' these more complicated schemes, and hence check that the overall surface energy and water balance is well simulated.

Figure 5.8 Distribution of generalized types of ecosystem on a 5° latitude × 5° longitude grid. The coarse spatial resolution and simple ecological classification required by most GCMs is difficult to derive from observational data.

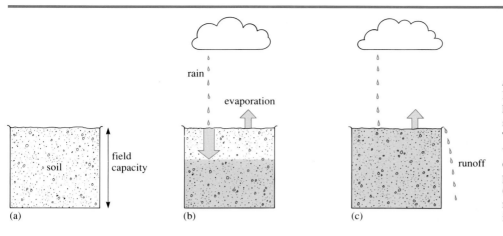

Figure 5.9 Representation of the Budyko 'bucket' model — a highly simplified parameterization scheme for land surface hydrology. The soil is represented as a bucket with some maximum or 'field' capacity (a). The bucket fills when precipitation exceeds evaporation (b): when it is full, excess water runs off, and plays no further part in the hydrological cycle (c).

In summary

At present, GCMs put together as outlined here are the most complete, and potentially powerful, tools for simulating climatic change. But the deficiencies we have highlighted sound a cautionary note. In reality, existing GCMs contain oversimplified, approximate and incomplete descriptions of many important climatic processes — shortcomings that arise partly from computational constraints, and partly from a lack of observational data and inadequate understanding of the controlling mechanisms. This is not to imply that simplification is necessarily a bad thing. Indeed, it is the essence of modelling. Moreover, relatively simple parameterizations are usually easier to understand, and to formulate in terms that a computer can use, than are more complicated or physically more complete descriptions. On the other hand, it is clearly important to check whether the simplified formulations in existing GCMs seriously undermine their simulation skills — a step usually referred to as 'model validation'.

5.4 Model validation

One obvious approach is to check the extent to which GCMs can reproduce the present climate, and its geographical and seasonal variations. Note that, in *climatological* terms, 'the present' never means the current year, *taken alone*. Because of natural variability (more on which in Chapter 6), climate statistics always relate to weather observations over a period of years — usually two or three decades. The analysis of such observations provides '**climatological averages**' — values of important climate parameters (such as the mean surface-air temperature or mean daily precipitation for each month, say) averaged over the years in question — together with some (statistical) measure of the interannual variability. The point to register is that the 'present-day climate' strictly means 'the climatological average over the recent past', the period usually used for model validation being the 30 years from 1951 to 1980 (although the shortness of some observational records sometimes dictates otherwise).

The check referred to above involves running a so-called **control simulation**, with model inputs appropriate to this definition of present-day conditions. Apart from the factors outlined in the previous section (not least the observational data effectively embedded within the various parameterization schemes), that comes down to specifying the atmospheric burden of greenhouse gases. Here, the *fixed* concentrations input to the atmosphere model typically reflect the average values during the

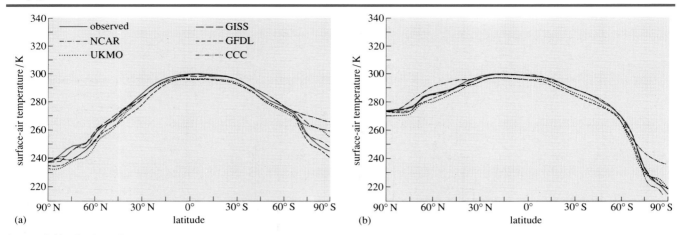

(a) latitude

(b) latitude

Figure 5.10 Surface-air temperature, averaged for 3-month periods and around latitude bands (zonally-averaged), predicted by various GCMs and as observed for (a) December–January–February (DJF), and (b) June–July–August (JJA). Models were developed at the National Center for Atmospheric Research (NCAR), the United Kingdom Meteorological Office (UKMO), the Goddard Institute for Space Studies (GISS), the Geophysical Fluid Dynamics Laboratory (GFDL), and the Canadian Climate Centre (CCC).

reference period, e.g. some 330 p.p.m. for CO_2. Generating the simulated climate then involves stepping the model's governing equations (10–30 minutes at a time) through a model year — as the solar input runs through its prescribed seasonal cycle, SSTs are computed and updated by the ocean model, and so on (as noted in Section 5.3.1). The model climate will vary somewhat from year to year, as it does in reality. Thus the simulation has to be extended over several model years (typically a few decades) in order to assemble statistics on the monthly and annual means of the computed climate parameters, together with their interannual variability. These are then compared with the observed climatological averages (if available).

The IPCC report contained a fairly exhaustive validation exercise along these lines, taking in GCMs developed by some of the major climate modelling groups. Space does not permit us a detailed look at that assessment, but the main conclusions are pertinent as a background to the global warming scenarios we shall examine in the next section.

All recent models produce a global climate that is generally realistic on large scales, capturing major features such as the strong temperature contrast between low and high latitudes (Figure 5.10); the prevailing westerlies at mid-latitudes (and the transient weather systems — cyclones and anticyclones — associated with them, Figure 2.24); and the wet Intertropical Convergence Zone near the Equator (Figure 5.11). They also reproduce a recognizable (if flawed in detail) seasonal cycle in the atmospheric circulation, snow cover, precipitation and surface-air temperature. The latter is important because, averaged over each hemisphere, these twice yearly (winter–summer– winter)

Figure 5.11 Zonally-averaged daily precipitation (averaged over 3-month periods) predicted by various GCMs and as observed for (a) DJF, and (b) JJA. Acronyms as in Figure 5.10.

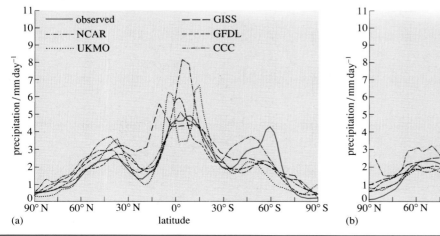

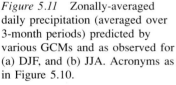

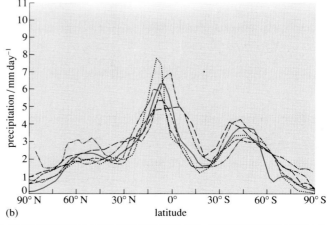

(a) latitude

(b) latitude

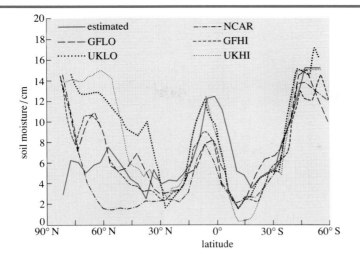

Figure 5.12 Zonally-averaged soil moisture for land grid points as estimated for July, and as modelled for JJA. GFLO, GFHI and UKLO, UKHI refer to low and high resolution versions of the GFDL and UKMO models, respectively. 'Soil moisture' is usually recorded (as here) as the 'soil moisture deficit', in terms of the centimetres of rainfall required to restore the soil to its field capacity (Figure 5.9).

temperature changes are several times larger than the variation between glacial and interglacial, or between current mean temperatures and those projected on the basis of anthropogenic greenhouse warming.

An equally strong message, however, is that there are significant errors on the regional scale (2 000 km or less) — already evident to some extent in the zonal averages recorded in Figure 5.10, and even more so in Figure 5.11. Here the limitations identified in the previous section become apparent. For example, all models tend to overestimate precipitation in winter, especially in the Northern Hemisphere, and most give a generally inadequate account of crucial phenomena, such as the southeast Asian monsoon, for example. At the regional level, errors range from 20% to 50% of the average seasonal rainfall, depending on the model. This is important, because errors in simulating precipitation further compound those associated with the relatively crude surface hydrology schemes mentioned earlier, as is evident from the soil moisture data collected in Figure 5.12. Bear in mind, however, that here the observed values are themselves uncertain, since no global data sets for soil moisture yet exist.

Finally, one stringent test of a model is whether it can correctly reproduce the energy exchange between the whole Earth–atmosphere system and outer space — as measured by the simulated flux of outgoing longwave radiation (i.e. F in Figure 5.2) and the simulated albedo; Figure 5.13 shows a comparison with the observed latitudinal variation of these two quantities (recall Figure 2.21).

Figure 5.13 Zonally-averaged (a) outgoing longwave radiation, and (b) average albedo, as modelled for DJF and as observed (from satellite data) for January.

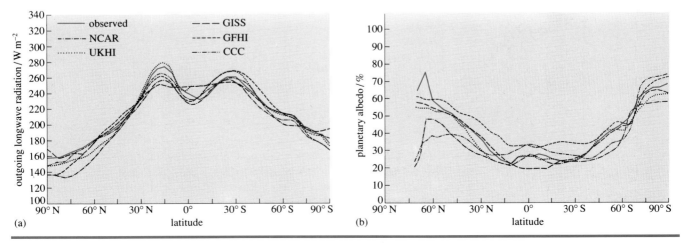

(a)

(b)

This activity serves to highlight one difficulty with any validation exercise; because climatic processes are so firmly interlocked with one another, it is often difficult to diagnose just where the deficiencies lie in any given model. Nor is it possible to identify a 'best' model; one may be more reliable than another for a particular climate parameter, but less so elsewhere. Another inevitable limitation is that many parameterization schemes are anyway 'tuned' to satisfy 'present-day' observational constraints, as noted earlier.

A related point, well brought out by the IPCC assessment, is the crucial importance of accurate sea-surface temperatures for a realistic simulation not only of atmospheric processes, but also of sea-ice. In control simulations with a simple mixed-layer ocean model, SSTs are maintained near to observed values through various parameterized formulations, as mentioned in Section 5.3.2. This also helps to ensure a good simulation of the extent and seasonal variation of sea-ice. As we noted at the time, however, the aspects of oceanic heat storage and transport represented by these schemes are commonly assumed to be unchanged when the model climate system is perturbed (by doubling CO_2, say), and thus take no account of possible changes in oceanic circulation. On the other hand, the fact that broadly realistic simulations of the *present* climate are achieved, *given accurate SSTs*, suggests that existing models capture ocean–atmosphere interactions quite well.

Another strand to model validation comes from experiments designed to simulate climates of the more distant past. Suffice it to say here that modelling studies with GCMs have helped to confirm the climate's sensitivity to changes in the Earth's orbital parameters (as discussed in Chapter 3), and to suggest some of the mechanisms responsible for major shifts in temperature and precipitation patterns evident in the palaeoclimatic record for the period since the last glacial maximum (18 000 years ago). Such studies are important in their own right. They also generate confidence that existing models can simulate important features of climatic regimes radically different from our own.

5.5 Equilibrium climatic change scenarios

To date, perceptions of the scale and geographical distribution of greenhouse-gas induced climatic change have been shaped mainly by simulations of the *equilibrium* response to a CO_2-doubling, in the sense defined in Section 5.2. As mentioned earlier, such studies are important because they allow assessments of the climate sensitivity produced by different models to be compared directly. So far, the term 'climate sensitivity' has been identified — at least implicitly — with the value of the parameter λ in Equation 5.2. In the present context, however, model results are more often compared in terms of the equilibrium increase in the global-mean surface temperature, i.e. the value of ΔT_s in Equation 5.2, in response to a CO_2-doubling (equivalent to a radiative forcing of some $4 \, \mathrm{W \, m^{-2}}$): this is commonly given the symbol $\Delta T_{2\times}$ (read as 'delta-t-two-times') *and is itself referred to as the climate sensitivity.* One final point to bear in mind: these equilibrium studies (or 'experiments') produce global warming scenarios, *not* forecasts as such. Specifically, they cannot simulate the *time-evolving* response to the continuing buildup in CO_2 (and all the other greenhouse gases) actually happening in the real world; more information on how that task is handled is in the next section.

There are two stages to constructing an **equilibrium scenario**. First, a control simulation is run to establish a 'present-day' model climatology, as outlined in the previous section. Then the concentration of CO_2 input to the atmosphere model is doubled instantaneously, and the simulation is extended until the model climate settles to a new 'perturbed' equilibrium state. With an AGCM coupled to a simple mixed-layer ocean model, this requires some 10–20 years of simulated time. To put the computational constraints mentioned earlier into some sort of perspective, it is worth recording here that with an atmosphere model of average resolution (say $5°$ latitude $\times 7.5°$ longitude), two 20-year simulations need something like 400 computational hours (at \$1 000 per hour) on a Cray XMP computer. Halving the grid (as has been done in the most recent 'high resolution' models) increases the time required by almost an order of magnitude — to nearly 6 months of dedicated supercomputer time. Gosh!

Averages taken at the end of the 'control' and 'perturbed' simulations are then used to infer the geographical patterns of climatic change — with due (i.e. statistical) regard to the model climate's inherent variability. Changes in the global-mean surface temperature (i.e. $\Delta T_{2\times}$) and in the hydrological cycle are also computed.

Following their review of twenty or so simulations carried out by nine modelling groups during the late 1980s, the IPCC reported the following broad conclusions about these globally-averaged quantities:

o   All models indicate that doubling the atmospheric concentration of CO_2 would result in significant global warming — with the more recent studies (some with high resolution models) giving values of $\Delta T_{2\times}$ ranging from $1.9 \, °C$ to $4.4 \, °C$.

o   All models simulate a substantially moister atmosphere (the water vapour feedback loop in action), with increases in average global precipitation and evaporation ranging from 3% to 15%. In general, the greater the warming, the more the global hydrological cycle intensifies.

o   Details vary from model to model, but sea-ice is commonly less extensive, and the area of seasonal snow cover diminishes.

Question 5.3   Given the points noted above, what conclusions can be drawn about the *net* effect of the radiative feedback mechanisms discussed in Section 5.2.1? (Hint: think about the quoted range of $\Delta T_{2\times}$ values.) Can you say anything about the sign and magnitude of cloud feedback, taken alone?

Attempts have been made to 'disentangle' the values of $\Delta T_{2\times}$ produced by various GCMs, and so assess the contributions made by the individual feedbacks. The most recent such study (reported by the IPCC) involved a rather different type of 'climate change' simulation — one specifically designed to *suppress* snow–ice albedo feedback. We shall not dwell on the details. Suffice it to say that existing GCMs appear to be in remarkable agreement as regards the strength of water vapour feedback — not just with one another, but also with the value deduced from observational data (referred to in Section 5.2.1). By contrast, there is something like a threefold variation in the simulated strength of cloud feedback. In short, cloud feedback is *the* major source of uncertainty in current estimates of the overall climate sensitivity ($\Delta T_{2\times}$) — a conclusion foreshadowed in Section 5.3.1, following our brief discussion of the deficiencies in existing cloud parameterization schemes. In particular, whether possible changes to cloud radiative properties would tend to enhance or reduce the *positive* cloud feedback indicated by most modelling studies remains an open question. Here, the paramount problem is how to validate parameterization schemes that do attempt to incorporate important 'microphysical' factors, such as the liquid water content of clouds and so on.

More telling than any particular source of uncertainty, however, is the fact that the IPCC found no compelling evidence to alter, *or narrow*, the range of possible $\Delta T_{2\times}$ values (1.5–4.5 °C) identified more than a decade earlier following a careful assessment by the US National Academy of Sciences.[*] This is important — a timely reminder of one of the central issues in the on-going debates about global warming; defining the point at which available scientific understanding is deemed sufficient to trigger a societal response, as distinct from simply generating further research. We address this issue more directly in the next chapter.

Returning to the equilibrium scenarios produced during the late 1980s; in spite of the large range of estimates for $\Delta T_{2\times}$, certain broad features of the geographical distribution of the surface warming stand out from all of them. They are evident in the results from three recent studies with high resolution models, shown in Plate 5.2.

o   The temperature changes do not occur uniformly across the globe; the warming is greatest at high latitudes in late autumn and winter, particularly over regions presently covered by sea-ice (i.e. the Arctic Ocean and around Antarctica).

o   The surface warming and its seasonal variations are least in the tropics.

o   The continents warm more than the ocean — a trend apparent at northern midlatitudes in Plate 5.2.

The first point above is a manifestation of the *geographical* nature of snow–ice albedo feedback, as noted earlier (Question 5.2). In practice, however, the enhanced warming at high latitudes, especially in *winter*, seems to be a little more complicated than the discussion there would suggest. Over ocean areas, a crucial factor is the melting of sea-ice during the *summer* months of the warmer (CO_2-doubled) climate. The less reflective surface then allows more heat to be stored in the ocean's mixed layer during the ice-free months. This, in turn, both delays the onset of sea-ice formation and reduces its extent during the following autumn and winter; ice-free ocean can then continue to release heat throughout the winter. Over continental regions, the reduced extent and earlier melting of high albedo snow cover similarly acts to amplify the surface warming.

Apart from the large scale features listed above, the detailed pattern of regional change clearly varies considerably from model to model — a picture that emerges with yet greater force when simulated changes in precipitation and soil moisture are compared. For example, models consistently produce enhanced precipitation at high latitudes and in the tropics throughout the year — and at northern midlatitudes in winter, married in the most recent studies (such as those reported in Plate 5.3) to a slight decrease in summer. Beyond these broad generalizations, however, existing models clearly provide little basis for reliable predictions on the sub-continental scale — especially in the tropics and subtropics, where many nations are highly vulnerable to slight shifts in the pattern and intensity of seasonal rainfall.

Even where models are in reasonable agreement as to surface warming and precipitation, there can still be marked discrepancies in their simulation of changes in soil moisture. Figure 5.14 illustrates the point.

---

[*] US National Academy of Sciences (1979) *Carbon Dioxide and Climate: A Scientific Assessment,* Washington DC.

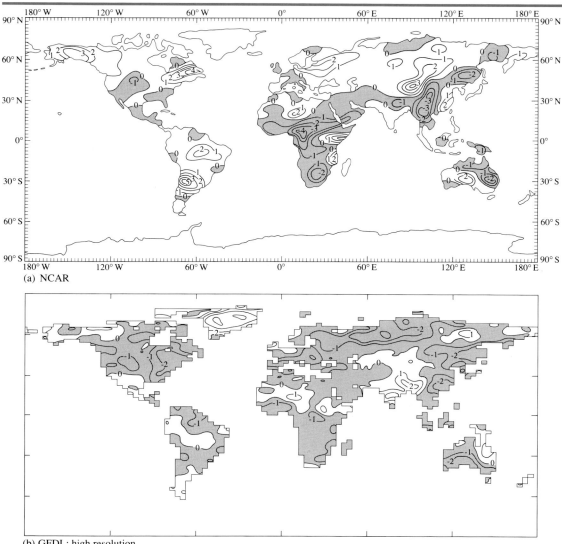

(a) NCAR

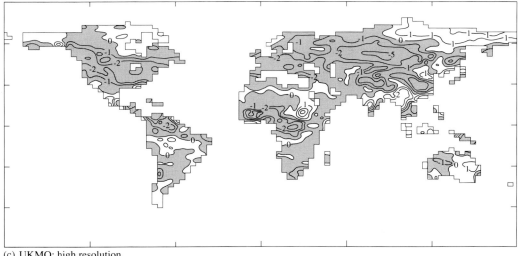

(b) GFDL: high resolution

(c) UKMO: high resolution

Figure 5.14 Scenarios for changes in soil moisture (JJA averages) following a doubling in the atmospheric concentration of CO_2. Negative figures correspond to a decrease in soil moisture (i.e. a drier surface) shown in grey.

Activity 5.3

Look at the northern midlatitudes in Figure 5.14. How do the predicted changes in soil moisture in summer (JJA) compare in the three different models?

Because these latitudes take in the world's major grain growing areas — the US corn belt, for one — inconsistencies like those you identified in Activity 5.3 have warranted close examination. Several factors appear to be involved. Some have to do with the way key surface processes are formulated in the various models (e.g. the degree to which snow melt in spring is absorbed by the soil, or runs off if the ground is frozen), and the impact that has on the computed soil moisture in the *control* simulation. If this is far from saturation in *winter* (as in the NCAR model, for example), then surface warming and enhanced precipitation during the winter (in the CO_2-doubled run) adds to the store of water in the ground, and helps to ameliorate summer drying. Other factors appear to involve complex soil moisture/evaporation/cloud feedbacks.

This sensitivity to the way surface processes are parameterized in the different models, plus an awareness that *all* existing schemes are pretty crude anyway, led the IPCC to be fairly cautious about the 'mid continental drying' scenario that is, in fact, a feature of most existing model studies.

At this stage, it is well to stand back from the details of this, or any other, discrepancy between the various model scenarios — and to restate the general points on which they agree.

o All models show substantial changes in climate when the atmospheric concentration of CO_2 is doubled, with the climate sensitivity (in terms of $\Delta T_{2\times}$) lying in a range of 1.5–4.5 °C. Here, we use the word 'substantial' advisedly. Recall that the world was only some 5 °C colder, on average, during the last glacial period.

o All models agree on certain large scale features of the likely geographical distribution of CO_2-induced climatic change.

The fact that global warming is not uniformly distributed around the world implies that *regional* climates — the seasonal pattern of temperature, winds, rain, snow and so on — are almost certain to change. The differences highlighted here do not alter that general conclusion. But they do make detailed predictions of regional climatic change highly uncertain. And those uncertainties are further compounded by the question to which we now turn; how will the changes evolve in time?

5.6 Assessing the pace of climatic change

The scenarios discussed in the previous section are like 'snapshots' in time — images of the climatic regime on a world where the Earth–atmosphere system has come into balance following an abrupt change in radiative forcing. But as long as the atmospheric burden of greenhouse gases goes on increasing, the climate system will be continually perturbed; no new equilibrium will be reached. A further — and crucially important — issue was foreshadowed in Section 5.3.2; the primitive ocean models employed in equilibrium studies fail to simulate the sinking of surface waters, especially at high latitudes. In reality, as the surface ocean warms, vertical mixing will carry some fraction of the enhanced radiative heating into the deeper ocean, where it may be sequestered for decades — or far longer — thus *delaying* the atmospheric response to the time-evolving increase in greenhouse gases. Shifts in ocean currents — or indeed, in the large-scale thermohaline circulation — could also produce a geographical distribution of surface warming different from that computed in equilibrium studies.

To capture these effects — and hence simulate the *time-evolving* phase of climatic change — strictly requires an AGCM to be coupled to a dynamic, three-dimensional ocean model; an OGCM, in short. Basically, the mathematical formulation of an OGCM mirrors that of an AGCM (since the ocean, too, is a fluid on a rotating planet, etc.) — if, that is, the equation governing atmospheric water vapour is replaced by one describing oceanic salinity. Again, computational constraints impose much the same coarse grid structure as in an AGCM. However, the attendant parameterization problems are far sharper. Many sub-grid scale phenomena (e.g. mesoscale eddies) and mixing processes are crucial components of the oceanic system for transporting heat — both vertically and horizontally. But how they interact with and influence the large-scale circulation is not clear.

One fundamental problem here — as so often in this unfolding story — is the totally inadequate observational data base from which current understanding of the oceanic circulation is inferred, and against which ocean models are tested. In an attempt to remedy this situation, an intensive international research programme is currently underway — the **World Ocean Circulation Experiment (WOCE)**. As part of the World Climate Research Programme, the ultimate aim of WOCE is to understand the role that the oceans play in controlling the Earth's climate. This awesome task will involve many of the world's physical oceanographers working full time during the 1990s. At the time of writing (1992), three core projects were in place, running in parallel with theoretical and modelling work (Figure 5.15).

o The first aims to take a comprehensive global 'snapshot' of the physical properties of the ocean, by combining global satellite surveillance of sea-surface conditions, with *in situ* measurements (from research ships, and thousands of instruments floating on, or suspended, in the sea).

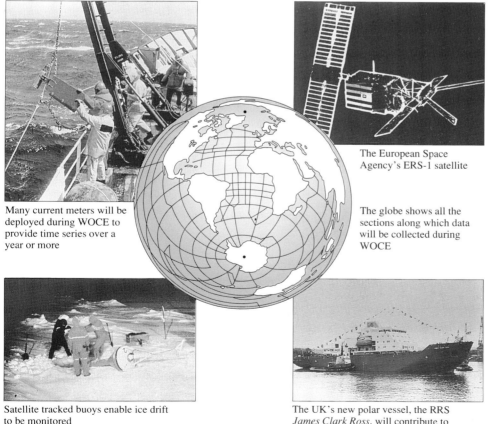

The European Space Agency's ERS-1 satellite

Many current meters will be deployed during WOCE to provide time series over a year or more

The globe shows all the sections along which data will be collected during WOCE

Satellite tracked buoys enable ice drift to be monitored

The UK's new polar vessel, the RRS *James Clark Ross*, will contribute to WOCE in the Southern Ocean.

Figure 5.15 A 'montage' of some features of the World Ocean Circulation Experiment (WOCE).

o   The second is concerned with the Southern Ocean and the way it links the circulation of the world's major oceans.

o   The third will study in detail the physical processes that have the greatest influence on models of ocean circulation, and the way in which the atmosphere and ocean interact.

These projects are still at an early stage. Inevitably, then, coupled AGCM/OGCM simulations of the time-evolving climatic response to an *on-going* increase in greenhouse gases have so far used coarse-resolution ocean models, with fairly crude parameterizations of small-scale mixing processes. Such models appear to simulate the exchange of surface waters with the deeper layers of the ocean in a broadly realistic way. For example, they do simulate strong vertical pathways in the northern North Atlantic (induced by increased surface salinity in winter), and in the Southern Ocean around Antarctica (through wind-driven upwelling/downwelling). On the other hand, existing models have certain known deficiencies (they tend to underestimate horizontal heat transport, for example); doubtless others will become apparent as the WOCE data are processed.

Bearing these limitations firmly in mind, we focus now on the key features revealed by a **'time-dependent' simulation** using a coupled AGCM/OGCM developed at the GFDL in Princeton (one of only two such studies that had been published at the time of the IPCC report). In this study, the control simulation was run for 100 model years (think of the computer resources!). It was then perturbed by increasing the atmospheric concentration of CO_2 at 1% a year, compounded (like compound interest, that is), *so that it doubled after 70 years.* Because of the absorption characteristics of CO_2, this translates into a *linear* increase in radiative forcing (Figure 5.16), and at a rate roughly equivalent to that currently being induced by increases in the entire suite of greenhouse gases. In other words, here — as in equilibrium studies — CO_2 is effectively a surrogate for *all* infrared absorbing trace gases (except water vapour, of course).

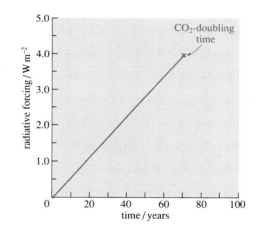

Figure 5.16   The variation with time of the radiative forcing due to an increase in atmospheric CO_2 at 1% a year, so that it doubles after 70 years.

Now have a look at Plate 5.4. Part (a) shows the geographical distribution of the surface warming computed after 70 years of the time-dependent simulation with the coupled AGCM/OGCM. Or to put it another way, it records what is often termed the **'realized warming'** at a given time — when the atmospheric concentration of CO_2 actually doubles in this case. For comparison, part (b) shows the *equilibrium* response to a CO_2-doubling, produced when the *same* AGCM is coupled to a mixed-layer ocean model — averaged over a whole year, that is (cf. the 'DJF' and 'JJA' scenarios produced by this GFDL model in Plates 5.2b and e, respectively). This equilibrium scenario represents the surface warming that would be 'expected' to occur *eventually* — once the whole atmosphere–ocean system has come to a new stable equilibrium, that is (in the sense defined in Section 5.2). Thus, the global-mean warming recorded in part (b) is the climate sensitivity (i.e. the value of $\Delta T_{2\times}$, as shown) of this particular AGCM.

Activity 5.4

According to the global-mean temperature changes recorded in Plates 5.4a and b, what fraction of the *eventual* equilibrium response to a CO_2-doubling (i.e. the value of $\Delta T_{2\times}$) is actually *realized* at the time when that occurs (after 70 years) in the time-dependent simulation? Now concentrate on part (c) of Plate 5.4. Identify two geographical regions where the realized warming is a significantly *smaller* fraction of the equilibrium response than this global average figure. Can you suggest a plausible explanation? (Hint: Have another look at the opening paragraph to this section.)

To take your thoughts on Activity 5.4 on a stage, refer to Figure 5.17. Here, the black points record global-mean values of the *realized* warming at various times *during* the GFDL time-dependent simulation: the final point (at 70 years) corresponds to the value (2.3 °C) recorded in Plate 5.4a. For comparison, the blue line records the expected *equilibrium* temperature response *appropriate to the radiative forcing at any given time*: values of the latter (taken from Figure 5.16) are indicated by the blue scale along the top of Figure 5.17. Strictly speaking, the known climate sensitivity of this particular AGCM (i.e. $\Delta T_{2\times} = 4\,°C$, as noted in Plate 5.4b) provides just one point on our blue line — that marked by a cross in the figure. Provided λ remains constant in Equation 5.2 (i.e. $\Delta T_s = \lambda \Delta F$), however, the equilibrium temperature-response to *any other* radiative forcing must lie on a line joining this point to the origin, as shown.

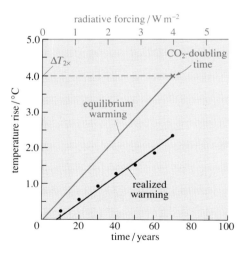

Figure 5.17 The variation with time (black) of the realized warming simulated by the coupled AGCM/OGCM developed at the GFDL, with the atmospheric CO_2 concentration increasing at 1% a year, such that it doubles after 70 years. This translates into a linear increase in radiative forcing in time (Figure 5.16), as indicated by the blue scale along the top of the figure. The blue line records the 'expected' equilibrium temperature response to each value of the forcing, as described in the text.

Concentrate now on the black line in Figure 5.17: this is a best straight-line fit through the calculated values of the realized warming. Notice that it cuts the time axis just short of 10 years: thereafter the time-evolving temperature response to the linear increase in forcing with time shown in Figure 5.16 is itself very nearly linear in time. This is important. It suggests that (after a brief initial phase of a decade or so), the realized warming at any given time *is always* proportional to the prevailing radiative forcing — but is of a *reduced* magnitude compared to the corresponding equilibrium response (around 60% in this case, as you found in Activity 5.4).

One possible explanation for these results links this global-mean picture with the regional 'anomalies' you identified in Activity 5.4. Put simply, it can be couched as follows. The strong vertical pathways that operate at high latitudes in the ocean effectively 'short circuit' a fraction (here some 40%) of the 'enhanced' radiative heating — whence it is sequestered in the deep ocean. This partly suppresses the surface warming in these regions. But elsewhere, a decade or so (the 'time-lag' referred to above) is sufficient to bring the atmosphere and the upper layers of the model ocean to an approximately balanced state, commensurate with the remaining portion (here 60%) of the radiative forcing.

To sum up. The results reviewed here add substance to the points raised at the beginning of this section. Certainly, they well exemplify the crucial role of the oceans in governing the pace of greenhouse-gas induced climatic change. Furthermore, the comparison in Plate 5.4 suggests that the geographical distribution of the evolving temperature rise (and, quite possibly, of changes to other key climate parameters as well) could indeed be different from that likely to characterize the eventual equilibrium response — as regards enhanced warming at high latitudes, for example.

That said, we should stress again that these are very early days for such coupled AGCM/OGCM studies. Many important questions remain. For example, what if the AGCM used had been one with a climate sensitivity toward the lower end of the IPCC range? What fraction of the enhanced radiative heating effectively removed from the atmosphere–upper ocean system is stored in truly deep, as opposed say to intermediate, waters? This is a vital (and as yet unresolved) issue for the time-scale over which it could, in turn, affect surface warming (see Figure 5.18). But perhaps most telling of all, there were indications in the GFDL study that downwelling and deep vertical mixing in the North Atlantic was becoming systematically weaker toward the end of the perturbed run. Could it cease altogether? And if it did, how would this affect regional climates, and the thermohaline circulation in general?

Figure 5.18 (a) Schematic representation of a hypothetical change in radiative forcing, which follows the linear increase in Figure 5.16 for 70 years, but is then held constant *indefinitely* at a value equivalent to a CO_2-doubling. (b) Sketch of the realized warming in response to the radiative forcing in (a), assuming $\Delta T_{2\times} = 4\,°C$ (as in Figure 5.17). With the forcing constant (after 70 years), temperatures would continue to rise slowly, but it is not yet clear whether it would take decades or centuries for most of the remaining rise to equilibrium (i.e. the *un*realized response to the CO_2-doubling) to occur.

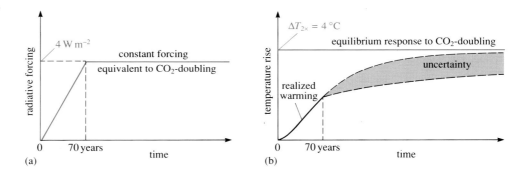

Issues like these can only really be addressed through more, and yet longer, runs with coupled, dynamic climate models. But there are other, equally pressing, demands on existing computer resources — or on any foreseeable increase therein. By now, examples should come readily to mind; better spatial resolution, improved treatment of surface processes, more detailed cloud parameterization schemes, and so on — together with the need (touched on at the beginning of Section 5.3) to incorporate the *biosphere* in a fuller and more interactive way.

To date, the pragmatic response to this situation has been to use a very much simpler type of climate model to make assessments of the pace of climatic change. In outline, this involves calculating the realized surface warming at any given time from what amounts to a simple global energy balance, which is determined by:

1   a *prescribed* value for the overall climate sensitivity (i.e. the value of $\Delta T_{2\times}$);

2   a prescribed rate of increase in the atmospheric burden of greenhouse gases, and hence in the radiative forcing; and

3   the oceanic uptake of the 'excess' radiative heating, as computed by a very simple ocean model, broadly similar to the upgraded 'box model, with polar outcrop' still widely used to simulate the oceanic uptake of 'excess' CO_2 — and described, in that context, in Chapter 4 (Figure 4.15b, Section 4.2.4).

You should be clear that this simple type of model treats neither atmospheric nor oceanic dynamics explicitly. Vertical and horizontal mixing within the ocean, and the associated heat transfer, are effectively reduced to a few globally averaged figures — for the rate at which water downwells in the 'polar outcrop', for example, or is exchanged between model layers in the 'non-polar' region, and so on. The atmospheric response to the radiative heating *not* sequestered by the model ocean is essentially prescribed by fixing the climate sensitivity.

Now have a look at Figure 5.19, which was produced by such a model — with the inputs under points 1 and 2 above specified to match those in the GFDL study recorded in Figure 5.17. Clearly, the two models simulate a broadly similar time-evolving temperature rise. Or at least they do on the decade–century time-scale where a comparison is possible — just the time-scale of most immediate concern when it comes to assessing the likely impacts of climatic change. This is important. The great strength of these simple climate models is that they are computationally fast, so long simulation runs are perfectly feasible. And they can be readily repeated, with changed inputs, thus allowing at least some estimate to be made of the time-evolving temperature rise:

1   for various radiative forcing 'scenarios', both past and future; and

2   for *different* values of the climate sensitivity, set in the range (1.5–4.5 °C) indicated by the equilibrium studies reviewed in Section 5.5.

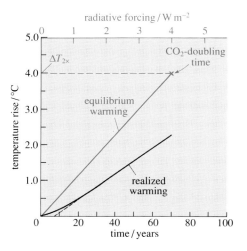

Figure 5.19 The realized warming as simulated by 'feeding' a prescribed linear increase in greenhouse forcing (chosen to match that in Figure 5.17) into the much simpler type of climate model described in the text. The prescribed climate sensitivity (i.e. the equilibrium response to a CO_2-doubling, $\Delta T_{2\times}$) was 4 °C.

In the next two chapters, we examine how the results of such studies feed into some of the more contentious issues in the on-going debate about human interference with climate.

Activity 5.5   *You should spend up to 20 minutes on this activity.*

Much of the material developed in this chapter is used and reinforced in the two that follow. Nevertheless, it would be a good plan to pause before you move on, and try to summarize in note form what you consider to be the key points. Make sure your summary includes a reference to each of the following:

o   radiative forcing;

o   climate sensitivity;   *(continued overleaf)* o radiative feedbacks;

o GCMs, and their shortcomings;

o equilibrium scenarios;

o realized warming.

Then compare your summary with the one below.

Summary of Chapter 5

1   In simple terms, anthropogenic greenhouse warming can be viewed as a two-stage process. An increase in the atmospheric burden of greenhouse gases constitutes a radiative forcing of the climate system, i.e. it disturbs the radiation balance at the top of the atmosphere. Global warming acts to restore the balance; the new equilibrium climate is characterized by a higher global-mean surface temperature (T_s).

2   The 'climate sensitivity' is commonly discussed in terms of the equilibrium change in T_s (ΔT_s) in response to a doubling of the atmospheric concentration of CO_2 (which translates into a radiative forcing of some $4\,W\,m^{-2}$): this is given the symbol $\Delta T_{2\times}$.

3   Depending on their sign, radiative feedback mechanisms can act to either increase or reduce the climate sensitivity. Important examples include water vapour feedback, snow–ice albedo feedback and cloud feedback. These feedbacks are a manifestation of the complex interactions between the atmosphere and the other components of the real climate system — the oceans, cryosphere, land surface and the vegetation that grows there.

4   General circulation models (GCMs) are powerful tools for simulating the behaviour of the climate system, and its response to a radiative forcing. Most current versions attempt to incorporate the interactions under point 3 above by coupling a dynamic model of the atmosphere (an AGCM) to an array of much cruder models at the planetary surface. At present, computational constraints impose a fairly coarse spatial resolution; small-scale processes are incorporated through parameterization techniques. Overall, existing GCMs contain oversimplified, approximate and incomplete descriptions of many important climatic processes; examples include cloud formation, precipitation, oceanic heat transport, sea-ice formation and many of the surface processes collected in Figure 5.7.

5   Nevertheless, validation studies generate confidence that such models can simulate important features of the Earth's present (and past) climate. Control runs do, however, reveal significant errors in the simulation of regional climates.

6   Equilibrium scenarios generated by different GCMs suggest that doubling the atmospheric concentration of CO_2 (or its radiative equivalent in terms of the other greenhouse gases) would induce significant surface warming; the climate sensitivities produced lie in the range 1.5–4.5 °C. Uncertainties about cloud feedback are thought to be a major factor in this wide range of estimates. All of the models assessed by the IPCC agree well with a recent observational determination of water vapour feedback.

7   Likewise, all equilibrium scenarios agree on certain large-scale features of the likely geographical distribution of greenhouse-gas induced climatic change, e.g. enhanced warming at high latitudes, especially in winter (linked to the snow–ice albedo feedback loop). But the detailed pattern of regional change (especially as regards precipitation and soil moisture) is markedly model dependent.

8   Early studies with an AGCM coupled to a dynamic ocean model (an OGCM) suggest that vertical mixing in the oceans (which is neglected in simple mixed-layer models) could significantly delay the atmospheric response to an on-going increase in

greenhouse gases, i.e. the 'realized' warming at any given time is less than the 'expected' equilibrium response to the prevailing radiative forcing. An important mechanism here appears to be the sequestering of 'excess' heat via the strong vertical pathways that 'feed' surface waters into the deep ocean at high latitudes. The existing simulations suggest that this may also suppress enhanced high-latitude warming during the time-evolving phase of climatic change.

9   Because the simulations referred to under point 8 are so computer-intensive, most existing assessments of the pace of climatic change have been based on studies with a much simpler type of climate model. Here, the 'excess' radiative heating effectively removed from the atmosphere–upper ocean system is computed by the type of ocean model still widely used to simulate the transfer of 'excess' CO_2 into the deep ocean. The global warming induced by the 'residual' heating is determined by the prescribed climate sensitivity. The results of such studies will be discussed further in Chapters 6 and 7.

6 The 'detection issue'

6.1 The issue

As we said in Chapter 1, the late 1980s saw an explosion of (often highly sensationalized) media reports about the potential consequences of the 'greenhouse forcing' experiment going on in the real world. Many unusual weather events were blamed on the greenhouse effect — the most potent such link undoubtedly being that prompted by the 'Summer of 1988' in the United States. Temperatures soared across the country. Thousands of barges were stranded on the Mississippi River and devastating drought gripped the Mid-West (Figure 6.1) — an echo of the dust-bowl years of the 1930s that reached deep into the American psyche, as did images, as the summer wore on, of fire sweeping through Yellowstone National Park. At the time, the message conveyed by the headlines was clear: greenhouse warming had arrived!

Greenhouse warming grips American corn belt

Ian Anderson, San Francisco

Echoes of droughts in the 1930s. Is the greenhouse to blame?

Figure 6.1 Of the unusual weather conditions of the late 1980s blamed on the greenhouse effect, few exerted such a powerful hold over the media — and through them, the public imagination — as the record-breaking heat and drought in the USA in 1988. That, coupled with the comments by James Hansen referred to in this extract from *New Scientist* (30 June 1988), sparked off the (equally heated!) 'detection debate' of the late 1980s: more on that in the text.

Scientists at NASA sparked a controversy among climatologists last week by declaring that the drought now devastating much of the American Midwest and the prairies of Canada may be an early manifestation of the greenhouse effect. Global temperatures so far this year are the highest on record, continuing a strong warming trend through the 1980s.

'It is time to stop waffling so much and say that the evidence is pretty strong that the greenhouse effect is here' said James Hansen, the top climate modeller at NASA's Goddard Institute for Space Studies in New York.

Other scientists said last week that both the drought in the US and the recent rise in global temperatures could be explained by natural fluctuations ...

The drought has lasted for three months. Conditions are the worst since the famous 'dust bowl' drought that lasted from 1934 to 1936.

Reflecting later on this period, Stephen Schneider somewhat ruefully remarked:

... overly dramatic coverage of the Summer of '88 and overstrong association with the greenhouse effect inevitably created a backlash ... a debate in 1989 that

is largely irrelevant to the scientific validity of the greenhouse effect was turned into a trial-by-media of a phenomenon whose existence is proved essentially beyond doubt.

(S. H. Schneider, 1990, Global Warming)

The important point being made here is the distinction between the greenhouse effect *per se* (i.e. the heat-trapping properties of certain trace gases in the atmosphere, about which there is no dispute) on the one hand — and on the other, a debate during 1989 that was largely about various facets of the **detection issue**.

Put simply, that comes down to the question: Have we yet detected the *enhanced* or *anthropogenic* greenhouse effect? Or to spell it out a little: we have a good record of the buildup of the main greenhouse gases (CO_2, CH_4, N_2O and the CFCs) since pre-industrial times. For each greenhouse gas, the radiative forcing associated with the observed increase in its atmospheric concentration (above the pre-industrial level recorded in Table 4.1, that is) can be calculated, as outlined for a CO_2-doubling in Section 5.2. Adding these separate contributions together produces a figure for the *total* radiative forcing at any given time during the past century — and hence of the way that total has evolved to date, as shown in Figure 6.2: as of 1990, it amounted to some $2.5\,\mathrm{W\,m^{-2}}$. The central question is then: Has the world seen changes in climate over the past century or so that can confidently be attributed to *this particular* history of radiative forcing?

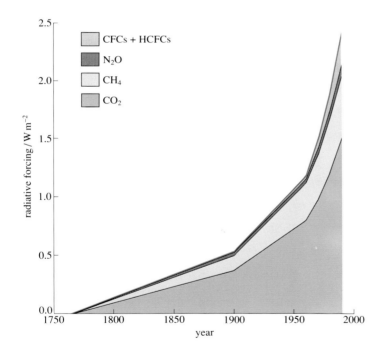

Figure 6.2 Estimated contributions to the *total* radiative forcing of the climate system (the blue line) due to the build up of various greenhouse gases since 1765.

Thus, detection embraces two problems. The first relates to the observational record, and the evidence for recent climatic change — usually (though not exclusively) identified with long-term global warming. The second is the question of attribution. In brief, that involves 'feeding' the radiative forcing in Figure 6.2 into a climate model, and then assessing the significance of any similarities (or indeed differences) between the model-predicted 'signal' of greenhouse gas-induced climatic change (or the **'greenhouse signal'**, for short) and that observed in the real world.

A major aim of this chapter is to examine the reasons why detection is an extremely difficult problem — and why, indeed, it is not as yet possible even to define a set of objective criteria that would constitute clear 'proof of detection'. But we shall also weave into the discussion some of the questions raised during the noisy, and some-what acrimonious, 'climate debate' of the late 1980s — questions that were seen, or at least represented, at the time as highly contentious issues. Finally, we aim to set the whole detection problem into a broader, and arguably more important, context.

6.2 Global warming trends: the instrumental record

The extract in Figure 6.1 refers to 'a strong warming trend through the 1980s'. There are similar references in the cuttings collected in Figure 1.2 — one of which (from a *Nature* report in early 1991) contains a figure depicting the trend in global-mean sur-face temperature this century. The temperature records we shall work with here are those shown in Figure 6.3: they come from the IPCC report published in 1990. Con-centrate for now on the global picture, in Figure 6.3a. Immediately striking are the marked fluctuations from year to year. Moreover, the averaging that produced the smoothed curve brings out considerable variability over periods of a decade or so as well. But equally, there clearly has been a general warming during the past century; by eye, it amounts to something like 0.5 °C. Before engaging further with the details of that trend, it is pertinent to ask how the hemispheric and global records in Figure 6.3 were put together.

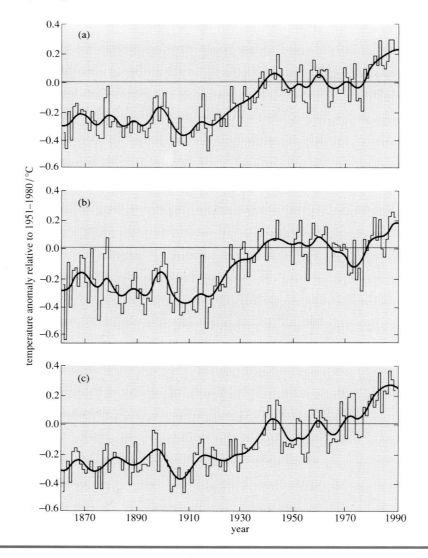

Figure 6.3 Reconstructions of the annual-mean surface temperature variations over the period 1861–1989 for (a) the whole globe, (b) the Northern Hemi-sphere, and (c) the Southern Hemi-sphere. In each case, the data (calculated from combined land-based measurements and sea-sur-face temperatures) are plotted as deviations ('anomalies') from the mean for 1951–1980. The smooth curves were obtained from a mathematical averaging procedure, roughly equivalent to plotting 15-year running means, i.e. averages over the current year and the previous 7 and following 7 years (e.g. the 15-year running mean for 1900 averages over the years 1893–1907, and so on).

There were clues in the extract from *Nature* in Figure 1.2 ('... based on data from land- and sea-based monitoring stations'), but little sense of the difficulties involved. In practice, it is a complex and time-consuming business to 'aggregate' weather observations (be they on land or at sea) from around the world into hemispheric or global averages, and hence construct the kind of climatological time series shown in Figure 6.3. Moreover, in the present context, these series need to be *reliable* enough to determine changes of the order of a few tenths of a degree Celsius over a period of 100 years or so.

For land-based measurements, something approaching a crude world-wide network of weather recording stations was in place by the late 19th century — but it was far from complete (think about it!). As late as the 1920s, data are lacking for many continental regions — parts of Africa, China, the former USSR and tropical South America, for example, and the whole of Antarctica. Even today, stations tend to be concentrated in heavily populated regions of the industrialized world; more remote areas are often poorly monitored. This is important. An uneven spatial coverage effectively 'samples' the Earth's temperature non-uniformly. Unless allowed for in some way, it can bias the hemispheric, and hence global, averages toward the figures for areas with many recording stations. *And as the spatial coverage changes over time, spurious trends can then become embedded in the historical record.*

But this is far from the only potential source of error that researchers — such as the groups referred to in the *Nature* article — have to contend with. Other problems relate to the station data themselves, where apparent jumps or trends in the record may be an artifact of some local effect. For example, changes in instrumentation or observing times, or in station location or the local environment can all affect the reliability of the data. Environmental factors that may introduce a persistent bias are the most serious, especially if the phenomenon is widespread. The classic (and much discussed) example here is the spurious warming associated with the growth of towns and cities around (or near) weather recording stations — the so-called 'urban heat island effect'.

Since over two-thirds of the Earth's surface is ocean, a truly global (or indeed hemispheric) temperature record must also include marine data. Again, problems arise over a skewed, and changing, spatial coverage (somewhat serendipitous in this case, as most marine observations are made by 'ships of opportunity') — and over data reliability (see Figure 6.4!).

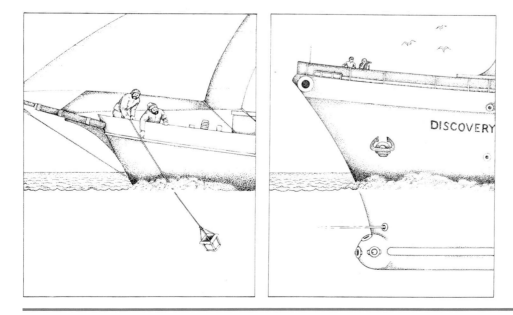

Figure 6.4 Since the 1850s (largely due to the pioneering efforts of a US naval captain — one Matthew Fontaine Maury) the maritime nations have archived logbooks containing millions of marine weather observations. But problems over biases and data reliability are, if anything, more pressing than for land-based measurements. Before about 1940, sea-surface temperatures (SSTs) were measured by hauling up a sample in a bucket (left): depending on the insulating properties of the bucket, the water tends to cool. Canvas, wood and metal have all been used — so not all bucket measurements are equal! Then, around World War II, there was a shift to measuring the temperature of the seawater in engine intake tubes (right). Such readings can be 0.3–0.7 °C warmer than canvas bucket measurements.

Different groups have used various techniques in a painstaking effort to screen the available records (both land-based and ocean-based) — applying corrections where possible, or simply rejecting unreliable data — and to minimize the impact of spurious trends and biases, and the potential 'sampling errors' noted above. We cannot go into the details here.* Suffice it to say that, following a careful assessment of the resulting data sets, the IPCC endorsed the reconstructions in Figure 6.3 (appropriately, i.e. by area, weighted averages of land and ocean data) as the most reliable guide to our planet's recent temperature history then available. So what of the trends they reveal?

This brings us back to the points noted earlier. For now, we concentrate on the *overall* warming trends in the hemispheric and global-mean surface temperature records of Figure 6.3. Judging that 'by eye', one tends to focus on the two end points of the smooth curves — themselves the result of an averaging process. A better technique is to put a line through the 'raw' (i.e. annual) values. There is a standard procedure for achieving the 'best linear fit' to a set of data. Applied to the data in each part of Figure 6.3 in turn, it yields the average warming rates collected in Table 6.1 — depending on how much of the early, and generally less reliable, part of the record is brought into the analysis.

Table 6.1 The results of fitting linear trends through the data in Figure 6.3 between (i) 1890 and 1989, and (ii) 1870 and 1989.

	Average warming/100 years	
	(i)	(ii)
Northern Hemisphere (b)	0.47 °C	0.39 °C
Southern Hemisphere (c)	0.53 °C	0.43 °C
Globe (a)	0.50 °C	0.41 °C

With uncertainties like this — and others linked to the fact that no amount of careful screening can entirely eliminate sampling errors and other biases from the record — the IPCC quoted their 'best estimate' of the global warming since the late 19th century as 0.45 ± 0.15 °C, i.e. in the range 0.3–0.6 °C. This broad range acknowledged a special concern that there could still be a small warming bias due to urbanization not eliminated from the temperature records — difficult to estimate (since the effects seem to be highly regional and time-dependent), but currently put at 0.05 °C at most.

Only the most carefully screened of the independent data sets so far assembled (and these cover marine air temperatures, as well as those over land and SSTs) were actually fed into Figure 6.3. But it is important to note that each set indicates a long-term warming trend, broadly consistent with the range cited above. Moreover, the past century has also seen a marked retreat of mountain glaciers in all parts of the world, and a general rise in sea-level. We return to the interpretation of such changes in Chapter 8; for now it is sufficient to appreciate that they provide some independent evidence for recent global warming, in that they draw on measurements not based on reading a thermometer. In short, the available evidence points consistently to a real warming trend over the past century — with six of the seven warmest years on record bunched in the years since 1980.

But, as Figure 6.3 makes abundantly clear, the upward trend has been both irregular, and somewhat different in the two hemispheres. Moreover, within each hemisphere, there are pronounced variations in *regional* temperature trends — apparent for the 20 years from

* A brief account of the procedures used by the group at the Climatic Research Unit at the University of East Anglia is given in a *Scientific American* article by P. D. Jones and T. M. L. Wigley (August 1990, pp. 66–73).

1967 to 1986 shown in Plate 6.1. During the late 1980s, it was often argued that the *irregular* warming of the Earth over the past century was inconsistent with the observed increase in the atmospheric burden of greenhouse gases, which translates into a relatively *smooth and accelerating* increase in radiative forcing (Figure 6.2). From this perspective, the more obvious discrepancies can be summarized as follows.

o As a whole (Figure 6.3a), the Earth appears to have warmed most rapidly during the 1920s and 1930s (with a particularly abrupt rise in the Northern Hemisphere, Figure 6.3b), followed by a period of relatively stable temperatures from the 1940s through to the 1970s (or even a slight cooling in the Northern Hemisphere), before the record took an upward turn again (since the 1960s in the south, but only after the early 1970s in the north). There is little direct correlation here with the pattern of radiative forcing in Figure 6.2, which shows the steepest increase after 1950 or thereabouts.

o Over the whole period, the average figures collected in Table 6.1 also suggest that the Southern Hemisphere has been leading slightly in the warming race, whereas the equilibrium scenarios we looked at in Section 5.5 might suggest the reverse — given that there is more ocean in the Southern Hemisphere, and the ocean is predicted to warm *less* (on average) than the land. That feature is also apparent in the results from the GFDL time-dependent simulation in Plate 5.4a.

The points noted above bear directly on the detection problem; we shall now sharpen the focus a little.

6.3 The question of attribution

Figure 6.5 is a better basis for the comparison outlined above. It incorporates the real-world temperature record from Figure 6.3a (in black), together with the model-predicted signal of greenhouse gas-induced global warming since the mid-19th century (in blue). In principle, the latter should be the time-evolving *realized* warming produced by feeding the historical increase in greenhouse gas concentrations into a variety of *different* coupled AGCM/OGCMs. In practice, no such simulations had been carried out at the time of writing — and computational constraints suggest they will not be immediately forthcoming. Thus, the blue curves in Figure 6.5 are from simulations with the much simpler type of climate model described at the end of Section 5.6. Here, the

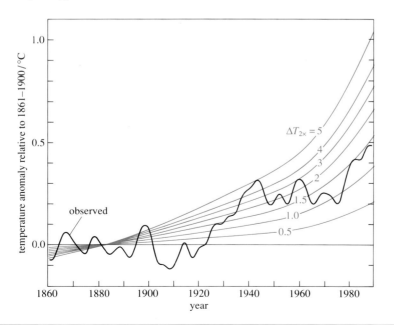

Figure 6.5 Observed global-mean surface temperature changes (1861–1989, as in Figure 6.3a, the black line) compared with the model-predicted realized warming (the 'greenhouse signal') for various prescribed values of the climate sensitivity, $\Delta T_{2\times}$ (the blue curves, described in the text). To provide a common reference level, modelled and observed data have been adjusted to have a zero mean over the period 1861–1900.

time-evolving radiative forcing 'fed' into the model was that in Figure 6.2. The *prescribed* climate sensitivity (labelled $\Delta T_{2\times}$) was set, in turn, to different values — both within the 'envelope of uncertainty' endorsed by the IPCC (i.e. 1.5–4.5 °C, and above and below it.

From this comparison, it would appear that the observed warming is just barely consistent with the 'accepted' range for $\Delta T_{2\times}$, even when discrepancies like the rapid warming between 1920 and 1940, and the slight cooling from then through to 1970, are effectively 'averaged out'. For example, judging the best match by eye from Figure 6.5 suggests a climate sensitivity of around 1.5 °C. In fact, a more rigorous analysis (analogous to the linear-trend analysis mentioned in Section 6.2, only this time between the 'raw' observed data in Figure 6.3a and the model-predicted curves for different values of $\Delta T_{2\times}$) produces a 'best fit', with a climate sensitivity closer to 1.4 °C.

▷ What is the implicit assumption in this analysis?

▶ That the observed warming can be attributed *solely* to an enhanced greenhouse effect.

But that amounts to assuming that all sources of *natural* climate variability have had *no net* effect on the planet's temperature over the past century — neither contributing a part of the observed warming, nor indeed, acting to offset what might otherwise have been a more substantial warming. In other words, the question of attribution — of establishing the 'guilt', if you will, of the prime suspect (the anthropogenic greenhouse effect) — is inextricably bound up with the task of weighing up the evidence against other possible 'suspects'. These can be collected under two broad headings: **internally-generated natural variability** — as distinct from climatic change induced by the kind of **external factors** ('external' to the Earth's climate system, that is) discussed in Chapter 3. Below, we look briefly at each of these categories.

6.3.1 Internally-generated natural variability

Most of the climate variability from year to year, evident in the records of Figure 6.3, stems from random fluctuations in the general pattern of atmospheric circulation — with consequent variations in cloudiness, for example, and in the exchange of heat with the planetary surface and oceans. Equally, spontaneous fluctuations in the oceanic circulation and in sea-surface temperatures can themselves 'force' the atmosphere and produce relatively short-term climatic anomalies.

More telling in the present context, however, is the possibility that the ocean's large 'thermal inertia' — and hence slow response to interannual fluctuations in atmospheric temperature — could, in turn, result in climatic variability on decadal, or even longer, time-scales. As noted earlier in the discussion of Figure 6.3, there *is* evidence of natural variability on time-scales of a decade or so in the historical temperature record. But that record is simply too short (and perhaps already 'contaminated' by greenhouse warming) to allow possible longer term *natural* fluctuations in global-mean surface temperature to be reliably identified — much less quantified. Under these circumstances, the only existing estimates of the effects that could arise have been obtained from computer simulations with climate models. Some typical results are collected and described in Box 6.1. Read this now, but don't worry too much about the details. The important general point to note is that such simulations reproduce the observed interannual and decadal scale variability in a broadly realistic way. But they also suggest that substantial *century-long* warming *or* cooling trends may occur — possibly as large as 0.2–0.3 °C.

Box 6.1   Model-simulated natural variability: the 'butterfly effect'*

6.1

The governing equations embedded in an AGCM have a key feature; they contain what mathematicians call 'non-linear' terms. These terms amount to a sort of 'internal feedback' — links through which the relationships between the different variables (temperature, pressure, wind speed, etc.) constantly shift and change and are impossible to pin down. As James Gleick has written, analysing the behaviour of such a system 'is like walking through a maze whose walls rearrange themselves with each step you take'.

To borrow an image from Gleick, the 'demon of non-linearity' is the ultimate source of internally-generated natural variability — the random fluctuations that produce the rich repertoire of real Earthly weather. In this coupled, non-linear system, many motions are inherently unstable. Small perturbations (the proverbial flap of a butterfly's wings) are not 'damped out'. Instead, seemingly small differences, between two similar atmospheric states say, can blow up rapidly as the system evolves in time, generating quite different weather patterns. In short, *even without any external disturbance*, the weather never exactly reproduces itself from one year to the next — not in the real world, and not in the model world either.

Now concentrate on Figure 6.6. The top panel (a) comes from the 100-year *control* run with the GFDL's coupled AGCM/OGCM referred to in Section 5.6. It shows random fluctuations in global-mean surface tempera-

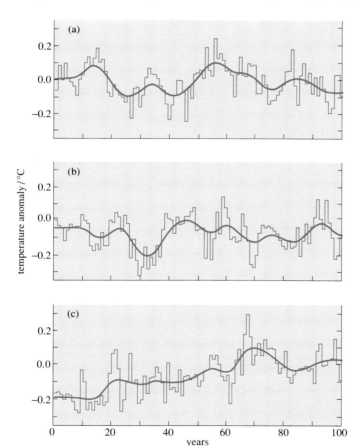

Figure 6.6 Computer simulations of fluctuations in global-mean surface temperature due to internally-generated natural variability, produced by (a) the GFDL's coupled AGCM/OGCM, and (b) and (c) the much simpler type of climate model described at the end of Section 5.6. Further details are in the text.

---

* The profound implications of the butterfly effect were first recognized in the early 1960s by Edward Lorenz, then a mathematician in meteorologist's clothing at the Massachusetts Institute of Technology. From that seed has grown arguably the most important revolution in scientific thinking of the late 20th century. If you are interested, I urge you to read *Chaos: Making a New Science* by James Gleick (Cardinal, 1988). It provides a fascinating, always readable, and often provocative, introduction to this new way of looking at the behaviour of complex dynamic systems. The references to Gleick in this Box come from p. 24 of his book.

ture from year to year. But there are also larger, longer-term, trends (brought out by the smooth curve) which have been ascribed to the modulating effect of the ocean's large thermal inertia.

The lower two panels, labelled (b) and (c), are two different '100-year sections' from a very much longer simulation (it was run for *100 000* model years!) with the much simpler type of climate model used to produce the curves in Figures 5.19 and 6.5. Here, $\Delta T_{2\times}$ (= 4 °C) was chosen to match the climate sensitivity of the AGCM/OGCM of (a) — as it was in the simulation that produced Figure 5.19. Recall that the latter simulation involved 'feeding' a linear increase in radiative forcing with time (shown in Figure 5.16) into the model. This time, however, the model was 'forced' with a randomly fluctuating pattern of radiative changes designed to reproduce the kind of year by year (i.e. high-frequency) variability in global-mean

surface temperature observed in the real world. The *low-frequency* variability in these two panels (again brought out by the smooth curves) can only arise as these rapid fluctuations are modulated by the slower response of the model ocean.

The central panel (b) is one '100-year section' from the 100 000-year simulation run with this simpler model: it shows decadal-scale variability which is qualitatively indistinguishable from that evident in the AGCM/OGCM results in panel (a). Most 100-year sections show a broadly similar pattern. But a significant fraction show *century*-long warming or cooling trends as large as — or even larger than — that in the bottom panel (c). That in turn suggests that *longer* control runs with coupled AGCM/OGCMs may also reveal such century time-scale natural variability. And maybe that happens in the real world as well. ■

To sum up. Spontaneous fluctuations in global-mean surface temperature are an inherent feature of the Earth's climate system. This internally-generated 'noise' is bound to obscure the 'greenhouse signal' in the real world: deviations from the steady model-predicted warming trend (e.g. the blue curves in Figure 6.5) are only to be expected. That is the important general message. More specifically, the results outlined in Box 6.1 suggest that natural variability could have contributed a *significant* part of the observed warming to date — or alternatively, acted to offset the 'true' greenhouse signal.

Activity 6.1

For simplicity, take the observed global warming over the past century to be 0.5 °C (from Table 6.1). Suppose now that natural fluctuations could have contributed ± 0.2 °C during this period.

(a) What might the 'true' greenhouse gas-induced warming have been over this period?

(b) In qualitative terms, how would that affect the climate sensitivity deduced from the comparison in Figure 6.5?

One final point. The emphasis here has been on fluctuations in the global-mean surface temperature. This global picture effectively 'averages out' the influence of natural variability on a more local or regional scale — a familiar (and at times, devastating) fact of life for human populations around the world. The point to register is that natural variability makes the interpretation of *regional* temperature trends (like those in Plate 6.1, for example) an even more difficult and uncertain business.

6.3.2 The influence of 'external' factors

▷ Which of the factors discussed in Chapter 3 are known (or suspected) to influence the Earth's climate on a time-scale of years to a few centuries?

▶ Two such factors were identified in the answer to Activity 3.4: variations in solar irradiance (and hence the solar constant at Earth) and volcanic activity.

Of these, the possible effects of solar variability over the past century have been the source of much controversy and long debate. It is a complicated issue. As we said in Section 3.4, ongoing monitoring of solar irradiance (from satellite-borne instruments) has been in place only since 1978. That period is just sufficient to confirm that the solar constant varies by about 0.1% in step with the 11-year sunspot cycle — declining between 1978 and the mid-1980s, and recovering since then (Figure 3.19). A far more difficult question to resolve is the possibility that these sunspot cycle-related fluctuations in solar irradiance may be superimposed on larger, longer-term (a century or so) variations, as shown schematically in Figure 6.7. Arguments that this may indeed be so have drawn mainly on the *indirect* evidence from the palaeoclimatic record outlined in Section 3.4. In essence, that comes down to the possibility of a *causal* link between century time-scale variations in solar irradiance and the recurrence throughout the present interglacial (the Holocene) of relatively cold periods, more or less global in extent, and sometimes lasting for centuries.

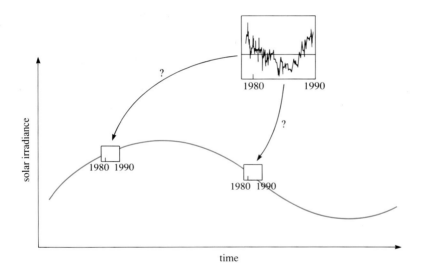

Figure 6.7 A visualization of the possibility that the observed short-term fluctuations in the solar constant that accompany the 11-year sunspot cycle (the box shows a repeat of the satellite measurements in Figure 3.19) could be superimposed on top of larger, century time-scale variations (the blue curve). The curve is purely hypothetical: there are no observational data about its shape, about the scales that should be attached to the vertical and horizontal axes, nor about whether we are presently 'sitting' on a rising or falling portion of the curve.

We should stress again, as we did in Section 3.4, that there is no agreed explanation for these recurrent 'Little Ice Age' type events. The evidence for a link with century time-scale solar variability was rehearsed at that stage: it is at best 'highly suggestive'. However, one key point was not brought out in our earlier discussion. In the terminology introduced in Section 5.2, a change in the solar constant, like a change in the atmospheric burden of greenhouse gases — or indeed, *any change that disturbs the radiation balance at the top of the atmosphere* — constitutes a radiative forcing of the climate system.

Figure 6.8 illustrates the point for a 1% change (up or down) in the solar constant, and hence in the globally-averaged solar flux incident at the top of the atmosphere (i.e. the '100 units' of incoming solar radiation in Figure 6.8a). Assuming that the overall planetary albedo is unchanged (at 31%), this produces a 1% change in the solar flux *absorbed* by the Earth–atmosphere system. Notice that the resulting radiative forcing, i.e. the imbalance at the top of the atmosphere, can have either a warming (Figure 6.8b) or cooling (Figure 6.8c) effect. In short, '**solar forcing**' (unlike the 'greenhouse forcing' recorded in Figure 6.2, say) can be *either* positive *or* negative.

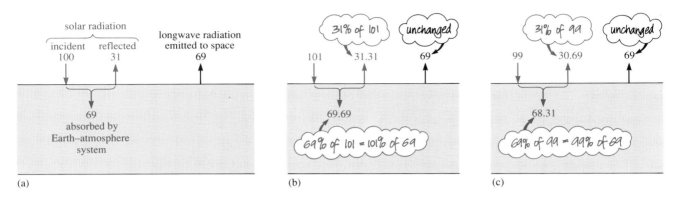

(a) (b) (c)

Figure 6.8 The global-mean radiation balance at the top of the atmosphere, and the effect on that of a 1% change in the solar constant. (a) Present situation, with figures expressed as a percentage of the incoming solar flux (100 units, as in Figures 2.14 and 5.2a). (b) and (c) The imbalance induced by a 1% increase or decrease, respectively, in the solar flux, assuming no change in the overall planetary albedo. See text for further details.

Question 6.1 According to Figure 6.8, what is the radiative forcing associated with a $\pm 1\%$ change in the solar constant? (Take 100 units to be equivalent to $342\,\mathrm{W\,m^{-2}}$, as in Figure 5.2.)

In the present context, modelling studies (analogous to those which produced the results in Figure 6.5, but using a *negative* forcing history to 'match' the *fall* in global-mean surface temperature deduced from the palaeoclimatic record) indicate that a prolonged (100–200 year) decline in the solar constant of several tenths of a per cent (in the range 0.2–0.6%) could explain the cold periods earlier in the Holocene. As we noted in Section 3.4, these figures are somewhat higher than other, more theoretically-based, estimates of possible century time-scale variations in solar irradiance (around 0.14%). But as yet, there is no *direct* observational evidence for such changes, and hence no way of assessing the reliability of these estimates: that will only come with further satellite measurements over the coming decades. More importantly, there are no hard data to either confirm or deny the possibility of a prolonged increase (or equally, decrease) in the solar constant over the *last* century. How does that situation affect the detection issue — the problem of attributing all (or some part) of the global warming this century to the enhanced greenhouse effect? The following activity gives you a chance to ponder on this.

Activity 6.2

(a) Suppose we adopt $\pm 0.5\%$ as a possible (if arbitrary) measure of the change in solar constant that *could* have occurred during the past century. What might the *total* (i.e. 'solar' plus 'greenhouse') radiative forcing of the climate system have been over this period. (Take the 'greenhouse' contribution to be $2.5\,\mathrm{W\,m^{-2}}$, as noted in Figure 6.2.)

(b) Suppose it were claimed (and it has been) that global warming this century can be explained *completely* by a long-term increase in the solar constant. Can you now spot the fundamental *logical* flaw in this assertion?

(c) In qualitative terms, how does your answer to part (a) affect the climate sensitivity (i.e. the value of $\Delta T_{2\times}$) deduced from the comparison in Figure 6.5? (Don't worry if you find this a bit tricky.)

To sum up. As far as detection is concerned, the uncertain history of solar forcing only reinforces the points made in Section 6.3.1 and Activity 6.1. Thus, estimates (of the kind you made in Activity 6.2a) suggest that century time-scale fluctuations in solar irradiance *could* have significantly enhanced — or acted to offset — any greenhouse gas-related warming over the past century. Whether or not it actually did remains an open question. In short, prolonged solar forcing is one 'alternative suspect' we have only just begun to keep under surveillance.

▷   Turning now to the other external factor identified at the beginning of this section, why can major volcanic eruptions, like Tambora (1815) for example, have a substantial — if largely short-term — *cooling* effect on surface temperature? (Refer back to Section 3.5 if need be.)

▶   Such eruptions inject into the *stratosphere* large amounts of dust and, in particular, sulphur dioxide (SO_2) — the latter being rapidly converted into sulphate aerosols. The major effect of such aerosols is through the back-scattering of incoming solar radiation. This effectively increases the planetary albedo (it amounts to a *negative* radiative forcing), producing a short-term cooling at the surface.

There is little of substance to add here, other than to note that the major eruptions over the past century (some of which were listed in Table 3.1) will have contributed to the short-term variability evident in the temperature records in Figure 6.3.

However, there is a related *anthropogenic* factor that was not discussed in Chapter 3. Since the pre-industrial era, human activities have undeniably been pumping a cocktail of different solid particles (smoke, ash, dust, etc.) and SO_2 into the *lower* atmosphere, often along with the archetypal greenhouse gas (CO_2) as fossil fuels are burnt. Could any, or all, of these other pollutants — collectively dubbed '**tropospheric aerosols**' — have had a significant impact on the Earth's radiation budget? The short answer is: perhaps. But the general dearth of observational data, together with the extraordinary diversity of tropospheric aerosols (in size, chemical composition, optical properties, atmospheric lifetimes and so on), makes it frankly impossible to reconstruct any kind of 'aerosol forcing' history for the past century. Or at least, it does with one partial exception.

The emission of volatile sulphur-containing compounds at the planetary surface is part of the natural 'sulphur cycle'. These 'sulphur gases' include both *inorganic* compounds (notably SO_2, but also hydrogen sulphide, H_2S) and a variety of *organic* compounds (principally dimethylsulphide, or DMS for short) of biogenic origin. The most important natural source of DMS is that released by marine phytoplankton, although terrestrial plants and micro-organisms in the soil also make significant (albeit much smaller) contributions. Without pursuing the atmospheric chemistry involved (the OH• radical again plays a pivotal role!), the ultimate fate of *all* of these naturally-produced sulphur gases is conversion to sulphate aerosols. As a result, the 'unpolluted' troposphere naturally contains a certain background level of such aerosols.

Some attempts have been made to estimate the *negative* radiative forcing associated with the *increase* in sulphate aerosols — above the 'normal' background level, that is — due to anthropogenic emissions of SO_2. These assessments take on board not only the *direct* radiative effects of such aerosols (analogous to their role in the stratosphere), but also a potentially important *indirect* effect — through their influence on cloud albedo. The link here comes from the importance of sulphate aerosols (whatever their source) as cloud condensation nuclei (Box 2.3 in Section 2.3.1), i.e. the air-borne particles that allow the condensation of water vapour to form the liquid droplets suspended in clouds. The argument goes that an increased load of aerosols produces clouds with a higher concentration of such droplets — and that such clouds are more reflective.

There is observational evidence (from the ERBE, for example, mentioned in the caption to Figure 5.3) consistent with this aerosol/cloud albedo connection — and suggestive of a possible large-scale effect linked to anthropogenic emissions of SO_2. But it is difficult to quantify. In 1990, the IPCC report quoted estimates of the radiative forcing since 1900 in the range of -0.25 to $-1.25\,W\,m^{-2}$ — *all* of it actually occurring in the Northern Hemisphere. There are two points to note here. First, these estimates suggest that the so-called '**sulphate compensation effect**' *could* have acted to offset a substantial part of the positive *greenhouse* forcing to date (some $2.5\,W\,m^{-2}$, recall). But second, whatever 'forcing compensation' there may have been has probably acted regionally, *not* truly globally. By contrast with the major greenhouse gases, SO_2 and the aerosols derived from it have limited tropospheric lifetimes, a few weeks at most; they return to Earth as acid rain (and snow)! Because of this, the augmentation of sulphate aerosols brought about by industrialization is not evenly distributed around the globe (Figure 6.9), unlike the steady buildup in greenhouse gases. Rather, it is concentrated in the Northern Hemisphere, predominantly over the most polluted regions of Europe and North America.

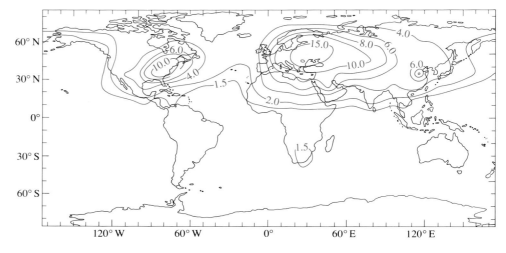

Figure 6.9 The contours mark out estimates of how much more sulphate aerosol there is at present in the troposphere than in the 'unpolluted' pre-industrial situation. (The figures are ratios. For example, sulphate levels have gone up by more than a factor of 10 over the most polluted regions of Europe and North America.)

Question 6.2 (a) Which of the 'discrepancies' listed at the end of Section 6.2 might possibly be a manifestation of this 'sulphate compensation effect'?

(b) At present, SO_2 emissions are being actively reduced in many industrialized countries. What impact might this be expected to have on any possible compensation effect in the coming decades?

6.3.3 The question of attribution: a summary

A pause to take stock is in order. By this stage, you should have a good feel for the problem at the heart of the detection issue. To spell it out a little, the existence of long-term global warming in the real world is clearly qualitatively consistent with the 'enhanced greenhouse' hypothesis; *all* climate models (whatever their differences as regards climate sensitivity and so on) agree on that. But this broad consistency does not *prove* cause and effect. To demonstrate that — to attribute all or part of the observed warming to this particular cause — other possible causes would need to be eliminated.

At present, that is impossible. Estimates of the warming, *or equally possible cooling*, trends that may be superimposed on any greenhouse-related signal can be, and have been, made. But in reality, the necessary historical data on other possible 'forcing' factors — whether natural (a prolonged change in the solar constant, for example), or anthropogenic (the tropospheric aerosol burden) — are lacking or highly uncertain, as discussed in Section 6.3.2. And on top of this, there is the 'noise' of internally-generated natural variability — spontaneous, and perhaps sustained and substantial, fluctuations of the global-mean surface temperature that seem to be an inherent feature of our planet's climate system (Section 6.3.1). All of which means, of course, that deviations from the 'expected' steady warming trend, and other apparent inconsistencies with model predictions, are only to be expected; they are not hard evidence *against* the enhanced greenhouse hypothesis.

Is there a way out of this impasse? Three strategies have been discussed. The first, being actively pursued at present, is generally known as the *'fingerprinting'* technique. This method acknowledges the message implicit in the resumé given above — effectively that changes in global-*mean* surface temperature are not, in fact, a particularly good signal of the enhanced greenhouse effect: there are too many other possible causes. Instead, the idea is to examine the observational records for evidence of other aspects of the model-predicted response to greenhouse forcing — a particular spatial pattern of climatic change, say. To date, such studies have used the more robust features of existing *equilibrium* scenarios (enhanced warming at high latitudes, for example) effectively to define the 'expected' greenhouse signal. But in reality, the actual time-evolving response to an ongoing increase in greenhouse gases could well have quite different spatial characteristics — as suggested by the results of the coupled AGCM/OGCM simulation we looked at in Section 5.6. Without more such simulations it will remain difficult to define a unique, greenhouse-related pattern of change — and, even more so, one that is likely to 'stand out' above the noise of natural variability. Nevertheless, the advocates of the fingerprinting method believe it holds the best hopes for *early* detection.

The other two detection strategies referred to above are essentially variants on the 'wait-and-see' approach.

o   Continue, or initiate, surveillance of the other possible **forcing factors** (i.e. solar irradiance, stratospheric and tropospheric aerosols), the aim being to quantify their influence, and so remove this from the temperature record *in the future*.

o   Simply wait until global warming is so large (perhaps another 0.5 °C say) that the enhanced greenhouse effect is the only possible explanation — the so-called **'unprecedented change'** approach. Current estimates (they depend, among other things, on the assumed climate sensitivity) suggest a wait of *at least* a decade, and probably longer.

In the meantime — and to pursue our legal terminology — the jury is still out on the question of attribution. All of the problems and uncertainties considered here (and in Section 6.2) conspire to make an objectively quantified judgement impossible — even one of a probabilistic kind, such as 'We are so many per cent confident that a certain observed change (or a certain fraction of observed change) over such and such a period is attributable to the enhanced greenhouse effect.'[*]

---

[*]T. M. L. Wigley, G. I. Pearman and P. M. Kelly (1992) Indices and indicators of climate change: issues of detection, validation and climate sensitivity, in Mintzer, I. M. (ed.) *Confronting Climate Change: Risks, Implications and Responses*.

Activity 6.3   *You should spend up to 20 minutes on this activity.*

To return to the sweltering summer of 1988; in June, James Hansen gave testimony before a US Senate Energy Committee hearing on global warming. His testimony included a statement that 'with a high degree of confidence we could associate the warming with the greenhouse effect'. This statement was seized on by the media and environmental pressure groups alike: it is referred to in the extract from *New Scientist* in Figure 6.1. Given the timing, and the weight of Hansen's scientific reputation, there is little doubt that it had a major impact on policy makers in the USA — and, through the media, on the wider public perception that greenhouse warming had 'arrived', and that it posed a serious threat to the future well-being of the planet. Equally, it was instrumental in provoking the backlash, referred to in our earlier quote from Stephen Schneider (Section 6.1).

The letters to the prestigious American journal *Science* reproduced as Extract 6.1 capture something of the ensuing debate within the scientific community. They appeared in response to a *Science* report (included in the offprints collection for this book if you are interested) on a 'Workshop on Greenhouse-Gas-Induced Climate Change' held in Amherst, Massachusetts in May 1989. Read through the letters, and then jot down (in note form) your thoughts on the following questions.

Is there any evidence here of a fundamental difference of opinion about the enhanced greenhouse effect *per se*?

What differences of opinion or emphasis *are* apparent — either explicitly or implicitly?

Extract 6.1   From *Science*, 4 August 1989.

Letters

Hansen and the Greenhouse Effect

Richard A. Kerr's article about James Hansen (Research News, 2 June, p. 1041) is, in my opinion, extremely misleading. Not only does it cast Hansen in a very bad light, it also gives the impression that the greenhouse problem could well be just another environmental false alarm. As a colleague who knows Hansen well, I would like to address these issues.

First, it should be pointed out that the meeting referred to in Kerr's article was organized by a group of people sympathetic to the Department of Energy's position that the greenhouse gas buildup cannot yet be taken seriously. In this regard I feel that the view of this group was not representative of the scientific community's stance. In a sense, Hansen was effectively entering a lion's den.

Second, most would agree that Hansen's depth of insight into the greenhouse problem is matched by few others in the field. He and his colleagues at the Goddard Institute of Space Studies have focused their major research efforts on this problem for the past decade. The papers they have published have had an enormous impact. In my estimation, none of the participants at the meeting can match Hansen's credentials and expertise. In fact, Hansen's group might be referred to as the Avis of climate modelling, while Michael Schlesinger, who organized the meeting, comes from a group that could be called the Rent-A-Wreck of climate modelling. I believe that Hansen is motivated only by his interests in the welfare of the planet and, while I do not agree with all the details of his congressional testimony, I support its major thrust.

With regard to the greenhouse problem, I feel that Kerr does not convey the fact that concern does not rest on whether a significant greenhouse warming has yet occurred. Rather, it rests on a host of model simulations and back-of-the-envelope calculations, all of which suggest that a substantial warming will occur. Further, the records of the last 150,000 years found in ice cores and in marine sediments scream to us that the earth's climate system is highly sensitive to nudges. The ozone hole demonstrates that processes generally considered unimportant in computer simulations can indeed prove to have serious consequences in the real world. The fact that we cannot prove that the warming during the last century was caused by man-induced greenhouse gases is not the major issue. Rather the issue is that, by adding infrared-absorbing gases to the atmosphere, we are effectively playing Russian roulette with our climate. It is essential that we plan a proper course of action should the consequences prove detrimental to agriculture and wildlife.

Hansen may prove to be incorrect in his prediction of the potential seriousness of the greenhouse gas buildup, but it should be understood that concerns such as his are born of a deep regard for the future of our planet and not by fame or funding.

W. S. BROECKER
Lamont-Doherty Geological Observatory
of Columbia University,
Palisades, NY 10964

Broecker states that the Workshop on Greenhouse-Gas-Induced Climate Change: A Critical Appraisal of Simulations and Observations "was organized and controlled by a group of people sympathetic to the Department of Energy's position that the greenhouse gas buildup cannot yet be taken seriously." Had Broecker accepted my invitation to participate in the workshop and made his contribution there, rather than in the pages of Science, he would have known this not to be the case. On the contrary, the 61 participants of the workshop from Australia, Canada, the Federal Republic of Germany, the Soviet Union, the United Kingdom, and the United States have an abiding concern for the climate future of the earth. This concern motivates them to understand this issue to the best of their ability lest society otherwise turn away from it in the near term, because of unrealized expectations, and thereby aggravate its solution in the long term. This concern is evident in the workshop press release which follows.

It is certain that increasing the concentrations of carbon dioxide, methane, chlorofluorocarbons and other trace gases will enhance the greenhouse effect. The concentration of these gases has increased substantially during the last 100 years as a result of human activities. Over the same period the average global surface air temperature has risen by about 0.5 degree Celsius, although this increase has not been constant in time or uniform over the globe. It is tempting to attribute this warming to the increase in greenhouse gases. Because of the natural variation of temperature, however, such an attribution cannot now be made with any degree of confidence. For the same reason, a temporary cooling should not be taken as evidence that greenhouse gas-induced warming in the next century is unlikely.

To increase our understanding of the long-term natural variations of climate requires detailed global information extending back over several centuries. Estimates of natural variability can be obtained from observations in the historic past and from simulations of climate with mathematical climate models on supercomputers.

Climate models are our best tool for estimating future changes in climate. These models project a global warming of a few degrees by the middle of the next century due to the continuing and projected increases of greenhouse gases. Such a change is several times larger than the warming of the past century. Changes in precipitation and other climate quantities are also projected. However, climate models give differing pictures of the regional features of climate change, including the frequency of droughts and storms.

Progress to improve our ability to project future climate will best be achieved by the further development, analysis, and verification of climate models, by the acquisition, assembly and analysis of climate data, by observational studies of climatic processes, and by providing the human and computer resources required for these tasks.

We, the participants in the international Workshop on Greenhouse-Gas-Induced Climatic Changes, conclude that the need to reduce the current uncertainties about the magnitude, timing and regional detail of future climatic changes is an urgent international priority.

MICHAEL E. SCHLESINGER
Department of Atmospheric Sciences,
Oregon State University,
Corvallis, OR 97331–2209

The article "Hansen *vs.* the world on the greenhouse threat" leaves the impression that James Hansen (or the position he has taken) is out of the mainstream of the climatological community and that his efforts are less than scientifically based. The major issue of contention is whether or not Hansen is stepping outside the bounds of reasonableness with his statement that "with a high degree of confidence we could associate the warming with the greenhouse effect" and with his communication of this to Congress.

Cause and effect is an incredibly difficult association to make in science. For greenhouse theory, there is no existing testable sufficient condition that would verify that the observed warming and greenhouse change are related. Rather, there are various testable necessary or circumstantial conditions that can be considered. The "fingerprinting" technique reportedly favored at the Amherst conference is just one of many tests that can be performed, and it has its problems like all of them. The fingerprinting technique uses the spatial pattern of climate change to detect greenhouse change, which is a noisier signal than the global average. In addition, studies to date with the fingerprinting method have considered only the predicted equilibrium response to greenhouse change in the absence of ocean currents for the purpose of comparison with observations (1). The actual transient response pattern could be quite different from the predicted equilibrium response (2).

The bottom line, however, is that all the circumstantial evidence in the world does not make a sufficient condition (be it for refutation or for confirmation). To say anything useful about the association between the theory and observations, all the circumstantial evidence must be considered, not just the results of any single statistical test. When one speaks of confidence in association of the warming and greenhouse change, then one is extrapolating on the basis of disparate information from various sources and tests. The confidence quoted cannot be associated with a particular statistical test and objective number. Rather, one is making value judgments over how much confidence to associate with the circumstantial evidence that is available When Hansen looks at the evidence and assigns a high degree of confidence to it, he is being no less, or no more, scientific than, say, fellow modeler Michael Schlesinger when he assigns a low degree of confidence on the basis of the same evidence.

The challenge presented by Hansen's manner of communicating his position (congressional testimony) is over how scientists resolve disputes over interpretation and communicate scientific information about contentious public issues. Should Hansen have gone before Congress? Should he have used the word "confidence," or something else? What is it about the science and the policy associated with this issue that makes a high confidence statement more or less defensible than a low confidence statement? How do the standards for certainty change (if at all) when a scientific issue has policy implications? Is there a "scientific" way of communicating information outside a field? Scientists need to consider how to speak out and how to respond to those who do and those who don't. Perhaps the logical follow-up from the Amherst meeting on greenhouse science is to hold another meeting where climatologists directly address the communication issues around which they have hitherto been skirting.

JAMES RISBEY
Center for Meteorology and
Physical Oceanography,
Massachusetts Institute of Technology,
Cambridge MA 02139

REFERENCES

1. T. P. Barnett and M. E. Schlesinger, *J. Geophy. Res.* **92**, 14772 (1987).

2. S. H. Schneider and S. L. Thompson, *ibid.* **86**, 3135 (1981).

Response: Broecker contends that the group assembled at the Amherst workshop on the greenhouse was not representative of the scientific community. To the extent that computer modelers play a role, the statement is unsupportable. There are five greenhouse modeling groups generally recognized as world-class. All were represented at the workshop. In addition, few if any researchers in the climate community have publicly agreed with Hansen's "high degree of confidence" statement.

Broecker says that concern does not rest on detection of the greenhouse warming. The reactions of Congress and the public suggest otherwise. True, the physics of the greenhouse and a wealth of circumstantial evidence require an eventual warming. But years of Capitol Hill testimony to that effect failed to sway Congress or the public. It was Hansen's claim of certain detection of the greenhouse, not hosts of calculations, that touched off last summer's media firestorm.

As Risbey ably points out, some might view Hansen's conclusion as scientific; his manner of presentation, however, might well be the subject of thoughtful discussion.

RICHARD A. KERR

6.4 The 'climate debate' of the late 1980s

To set Hansen's testimony in a wider context: June 1988 also saw a major international conference in Toronto. Entitled 'The Changing Atmosphere: Implications for Global Security', it was attended by over 300 government representatives, scientists and policy-makers from 48 countries. The debates were all the more pointed because of the heat and drought then gripping North America. Britain had a wet summer that year, but continental Europe fared differently: in Moscow it turned out to be the hottest summer of the century thus far. In August, Bangladesh was devastated by a flood that inundated almost 80% of its land and rendered 25 *million* people homeless. In September, Hurricane Gilbert brought a trail of destruction to the Caribbean in what the Jamaican Prime Minister described as 'the worst natural disaster in our modern history'. Just a month later, Hurricane Joan hit Nicaragua and flattened three-quarters of the trees in an area of $15\,000\,km^2$ of forest. In Africa, after years of continuing drought, there were unexpected torrential rains, which brought floods and plagues of locusts. At the end of 1988, scientists reported it to have been the hottest year this century (a record topped in 1990 — see the *Nature* extract in Figure 1.2).

Freak weather conditions can occur at any time, in any part of the world: there have always been storms, and floods and droughts. A spate of such events could easily be a further manifestation of natural variability. But in press reports of the late 1980s, many unusual weather patterns were 'blamed' on the greenhouse effect — and in the more lurid accounts or television programmes, used to conjure up frankly apocalyptic visions of the future.

To take just one example, tropical cyclones (also variously called hurricanes and typhoons, but properly referred to as 'tropical revolving storms') are fuelled by a convective cycle of evaporation and condensation above warm tropical seas (Section 2.3.2): SSTs of 27 °C or greater appear to be critical to their formation.

▷   What general features of the equilibrium scenarios we looked at in Section 5.5 could support the view that the frequency and/or intensity of such storms might increase in a warmer world?

▶   All equilibrium scenarios indicate an overall intensification of the hydrological cycle, and a general warming of the tropical oceans (Plate 5.2). Such changes could help to fuel more intense storms and/or alter their pattern of occurrence.

In practice, however, a more detailed analysis of existing model simulations reveals that they are somewhat equivocal about the prognosis for tropical storms in a warmer world — much as they are over the mid-continental drying scenarios we examined in Section 5.5. To date, it looks as if such storms could become more violent, but possible changes in their distribution and frequency of occurrence are less clear. The important general point is that a *single* extreme event (the 'great hurricane' of October 1987 over southern England, for example, or the 1988 drought in the USA) cannot, and *should not*, be attributed to the enhanced greenhouse effect. In climatological terms, such events assume significance only when their frequency and/or severity over a considerable period of time is clearly different from previous averages. So this is really another facet of the detection problem.

To pick up your thoughts on Activity 6.3, one of the key points made in Risbey's letter is worth stressing: scientific judgements — especially over tricky questions of 'cause and effect' — often do contain a subjective element. Given the same body of information, different scientists can, and do, reach different judgements about the evidence for or against a particular causal link. Disputes over interpretation are almost bound to arise, as they did in the wake of Hansen's testimony.

For all the reasons discussed in the previous section, it is not yet possible to make an *objectively* quantified judgement about whether or not the global warming this century is, in fact, a manifestation of the enhanced greenhouse effect. Hansen's more vocal critics (and there are hints to this effect in Schlesinger's letter) emphasized this lack of 'objective' evidence to support his 'high confidence' statement about detection. Indeed, many climatologists were (rightly) uneasy about the connections being made by the media. The more cautious were concerned that scientific credibility could be undermined by 'crying wolf' too soon; a return to more normal weather patterns, or a few cool summers in the early 1990s say, could then result in renewed public complacency.

On the other hand, scientists (Hansen and Broecker included) attempting to promote a wider awareness of the *potential* risks of climatic change argued that a 'no confidence' statement was equally misleading. It could convey the impression that the enhanced greenhouse effect (if not the greenhouse effect itself!) could be struck off the list of suspects. And their worst fears were later confirmed — recall the quote from Schneider in Section 6.1.

Given all of the uncertainties and difficulties that surround the detection problem, it is clear that a *polarized* debate about this issue is itself misleading, if not positively confusing. All that can be said at present is that there could be a substantial greenhouse signal embedded in the planet's temperature record, perhaps partially offset by some natural or anthropogenic cooling effect. Or alternatively, the signal could be quite small, having been supplemented by some other warming trend. Under these circumstances, perhaps a more pertinent question to ask is not 'How convincingly has detection been demonstrated?', but rather 'Why is detection important — or, indeed, is it important at all?'.

6.4.1 How important is detection?

To pose the central issue more sharply; if the question of attribution cannot be answered unequivocally, if it is always possible to deny detection by appealing to some mechanism about which there are few or no data, then should the prosecution (i.e. the scientific community) be required to prove the suspect (i.e. the enhanced greenhouse effect) guilty 'beyond a reasonable doubt'? Or in other words, should society's *response* rest on a presumption of 'innocent until proven guilty' or on the counter view, namely that a legitimate cause for concern — the prospect of greenhouse gas-induced climatic change — should evoke a verdict of 'guilty until proven innocent'? Of course, this rather begs the question of what constitutes a 'legitimate cause for concern'. If detection is not to be the critical arbiter of a 'need for action' — whatever form that action might take — what is? What lower level of scientific evidence should be deemed sufficient?

There are no simple or generally applicable guidelines here. On the contrary, this question is itself guaranteed to be the source of controversy. As climatic change issues have moved up the political agenda, the debate, although ostensibly about the scientific case for action, has sometimes taken on the characteristics of a propaganda war, rife with the conflicting statements of various opposing advocate groups. Without doubt, this process was at work in the late 1980s (recall the comment to that effect in Broecker's letter). By this stage in *Science Matters*, you will have met other examples already. In the present context — where the 'problem' is in effect an inadvertent by-product of human population growth and economic development, with consequences on a global scale — the list of 'actors' with a stake in advancing their own interests or world-view is a particularly long one; more on this in Chapters 7 and 9. The important general point is that an environmental problem as scientifically complex as this one — and with such all-embracing policy implications — inevitably provides plenty of scope for polemic and polarized debate. Fuel for good media copy, perhaps — but more likely to provoke a baffled or deeply cynical response from non-specialists than to promote a wide and rational debate about the choices we face.

To cut through some of the rhetoric *as far as the science of climatic change is concerned* (i.e. leaving aside for now all of the attendant social, economic and political factors), few researchers base their underlying concern about the buildup in greenhouse gases on the Earth's recent temperature history. Rather, it has been driven by a growing body of circumstantial evidence. From early 'back-of-the-envelope' type calculations (referred to in Chapter 1), on through the increasing sophistication of more recent climate models, *all* estimates suggest that doubling the atmospheric burden of CO_2 — or its radiative equivalent — would commit the planet to a significant rise in global-mean surface temperature. This central result, essentially unchallenged by over a decade of research, captures what might be termed the 'relentless logic' of the physics of the greenhouse effect. To borrow a favourite metaphor from Schneider, it is as if human activities are loading the climatic dice toward 'warmer' and away from 'cooler', whatever chance throw Nature may turn up in any particular year or season. Moreover, validation experiments (of the type outlined in Section 5.4) generate confidence in the basic physics built in to the models. Set against that, however, there are all the caveats about existing models, and attendant uncertainties in their predictions, that we dwelt on at length elsewhere in Chapter 5.

As you will see in Chapter 8, 'translating' the climatic futures conjured up by climate models into assessments of the likely consequences — for human populations and ecosystems around the world — is an even more difficult and uncertain business. For now, suffice it to say that scientific research has effectively identified a *potential* problem. Allowing greenhouse gases to go on accumulating in the atmosphere *could* have wide-ranging, and possibly portentous, implications. But at the same time, the 'threat' is not an immediate one, its seriousness is still highly uncertain, and its effects are not yet demonstrably manifest. And that poses a dilemma — one touched on in Risbey's letter. How can, or should, scientists communicate the central import of their findings to non-specialists — be they politicians, journalists or the wider public — while at the same time conveying an honest assessment of the remaining uncertainties?

As we implied in Chapter 1, one of the most powerful ways of 'getting the message across' is to put together a *consensus* view among scientists working in the field. To carry weight, that needs to involve as many independent researchers as possible — whatever the level of heated discussion and compromise that inevitably entails! And since future climatic changes could touch all peoples, everywhere, the consensus that emerges needs to be internationally-based as well. The IPCC report produced in 1990 fulfilled all those criteria. To a non-specialist (and it might help to know that I count myself firmly in that category), it is a fascinating, if at times bewildering, monument to the awesome complexity of the planetary system. The limitations of the 'current state of knowledge' are frankly acknowledged throughout. Nevertheless, the summary to the chapter on the detection problem closes with the following sentence.

> *The fact that we are unable to reliably detect the predicted signals today does not mean that the greenhouse theory is wrong, or that it will not be a serious problem for mankind in the decades ahead.*
>
> (IPCC, 1990, Executive Summary to Chapter 8)

In effect, the scientific community thereby endorsed a stance of 'guilty until proven innocent', i.e. that the continuing buildup in greenhouse gases *is* a 'legitimate cause for concern'. At the Second World Climate Conference (Geneva, November 1990) that was widely interpreted as a 'need for action' — by the whole international community, not just individual countries (see the quote in Chapter 1).

In reality, the IPCC (the *Intergovernmental* Panel on Climate Change) was part of an ongoing 'dialogue' between the scientific community and policy-makers. It was convened in the wake of the Toronto conference (June, 1988) under the auspices of the United Nations Environment Programme (UNEP) and the World Meteorological Organization (WMO, itself a UN agency). Three Working Groups of the IPCC were given the task of preparing reports — not only on the science, but also on the potential social, economic and ecological impacts (taken up in Chapter 8 of this book), *and on possible policy responses*. These reports formed the essential background material for the Geneva conference.

Behind the scenes, then, growing scientific concern — transmitted via previous 'authoritative' reports, countless hearings before governmental committees around the world, and so on — had already registered with the political community. Increasingly too, economists, environmental and social scientists, industrial representatives and others were being drawn into the parallel business of developing emission scenarios (Section 4.4) and making impact and policy assessments. However, there seems little doubt that the item was catapulted up the political agenda by the heightened *public* awareness of the late 1980s. In effect, the *reality* of global warming (whatever the true greenhouse signal may be), together with unexpected drought and severe storms (quite possibly the result of natural variability), lent warnings about climatic change a popular credibility they had previously lacked. (You may like to ponder on that at some stage.)

Perhaps too, the ozone hole over Antarctica played a part. When news of this phenomenon broke in May 1985 (and was later given dramatic force by NASA's satellite images, Plate 6.2), it was the first tangible sign of *global* atmospheric change induced by human activities. Strictly, it is not a 'hole in the sky', of course, but a massive loss of ozone from the lower stratosphere over Antarctica, which now recurs each southern spring: Figure 6.10 is a compelling example of what happens to the ozone profile. Certainly, it was shocking to recognize that this drastic upset in the natural atmospheric balance could be traced back to the everyday activities that release CFCs — getting rid of an old fridge, for example, or using a hair-spray.

Throughout the late 1980s, the ozone story frequently hit the headlines. The negotiations that produced the original Montreal Protocol (agreed in September 1987) received wide publicity: here the signatories pledged effectively to halve their use of CFCs by the end of the century. By early 1988 there was hard evidence linking the seasonal loss over Antarctica with CFCs. And there was growing evidence of actual stratospheric ozone depletion elsewhere as well. Just 18 months after the Protocol was signed, international opinion had hardened behind the need for a complete phase out, crystallized in the strengthened terms agreed in 1990 and further tightened in 1992 (recall Section 4.3.3).

One can speculate that coverage of these events did help to fuel public concern about the *other* possible consequences of global atmospheric change — namely greenhouse warming. You may have your own thoughts on this. Whatever the effect on public opinion, there was an important message here for atmospheric scientists and environmentalists — and, more importantly, for policy-makers as well. It warrants a brief digression.

6.4.2 'Lessons' from the debate about CFCs: the precautionary principle

In reality, the threat of damage to the ozone layer — to our planetary 'filter' of the shorter, and more dangerous, uv wavelengths in the incoming solar radiation (Box 2.2) — was the subject of debate for a decade *before* there was any evidence of actual

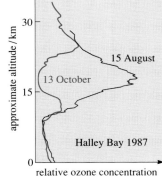

Figure 6.10 Between mid-August and mid-October 1987, some 95% of the ozone between an altitude of 14 and 23 km was destroyed over the British Antarctic Survey station at Halley Bay. It was measurements from this station (dating back to 1957) that first detected the large seasonal losses of stratospheric ozone over Antarctica — now known as the 'ozone hole'. The changes shown here now recur each southern spring, with ozone concentrations recovering again during the summer.

ozone loss. And that debate was again sparked off by a scientific hypothesis. First propounded by F. Sherwood Rowland and Mario Molina in 1974, it was prompted by the observed buildup in CFCs, and backed up by theoretical calculations based on general physical and chemical principles. (See Box 6.2 for a little more on that *if you are interested*.)

Box 6.2   CFCs and ozone depletion

At the heart of the original concern about CFCs lay two strands of reasoning:

1   Once released to the atmosphere, the only plausible fate for these (very stable) compounds was slow transport up into the stratosphere, followed by photolysis. That releases chlorine (Cl) atoms (recall Section 4.3.3, Figure 4.25).

2   Calculations, based on laboratory data, implied that Cl atoms could speed up the destruction of ozone. Here, the central mechanism, known as a 'catalytic cycle', can be written as a pair of reactions:

$$Cl + O_3 \rightarrow ClO + O_2 \quad (6.1)$$

$$O + ClO \rightarrow O_2 + Cl \quad (6.2)$$

Add (6.1) + (6.2): $O + O_3 \rightarrow O_2 + O_2 \quad (6.3)$

In the first step (Equation 6.1), Cl 'steals' an oxygen atom from ozone, forming chlorine monoxide (ClO). It can then 'hand this on', as it were, to another O atom, forming molecular oxygen (Equation 6.2). There are two points to note. First, the overall effect (the *sum* of the two steps, Equation 6.3) is just the same as the ozone-loss reaction you met earlier (Box 2.2, Equation 2.4). Second, and this is the crucial point, the Cl atom emerges unscathed, free to destroy many more O_3 molecules. As a result, model calculations — analogous to those used to simulate tropospheric chemistry (Section 4.4), but focused on *stratospheric* chemistry this time — predicted that tiny concentrations of CFCs could upset the natural balance that maintains the ozone layer, leading to a *net* loss of ozone from the stratosphere.

As we implied in Box 2.2, the controls over stratospheric ozone are actually a good deal more complicated than the simple scheme outlined there might suggest. And so too is the fate of the Cl atoms released as CFCs (and other halocarbons) are broken up. We shall not pursue the details. Suffice it to say that by the mid-1980s, ongoing research had produced a measure of confidence in the existing models, and hence in the forecasts of ozone depletion based on them. These suggested that continued release of CFCs *would* erode the ozone layer, but the agreed figures at the time implied a relatively slow attrition of something less than 1% per decade. In short, none of them predicted the ozone hole over Antarctica.

Without pursuing the matter, recent research has produced hard evidence that the Antarctic ozone hole *is* linked to enhanced levels of Cl in the stratosphere. However, the detailed mechanism involves a combination of meteorological and chemical factors that are peculiar to the *polar* stratosphere during the long dark winter months. That 'pre-conditioning' effectively sets the scene for a rapid loss of ozone as soon as sunlight returns in the spring. *None of the factors central to this pre-conditioning were included in the models being used to forecast ozone depletion in the mid-1980s.* There is growing evidence that this pre-conditioning of the polar stratosphere goes on during the winter over the Arctic as well, even though no northern 'ozone hole', as such, has yet been detected. (Or strictly, not as of 1992: you may be aware of developments since then.) ∎

We cannot go into the long-running saga about CFCs in any detail here.[*] But in retrospect, it can be viewed as an important testing ground for what has been termed **'the precautionary principle'** — in effect, the stance of 'guilty until proven innocent' mentioned earlier. The arguments for and against this principle were at their most stark during the earliest, and most heated, phase of the CFC debate, which erupted in the USA in the mid 1970s: it had all of the characteristics of a propaganda war (Figure 6.11)!

---

[*] If you are interested, I have written about this at some length elsewhere—see the Further Reading list.

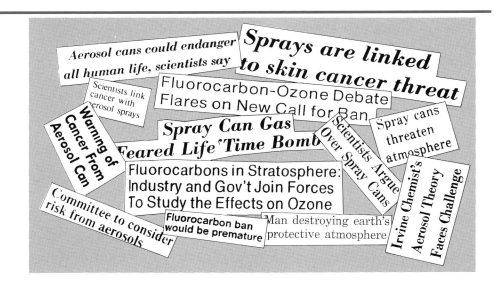

Figure 6.11 Montage of newspaper headlines from the mid-1970s — the height of the so-called 'spray-can war' in the USA. The link between ozone loss and increased incidence of skin cancer (through enhanced uv radiation at the surface) was a particularly emotive (and hotly debated) issue.

In brief, those with an interest in maintaining the status quo argued that a major industry should not be jeopardized on the strength of a *theoretical* prediction. They stressed the uncertainties in the calculations, and advocated a 'wait and see' approach. By contrast, those who argued for urgent action to control the release of CFCs stressed that stratospheric ozone is naturally highly variable — making it difficult to detect any underlying signal of a consistent long-term downward trend that could be attributed to human activities. In short (and I trust the argument has a familiar ring!), they contended that monitoring the atmosphere could not provide an '*early*' warning' of ozone loss. Rather, by the time a clear signal was detected, there would already be enough CFCs effectively 'stored' in the atmosphere (recall their long atmospheric lifetimes, Section 4.3.3) to keep the damage going for many decades — even if emissions were then halted at once. Just the circumstances we now find ourselves in.

As it turned out, unilateral action in the USA (where the use of CFCs as the propellant in spray cans was banned in 1978) was an important step towards acceptance of the precautionary principle by the wider international community. But it was a difficult and tortuous journey — and it took too long to avoid the problem completely.

Initially, further research provided substance to those who argued that international policy-making (i.e. action to curtail CFC usage world-wide) should await a better scientific understanding of the problem. Implicit (or sometimes explicit) in such arguments was the view that reducing the uncertainties in the calculations would somehow guarantee to reduce the seriousness of the threat as well. And throughout the early 1980s, there was a trend in that direction. As new facets to the problem were gradually uncovered and incorporated into ever more sophisticated computer models, so their forecasts of long-term ozone depletion came down to more modest levels (Figure 6.12).

Nevertheless, by the mid-1980s there was an emerging scientific consensus that continued release of CFCs was a 'legitimate cause for concern' (Box 6.2), even though the (potentially grave) consequences could be neither measured nor predicted with any certainty at the time. Recorded in a succession of national and international reports (the latter under the auspices of UNEP and WMO), that growing concern was a vital factor in the negotiations that produced the 'Vienna Convention for the Protection of the Ozone Layer', signed in March 1985. Although this Convention had

John Storey

Figure 6.12 As model forecasts of long-term ozone depletion came down to more modest levels, many argued that earlier predictions of cancer and 'eco-doom' had been exaggerated (J. Gribbin, *World Medicine*, 26 January 1980).

no regulatory powers, it did set an important precedent. It was the first time that nations agreed *in principle* to tackle a global environmental problem *before* its effects were manifest: news of the ozone hole broke two months later. The fact that this formal expression of 'international concern' was already in place certainly helped to expedite the subsequent negotiation of the explicit control measures in the Montreal Protocol.

Reflecting on the negotiations that produced the Montreal Protocol, Richard Benedick (then head of the US team) has written:

> *The ozone hole did not ... provide any clear signal for policy-makers at that time. Scientists in 1986 and 1987 were far from certain that CFCs were involved in Antarctica ... the phenomenon was contrary to known theory and did not conform to the global model predictions of gradual and pervasive long-term depletion. To add to the confusion, the downward trend was broken in late 1986 [see Plate 6.2 in this book] — just before the start of the diplomatic negotiations — when Antarctic ozone concentrations actually improved over the previous year.*
>
> (R.E. Benedick, 1991, Ozone Diplomacy)

For our present purposes, the crucial point is that none of the model forecasts of the mid-1980s contained any hint of a dramatic seasonal phenomenon like the ozone hole over Antarctica. And there is growing evidence that they seriously underestimated the ozone loss that has since been detected at other latitudes — and in both hemispheres — as well. In short, the ozone story now provides powerful support for the view that scientific uncertainties always cut two ways — especially when the problem to hand involves predicting the future behaviour of a complex and interconnected natural system. There is no *a priori* reason to suppose that incompletely understood factors — or hitherto unsuspected mechanisms (as seems to be the case as far as the ozone hole is concerned, Box 6.2) — will necessarily act to mitigate the perceived threat. They could, equally well, push the response of the real system beyond that indicated by model simulations.

Activity 6.4

What are the common factors between the debate about CFCs and stratospheric ozone depletion, on the one hand — and on the other, that about greenhouse gas-induced climatic change? Note down your thoughts on this question as a series of points. What light do they throw on the importance, or otherwise, of the detection issue?

6.4.3 Another perspective on detection

Whatever the precise mix of influences at work — and it would be overly simplistic to put this down to any 'lessons' conveyed by the ozone story alone — the fact remains that in many countries policy-making is running ahead of detection. In the developed world at least, governmental attitudes increasingly reflect a shift toward a more proactive (rather than reactive) stance about the prospect of future climatic changes. With that shift in place, the central issue is no longer detection *per se*. Rather, it is the need for more reliable forecasts of how serious those changes might be (i.e. their scale, pace and geographical distribution), given various possible courses of action.

▷ Apart from the future atmospheric burden of greenhouse gases (of which more in Chapter 7), what key model parameter effectively determines the response of the climate system to a given radiative forcing?

▸ The climate sensitivity, $\Delta T_{2\times}$.

Can detection help to reduce the uncertainties in the size of this crucial parameter, and so increase confidence in what the models tell us the future might be like? Perhaps. But recall another point touched on in Activities 6.1 and 6.2: the value of $\Delta T_{2\times}$ inferred from a simple comparison with the observational temperature record (as in Figure 6.5) is deceptive. In short, if the net effect of all other influences on climate over the past century — other than the accumulation of greenhouse gases in the atmosphere, that is — has been close to zero, then the global warming to date suggests a climate sensitivity at the bottom end of the model-predicted range (i.e. $\Delta T_{2\times} \approx 1.5\,°C$). It could be lower still, if all other factors have contributed some part of the warming trend. Alternatively, $\Delta T_{2\times}$ could be towards the high end of the model range (i.e. closer to $4.5\,°C$) if a substantial greenhouse signal has been partially offset by a natural cooling or other anthropogenic factors (e.g. sulphate aerosols).

The Workshop press release in Schlesinger's letter (Extract 6.1) captures the purely scientific response to this situation: a sustained international research effort, aimed at the deficiencies in existing models (recall the Summaries to Chapters 4 and 5); at monitoring other possible forcing factors, and the overall 'performance' of the planetary system (as part of the detection strategies outlined earlier); and so on. This should gradually reduce the present uncertainties about the sensitivity of the *real* climate system. But only in the medium-to-long term. And there are no guarantees. On the contrary, given the complexity of the processes involved, it is highly unlikely that a totally reliable estimate of $\Delta T_{2\times}$ will ever be achieved — just as an apparently 'reliable' estimate of long-term ozone depletion later proved to be illusory. As there, careful monitoring may itself reveal 'surprises' — perhaps some climatological analogue of the ozone hole — that would, in turn, cause modellers to adjust their crystal balls (more on this in Chapter 7).

The central dilemma, as it was in the long debate about CFCs, is how to formulate and implement 'appropriate' responses in the face of considerable, *and inherent*, uncertainty. That involves value judgements. All that science can do is feed into the policy-making process a series of plausible 'What if?' scenarios, based on the best available information at any given time. What if the climate sensitivity is 4.5 °C, as against 1.5 °C say, or below? What if we choose to delay action to curtail future emissions of CO_2 and the other gases by a few years or decades? What might the consequences be for ecosystems, for agriculture, for different economies, for coastal zones or islands subject to inundation if sea-levels rise? And so on. That is the subject of the next two chapters.

Summary of Chapter 6

1   Carefully screened data from weather stations on land and ships at sea have been used to reconstruct variations in the Earth's annual-mean surface temperature over the past century. Along with marked variability (on yearly and decadal time-scales), the record reveals a real global warming (in the range 0.3–0.6 °C) over this period. The upward trend has been both irregular, and somewhat different in the two hemispheres.

2   Detailed interpretation of the global warming to date — and hence convincing detection of the greenhouse signal — is frustrated by the lack of information about other possible causes of recent climatic change. These include other possible external 'forcing factors' (sustained changes in the solar constant, volcanic eruptions, a changing tropospheric burden of sulphate and other aerosols), together with the noise of internally-generated natural variability.

3   As yet, the difficulties under point 2 preclude a reliable empirical estimate of the climate sensitivity, $\Delta T_{2\times}$. Further research and monitoring programmes may narrow the present uncertainties in the model-predicted range of values (i.e. 1.5–4.5 °C) — and in the pace and geographical distribution of climatic change, as well. But only in the medium-to-long term — and there are no guarantees (compare with the 'ozone story'). It may also reveal surprises, not indicated by existing model-based scenarios.

4   Since the Second World Climate Conference in 1990, the prospect of greenhouse gas-induced climatic change is an item on the international political agenda. An important influence here (albeit not the only one) was undoubtedly the broad scientific consensus (embodied in the IPCC report) that a continuing buildup in greenhouse gases is a 'legitimate cause for concern' — the more so since most of the gases have long atmospheric lifetimes.

5   For all the reasons listed here (and discussed in previous chapters), there are *inherent* uncertainties when it comes to forecasting the response of the planetary system to a continuing buildup of greenhouse gases. Like the long-running saga about CFCs, the public and political debate about climatic change has been, and will no doubt continue to be, played out against the backdrop of these uncertainties. The 'detection debate' of the late 1980s is just one example of the way such uncertainties can, indeed almost inevitably will, generate disputes within the scientific community. That is the stuff of scientific argument. But picked up — and often magnified and/or distorted — by the media, and by various opposing advocate groups, this conveys a very confusing message to the 'wider public'. Retain your scepticism, but try not to become too cynical.

7 Future climates: projections and scenarios

To generate a range of 'What if?' global warming scenarios, the IPCC followed the strategy summarized in Figure 7.1. The starting point for this hierarchy of scientific modelling studies is a projection of future anthropogenic emissions of the various greenhouse gases. Fed into a carbon-cycle model (for CO_2) or a 'chemistry' model (for the other greenhouse gases), as outlined in Section 4.4, this produces a time-evolving picture of the total atmospheric burden of greenhouse gases — and hence the radiative forcing of the climate system. Thereafter, the calculations parallel those used to generate the predicted greenhouse signal over the *past* century shown in Figure 6.5 (Section 6.3). Thus the important new factor here is the emission scenario itself; it puts the technology and social science — and the politics — into the anthropogenic greenhouse effect.

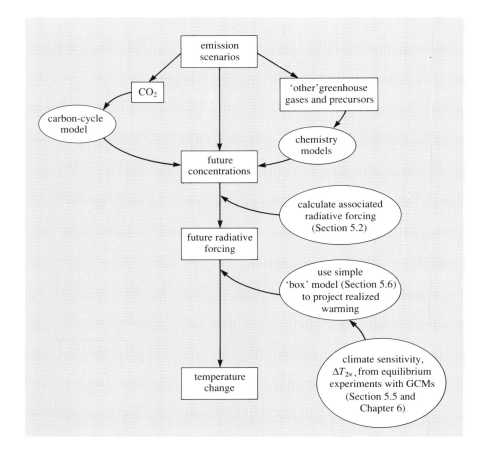

Figure 7.1 A schematic representation of the sequence of modelling studies used by the IPCC to transform emission scenarios into projections of the greenhouse gas-induced realized warming.

7.1 Emission scenarios

As we stressed earlier (in the wake of Activity 4.6), an emission scenario is not a definitive vision of the future. Rather, it is an image of what emission rates could be like, given certain basic *assumptions* about the future development of different human societies. To get a feel for how that task is handled we again take CO_2 as the leading example. First, a little extra background about its two major anthropogenic sources is in order.

7.1.1 Energy production and use

On current estimates (see Figure 7.2), the energy sector accounted for close to half of the radiative forcing incurred during the 1980s — the dominant contribution coming from the CO_2 released by burning fossil fuels. The key factors likely to influence such emissions in the future were identified in Section 4.4. To take that discussion on a stage, it helps to separate out the 'demand' and 'supply' sides.

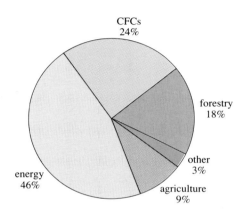

Figure 7.2 Estimated contributions of different human activities to the change in radiative forcing during the 1980s.

Energy demand

Put simply, there are two determinants of future energy consumption: the population level, and the energy demand per head of population. Figure 7.3 shows the projected growth in world population based on estimates drawn up in the late 1980s; the bulk of it occurs in countries of the developing world. There are inherent uncertainties here, of course, but the regional differences apparent in Figure 7.3 are common to all such projections.

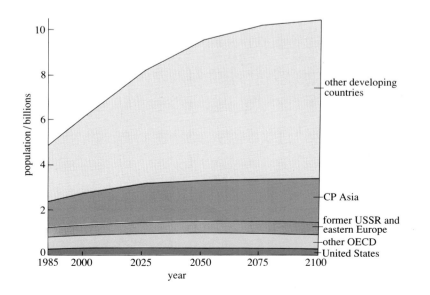

Figure 7.3 Anticipated global population levels by region, 1985–2100. CP Asia = centrally planned economies of China, Kampuchea, Vietnam, Mongolia and North Korea. See Box 7.1 for definitions of OECD and developing countries.

Box 7.1 Labelling groups of countries

There are difficulties in finding any precise and convenient way of labelling groups of countries. For the most part, the discussion in this chapter uses the following broad distinction:

The 'developed' world takes in the member countries of the Organization of Economic Co-operation and Development (**OECD**), which are roughly synonymous with the developed capitalist market economies (western Europe, the USA, Canada, Japan and Australasia). Sometimes (as in Figures 7.3–7.5, for example) the 'OECD' label is used to distinguish these countries from the other industrialized states in this group — the former USSR and eastern Europe: despite the dramatic political upheavals of recent years, these economies remain conditioned by decades of state socialist central planning.

The 'developing' (or 'Third') world is taken to include *all* other countries. As such, it is a somewhat crude umbrella term — spanning very poor countries like Bangladesh and many African nations, oil-rich states in the Gulf, and fairly industrialized countries in Asia and South America, such as China and Brazil.

One final point: it is important to appreciate that 'development' is itself a value-laden term, open to wide interpretation. Here, it is taken to imply 'economic development' in the sense commonly used in the industrialized world: a combination of economic growth and the assumed benefits this brings in terms of human progress and improvement. ■

At present, energy consumption is relatively low in developing countries compared with more economically developed regions; with over 75% of the world's population, they account for only some 22% of the global energy use. Translated into 'fossil carbon' CO_2 emissions per head of population, the contrast shows up in Figure 7.4. In short, economic well-being and the overall level of economic activity — commonly measured as the *gross national product* (GNP) — is one of the most important determinants of a country's per capita energy use. On the other hand, the marked variations between different industrialized countries evident in Figure 7.4 reflects the fact that this link is a complex one.

Figure 7.4 Annual CO_2 emissions (expressed as carbon-equivalent) from fossil-fuel burning per head of population (capita) in the late 1980s: 1 tonne = 10^3 kg = 10^6 g. (Note: if emissions from deforestation or other sources were to be taken into account, the per capita emissions from some countries, notably Brazil, would increase greatly.)

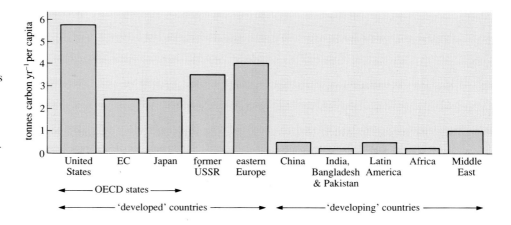

In reality, every country is different, with energy consumption driven by its own particular mix of more or less energy-intensive sectors — different industries, transport and residential needs, commercial and service activities, and so on. Differences in climate, geography (e.g. in land area, and hence transport distances) and such like also come into the equation. But a key factor in the *overall* **energy intensity** (the energy used per unit of GNP, that is) of different economies — and more importantly, in the way economic growth translates into changing energy demand — is '**energy**

efficiency and conservation'. In Japan, for example, where energy saving measures have been actively supported by government programmes, consumption was lower in 1990 than in 1973, despite an increase in GNP by some 45%. Given that robust economic growth is certainly the goal of most governments, what is the scope for greater energy efficiency in the future?

There is general agreement among experts that existing, or emerging, technologies and designs could achieve substantial savings in most areas of energy use in the near to medium term. Buildings, cars and other vehicles, and a whole range of industrial processes could all be more energy efficient, as could the generation of electricity in coal-fired power stations. However, technical feasibility is not the only, nor indeed central, issue. In the past, the take up of more energy efficient technologies and designs has proved to be notoriously slow and partial.

Activity 7.1

Think about your *personal* (i.e. non-work related) life-style for a moment. Jot down any ways in which you could 'save' energy. What stops you?

Hopefully, this rather blunt question prompted you to reflect on some of the barriers to improved energy efficiency that operate at all levels — not just the personal. Financial constraints may be paramount. Even if not, the 'pay back' period over which investment in energy saving measures becomes cost-effective invariably is. And that, in turn depends on capital costs as against energy (i.e. fuel and electricity) costs. Awareness of (which means availability of information about) alternative options and products comes into the equation — as do consumer and management attitudes and priorities in general.

Widening the perspective, certain *structural* changes could also greatly reduce energy demand. For example, in typical OECD countries, the transport sector currently accounts for over a third of total energy use, (Figure 7.5a); passenger cars and lorries contribute some 83% of that. Significant savings could be achieved if more freight was carried by rail, or more people shared cars or used public transport, or worked from home (through the growing influence of information technology). However, that would require not only changes in personal behaviour — and possibly quite radical ones — but also government policies designed to promote and facilitate such moves. More generally, numerous studies have concluded that rapid improvements in overall energy efficiency are unlikely in the absence of active government support (witness the Japanese example). In which context, it is worth noting that direct or indirect state subsidies for energy users in many countries currently encourage wasteful practices; in 1984, energy subsidies in the USA alone totalled around $44 billion.

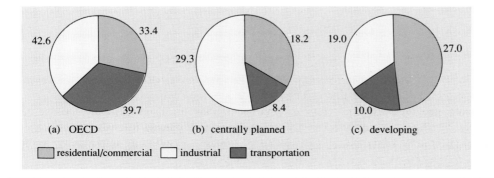

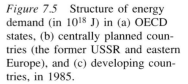

Figure 7.5 Structure of energy demand (in 10^{18} J) in (a) OECD states, (b) centrally planned countries (the former USSR and eastern Europe), and (c) developing countries, in 1985.

Outside of the OECD states, the barriers to improved energy efficiency are even more fundamental. For example, in the former USSR and eastern Europe most energy was used for industrial purposes (Figure 7.5b); by western standards, much existing plant is outmoded and very inefficient in energy terms. If these economies were only to achieve the overall energy intensity typical of western Europe in the late 1980s, energy savings estimated at around 60% could result — and the profligate per capita emissions recorded in Figure 7.4 would fall correspondingly. However, this would require enormous capital investment and major economic restructuring. In the early 1990s, all these countries are in severe economic difficulties.

As far as the developing countries are concerned, an urgent priority is alleviating widespread poverty, and achieving social and economic development. If most of these countries attempt to pursue these goals through the traditional path of heavy industrialization, this is bound to entail a sharp rise in energy intensity — a trend already apparent in parts of Asia. In general, these countries simply lack the capital to invest in new, more energy-efficient plant and equipment. Indeed, massive Third World debt resulted in a net capital transfer of some $30 billion per year from them *to* the OECD states in the late 1980s.

Energy supply

Energy demand translates into CO_2 emissions through the combination of energy sources used to supply that demand. Of the fossil fuels, coal is the most 'carbon intensive', i.e. burning coal releases more CO_2 per unit of energy generated than the other fuels (see Figure 7.6). In the electricity sector, for example, substituting natural gas for coal could reduce CO_2 emissions from a typical power station by an estimated 40–45%. More generally, a major shift in the mix of fossil fuels used — toward a greater reliance on natural gas, and away from coal in particular — could act to slow the growth in CO_2 emissions.

However, it is important to appreciate the constraints on such fuel switching. The estimates collected in Figure 7.7 reveal that known reserves of the different fossil fuels are distributed very unevenly around the globe. Notice the dominant position of the Middle East as far as oil is concerned. Together with the former USSR, this region also accounts for some two-thirds of the world's proved reserves of natural gas. By contrast, over 60% of coal reserves are held by the USA, China and the former USSR. In short, the scope for switching to natural gas varies greatly from one country or region to another — as would the economic consequences of a concerted move in that direction. More telling in the longer term is the message implicit in Figure 7.8; at the global level, a fossil fuel-based future looks set to become *increasingly* reliant on coal.

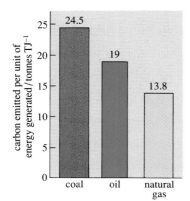

Figure 7.6 Average CO_2 emissions (expressed as the carbon equivalent) per unit of energy generated for coal, oil and natural gas. (1 TJ (terajoule) = 10^{12} J.)

▷   What other broad strategy would act to reduce CO_2 emissions for a given level of energy demand?

▶   Expanding the role of non-fossil fuel energy sources.

Some countries (France, for example) already rely heavily on nuclear and hydro-electric power. But the list of alternatives also includes other 'renewable' energy sources — solar, wind, wave, tidal and geothermal. Their *potential* contribution to electricity generation has been assessed in numerous national and regional studies. In the UK, for example, official estimates put the figure somewhere between 18%

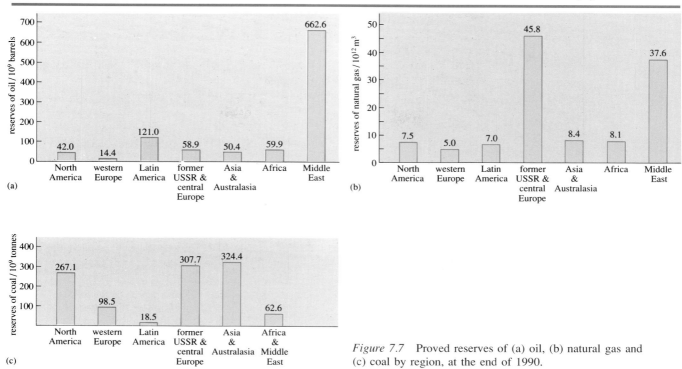

Figure 7.7 Proved reserves of (a) oil, (b) natural gas and (c) coal by region, at the end of 1990.

and 28% by 2025; it could be equal or greater elsewhere. Climate and geography apart, such studies identify economic and technological factors as the major barriers to a rapid 'deployment' of renewable energy sources in practice. Lack of investment in the past has left the technologies associated with several of them far from fully developed, and/or the electricity generated is uncompetitive at present prices.

Economic arguments also come into assessments of an expanding role for nuclear power. But so too does its own set of environmental, health and security problems — some of which have the same kind of long term, *intergenerational* dimension as greenhouse warming. Suffice it to say that this new context further complicates the already difficult and contentious issues that permeate debate about the nuclear option (see Figure 7.9).

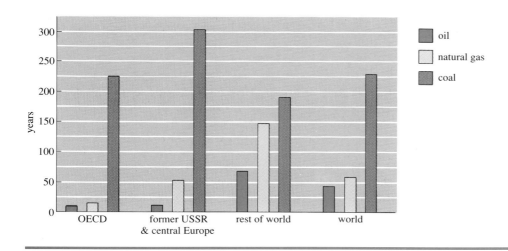

Figure 7.8 Estimates of the time (in years) that proved reserves of oil, gas and coal will last if *current* (1990) production rates continue. According to these figures, the world's reserves of coal will last twice as long as the combined reserves of oil and gas.

Tuesday 3 July 1990 THE INDEPENDENT

The Marshall nuclear plan

Global warming has given atomic energy a decisive role that is threatened by inept political meddling, argues **Lord Marshall**

LESSONS which should be learnt from the fiasco of nuclear power privatisation have been ignored by the Government's select committee in its report last Wednesday.

First, governments are best kept out of the nuclear power industry because politicians – certainly British politicians – are driven by motives different from those needed for a successful business. Political motives have now determined and destroyed four separate attempts at nuclear power in the UK.

In the late 1950s, a British government eager to develop alternative energy sources in the wake of the Suez crisis decided on a crash programme to build the Magnox reactors. Britain's first generation of nuclear power stations. Britain was proud to be the first to develop this new technology. Engineers at the time accurately assessed the cost of operating the reactors and their work has stood the test of time, despite the erratic technical performance of the Magnox reactors. But they also thought uranium was rare, reprocessing was easy and waste disposal a minor problem. All three judgements were wrong, and it is the escalating costs of the "back-end" of the fuel cycle, rather than the operating costs, that has made the Magnox reactors uneconomic.

The experience shows that Britain likes to be the first into a new technology. This is a national characteristic we should stamp out. The man who is first usually gets it wrong. We ought to aim to be more like the Japanese, to take our time on fundamental decisions and aim to be second, third or fourth into a new technology.

The nuclear business lasts a long time. Nuclear decisions made decades ago are influencing us now. We started the nuclear business as a result of fears following the Suez crisis. Now, we are abandoning pressurised water reactors (PWRs), partly because we can afford ...their... plentiful in the ...are wrong.

'Britain likes to be the first into a new technology. This is a characteristic we should stamp out'

wanted to encourage competition in the supply and construction of nuclear power stations. As a result we had several nuclear consortia to design and build AGRs when the country did not realistically have the technical and industrial strength to launch a single design. All these consortia collapsed. The appalling consequence of this political mistake has taken 25 years to demonstrate. My concerns about AGR economics are so well known and of such long standing that I am accused of being disloyal to British technology.

Britain had a brief flirtation in the mid-1970s with the steam-generating heavy water reactor, which was chosen primarily because it was not invented by the Americans or the Canadians. Fortunately, we had a sudden attack of ...sense and, by the end of that ...a programme of...

work well in the UK also. Alas, that logic has failed because of the decision by this Government to introduce a unique, untried experiment into the structure of the electricity industry.

The PWR programme has survived arguments between design engineers and operating engineers; it has survived

'The solution to the problem of greenhouse warming will need a massive investment in nuclear power'

the Sizewell B public inquiry, which lasted from 1983 to 1985; it has survived plans to build first 12, then six, four, and now one power station; but it cannot survive this political decision. That is ...nuclear power is ...anco...

clear power – assuming you get everything right – come in the long term, not in the short term.

For the same reason, Britain under the new privatised power system is unable to build big coal-fired power stations. Neither can we enjoy a secure electricity system with an obligation to supply that is the dominant responsibility of all power utilities throughout the world and has been the prime purpose of the Central Electricity Generating Board for almost half a century.

Under the new system, generators will build new capacity only if the risk of failure of the electricity system is substantial enough; they will then build cheap gas turbines that burn extensive fuel. When the gas turns out our electricity supply system will become insecure, some new form of long-term obligation will be introduced by a wiser government, and our coal industry and our nuclear industry can be revived again.

'Investment in nuclear power will come as people realise it is the most benign electricity producer' *Photograph: John Voos*

What a sad story this is. Amid the confusion of claim and counter-claim, three things should be remembered. First, it was never plausible that the Magnox fuel cycle with its large waste stream could ever be privatised. Second, the AGR reactors have given so much difficulty for such a long time that it was always clear that putting a value to them in a privatisation exercise would be difficult. Third, for reasons which are more subtle, but which, nevertheless, are just as clear, any new nuclear power would be unable to survive the particular form of privatisation chosen by the Government.

I said all three things at the beginning of the privatisation process, and did so with the unanimous support of the CEGB board. It is no pleasure to be proved right.

What is to be done next? From new, independent position as chairman of the World Association of Nuclear Operators, I can say that the nuclear stations we have will be operated as well as the AGR stations inherited so our predecessors will be made to...

'The nuclear business lasts a long time. Decisions made decades ago are... influencing us now'

...as well as possible, and that the new team now working on Sizewell B, which will be Britain's first pressurised reactor, is the best nuclear team in the world.

They will make the best Sizewell project, despite the difficulties which this Government and the...will throw at them. When we decide to return to building nuclear power stations, I predict they will look very like Sizewell B.

We will need to build these stations. We can solve the environmental problem of the hole in the Earth's ozone layer without any great difficulty as we are well on the way to doing that. But our determination to eliminate acid rain is already there. But the solution to the problem of greenhouse warming will need a massive investment in nuclear power. This will come about as people realise that nuclear power is the most benign producer of electricity that decades of nuclear power have misplaced. This charge of being ready beginning to take place.

The author was chairman of the Central Electricity Generating Board.

Just how green are you about nuclear power?

ONCE UPON A TIME, green was just a colour.

Now it's a universal movement. And what shade of green you are says more about you than even class or status.

To a lot of people, however, being green presents somewhat of a dilemma:

How best to safeguard the future of mankind, _and_ accept nuclear power as playing an important part in that future.

We at BNFL believe nuclear power has a role to play in both.

By far the biggest threat to our future comes from the Greenhouse Effect.

Since the Industrial Revolution we've been burning fossil fuels like wood, coal, and oil in huge quantities.

The carbon dioxide produced by this has been lingering above the earth's surface, trapping the sun's heat and causing global warming.

While the scientists argue as to what the exact consequences could be, certain facts cannot be ignored.

In 1850 there were 280 parts of CO_2 to one million parts of air in the atmosphere.

In 1984 that had increased to 340 parts per million.

Unchecked it will reach 600 parts by the year 2050.

That could result in the earth being the warmest since the age of the dinosaur 65 million years ago.

A rather chilling prospect in fact.

Now, whilst the nuclear industry has never claimed to be the sole solution to the Greenhouse Effect, to say it can make no contribution to solving the problem is misleading.

Fossil-fuel power stations produce CO_2, which contributes to the Greenhouse Effect. Fact.

In France and Belgium, for example, they generate more than two-thirds electricity from nuclear power.

This has helped to reduce their output of carbon dioxide faster than the rest of Europe.

In Britain we could also reduce our output of carbon dioxide by increasing our investment in nuclear power.

So sure are we of a nuclear future that BNFL is currently investing £1½ million a day at Sellafield.

Might we suggest that those people who say that you cannot possibly support a nuclear future and be green might be looking a little on the black side?

— BRITISH NUCLEAR FUELS PLC. —
Risley, Warrington WA3 6AS

Scientists reject use of nuclear power to halt global warming

By Michael McCarthy, Environmental Correspondent

The edge of darkness

Nuclear power, declared Nicholas Ridley at the weekend, is good for us. Is it? And can it really help to save the atmosphere, and hence the world? **Tim Radford** peeps into the abyss

Climate changes for nuclear power

Robert Malpas argues that nuclear power can still be the energy of the future

N-power backed to slow global warming

By John Hunt, Environmental Correspondent

Figure 7.9 As this collection of headlines, etc. suggests, the prospect of greenhouse gas-induced climatic change has added another dimension to the on-going debate about nuclear power!

Activity 7.2

At the global level, the transport sector is heavily dependent on products derived from oil. However, in some countries relatively poor in fossil fuel reserves (Brazil, for example) vehicle fuels are already 'diluted' with ethanol (C_2H_5OH) derived from plant materials (biomass), via a biological fermentation process. There are also known chemical routes for producing methanol (CH_3OH) from biomass; research and development into engines able to run on pure methanol is being actively pursued at present.

(a) Write a balanced chemical equation to represent the combustion of ethanol in oxygen, with CO_2 and H_2O as the only products.

(b) Why should replacing petrol and diesel with fuels derived from biomass be a potentially useful strategy for slowing the further accumulation of CO_2 in the atmosphere?

(c) Assessments of the scope for — and impact of — this kind of fuel switching again have to grapple with many factors. Take a moment to jot down any questions that you think such assessments would need to address.

7.1.2 Deforestation in the tropics

As we noted earlier (Section 4.2.3), there is nothing new about the wholesale destruction of forests; estimates put the cumulative loss during the course of human history at around two billion hectares, mostly at temperate latitudes. Neither is there anything unique to the tropics about felling trees for fuel, timber, paper making and so on. Large areas of the forests at temperate and higher northern latitudes (the 'boreal' forests of North America and northern Eurasia, where coniferous species predominate) are exploited in this way — both on a commercial basis, and by indigenous peoples. The difference is that today forests at these latitudes are roughly in balance as regards carbon cycling — with loss of biomass in one region (be it through felling or wild fires and storms or whatever) more or less offset by planting and net growth elsewhere. Temperate forests in the Northern Hemisphere may even be acting as a net carbon sink at present — a possibility noted in Section 4.2.4.

The tragedy of the tropical forests is the scale and rate of their destruction, with only limited attempts being made to establish a sustainable (i.e. balanced) regime. A regional breakdown of the resulting net emissions of CO_2 is shown in Figure 7.10. However, concern about tropical deforestation goes beyond the contribution these emissions make to anthropogenic greenhouse forcing — estimated at about 18% over the 1980s (Figure 7.2).

The rainforests of the humid tropics cover only about 6% of the total land surface, yet contain at least half of the world's known species of plants and animals. Their

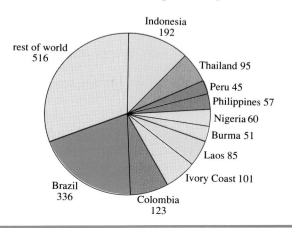

Figure 7.10 Estimated net emissions of CO_2 (expressed as PgC) from tropical deforestation in 1980, by region.

destruction only really got under way after World War II; averaged over the period since then, estimates suggest a *daily* extinction of some 15–75 species. In short, tropical deforestation is also a major *conservation* issue. Alongside the ecological damage is the cost to the indigenous tribes whose livelihoods and very means of existence depend upon the forests (see Figure 7.11, for example). Loss of forest cover also leads to soil erosion and flash flooding; it can cause drying of the local micro-climate and reduce rainfall over a wider area — recall the important role of vegetation in the regional hydrological cycle (Section 2.3.4). Experiments with climate models suggest that wholesale deforestation (of the entire Amazon Basin, say) could even interrupt the transfer of moisture and latent heat from the tropics to higher latitudes, thus influencing climate on a wider scale as well.

Figure 7.11 A plea from the Penan forest peoples of Malaysia. The Penan are nomadic: they live totally on the productive capacity of the forest, and express a profound understanding of its plants and animals. The relentless pressures of logging have forced most Penan to live in squalid slums: by the beginning of the 1990s only some 60 families remained completely nomadic.

Set against such concerns are the forces that drive tropical deforestation; clearing and burning for croplands and pasture; felling for local fuelwood, timber or animal fodder; and public and private development projects (such as logging for commercially valuable hardwoods, road building, mining, constructing dams, and so on). All these processes are partly responsible — and they are often interconnected. For example, the roads that provide access for commercial logging operations open up vast tracts of hitherto virgin forest to further clearance for agriculture (recall Plate 4.2). This 'colonization' compounds the initial damage to forest productivity — producing a net loss of carbon from both terrestrial reservoirs (as outlined in Section 4.2.3).

It is important to appreciate that behind these processes lie poverty, landlessness, population growth, and the chronic underdevelopment of Third World countries burdened by servicing their debt to the world's financial institutions. These are complex issues, involving governments and other agencies in both the developed and developing world, and cannot be done justice here. *If you are interested*, a brief account of the particular cast of 'actors' involved in the destruction in Amazonia is given in Extract 7.1. For our immediate purposes, it is sufficient to point to the central conflict; on the one hand, forests *must* be utilized and produce an economic return in order to survive — and on the other, that utilization can mean destruction. Or, as the declaration agreed at the IPCC Tropical Forest Workshop (held in São Paulo, Brazil in January 1990) put it:

> *The forest crisis is rooted in the agricultural sector and in people's needs for employment and income. Deforestation will be stopped only when the natural forest is economically more valuable than alternative uses for the same land.*

> *(In the report of the Response Strategies Working Group of the IPCC, issued in June 1990.)*

Extract 7.1 From P. M. Smith and K. Warr (eds) (1991) *Global Environmental Issues* (Book 4 of U206, *Environment*), pp. 229–234.

Deforestation in Amazonia

For many environmentalists the Amazon rainforest presents the greatest of all ecological challenges. The rate of forest destruction in Brazil is currently estimated to be in the region of 42 000 square kilometres a year — that is an area greater than the size of the Netherlands: see Figure. Only about one-fifth goes for commercial logging, the remainder being cleared and burned. The burning (through the *quiemadas* — giant forest fires) releases some 470 million tonnes of carbon dioxide annually into the atmosphere.

To appreciate the roles of the various 'actors' involved in the current drama, we need to go back a quarter of a century, to the setting up of 'Operation Amazon', by the generals in power in Brazil during the years of military dictatorship. The objective of Operation Amazon, to be centred in Manaus, was to 'flood the Amazon with civilisation', by attracting multinationals to invest in the region, and to encourage peasant 'settlers' to come to Amazonia purportedly to ease population pressure in Brazil's overcrowded coastal periphery. It also provided an easy means for cattle ranchers (*fazendeiros*) to establish land and property rights in the forest. This colonisation process was given full government support. Since Operation Amazon was launched, land speculation has resulted in more than 60 million hectares passing into private ownership, mostly concentrated in the hands of a few major land-owners. Yet the big ranches,

operating at a 'carrying capacity' of less than one animal per acre, have been an economic as well as an ecological disaster, and have only survived because of huge government subsidies, guaranteeing large profits for the land-owners. There has been an unholy alliance between successive governments and the powerful cattle ranchers union, the UDR. So huge sums of money have at the same time been fuelling the national debt, lining the pockets of the new land-owners, and producing forest destruction on a massive scale.

Side-by-side with this land speculation have come vast commercial projects, created under the auspices of Operation Amazon, and financed largely by international finance. Major logging centres have been established as roads have opened up the forests. In Paragominas, the 'saw-mill capital of the world', 500 mills handle 5 000 trees a day. A by-product of the logging is charcoal burning, which has become the new boom industry, principally to provide fuel for the smelting of pig iron. Iron ore is present in the Amazon in large quantities, and mining companies have moved in with massive investments. The largest scheme is the Carajas Iron Ore project, jointly financed by the World Bank, the European Community and Japan. This will convert an area of forest the size of France to industrial and agricultural use, with the production of pig iron for export. This type of development is being used to pay the interest

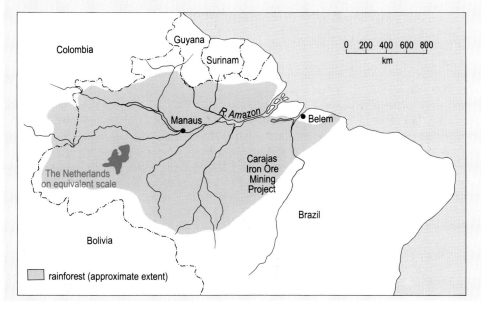

The Amazonian rainforest, Brazil.

on Brazil's world record foreign debt. Involved in the chain of destruction are dozens of developed countries who are helping to foot the bill through the aid financing of the World Bank and the IMF, and through the investments of multinationals.

The ecological devastation is matched by the suffering of the people: the indigenous Indian tribes who have lived for generations on a sustainable basis off the fruits of the forest, and the landless 'settler' peasants whose dreams of owning land have been thwarted since they cannot afford to buy, and squatting is outlawed — by the *fazendeiros*. They are forced to eke out a meagre subsistence, working for poor wages for the new industrialists, and cutting and burning further tracts of the forest to work the land for the sparse crops it will support. The plight of the Indians is worse: theirs is a cruel story of lost lands and dwindling culture. As contact with outsiders increases so too does the incidence of introduced diseases,

and there is little or no support from the state health services.

All of which sounds very depressing. It is easy to lose one's objectivity when assessing the consequences on this scale of so-called development. Yet our main purpose has been to highlight the processes involved, the interconnections between the developed and the developing world. There are indications that the Brazilian state is beginning to take steps to control the rate of development. Pressure from international environmental pressure groups and a change of government (in 1990) is producing some results. The Government Environment Office, IBAMA, now mounts annual forest monitoring by helicopter in an attempt to prevent unlicensed burning. Fines are levied on the worst offenders. But the power of the *fazendeiros* through the UDR and of vested commercial interests remains very strong; and the current state President reportedly is a close associate of the *fazendeiros*.[*]

Activity 7.3   *You should spend up to 45 minutes on this activity.*

At this point, a few calculations will serve to draw together some of the key issues identified above, and in Section 7.1.1.

(a) If global CO_2 emissions from the energy sector continue at the *present* rate (6 PgC per year) from 1990 through to the end of the next century, what mass of fossil carbon would this release? Explain (*in about 250 words*) why this is likely to be a serious underestimate without concerted government action at both the national and international level. (Your answer should include reference to the differences between the developed and developing worlds touched on in Section 7.1.1.)

(b) Now suppose that tropical deforestation also continues at the currently estimated rate, say 15 million hectares per year.

(i) Given that tropical forests contain, on average, about 150×10^6 g of carbon per hectare in *living* plant biomass, translate this scenario into a rough estimate of the carbon input to the atmosphere as CO_2 between 1990 and 2100, quoting your answer in PgC. What assumptions must you make in order to do that?

(ii) At present, tropical forests cover an estimated 2 billion hectares; under this scenario, what fraction would be lost by 2100?

(c) Several OECD states (e.g. the USA and Australia) have declared major tree-planting initiatives — promoted, in part at least, as one possible strategy for 'mitigating' their energy-related CO_2 emissions. Averaged over a 100-year period, one recent estimate suggests that a rapidly growing forest in the temperate zone can accumulate about 2.7×10^6 g of carbon per hectare per year. Suppose that fossil carbon CO_2 emissions from the USA alone were held at their present figure (around 1.4 PgC per year) over the next 100 years.

(i) What fraction of the continental USA (with a total area of some 8×10^8 ha) would the new growing forest need to occupy in order to match that output?

(ii) Would it go on acting as a net carbon sink indefinitely?

---

[*] To avoid impeachment for corruption, the president referred to here (Fernando Collor de Mello) resigned in December 1992.

(d) Now, putting together your thoughts on parts (a)–(c), comment (*in about 250 words*) on the following further statement from the São Paulo workshop on tropical forests referred to previously:

> *Although forests can assist in mitigating the effects of atmospheric carbon build-up, the problem is essentially a fossil fuel one and must be addressed as such.*

7.1.3 'Policy' scenarios

In their work for the Second World Climate Conference, the Response Strategies Working Group of the IPCC put together four alternative visions of the future. All of them were based on common assumptions about two important determinants of greenhouse gas emissions; the projected growth in world population (as in Figure 7.3), together with economic growth rates for different countries or regions taken from World Bank estimates. In other words, these variables were effectively 'factored out' of the equation. The variable they did focus on was essentially a political one — an emphasis foreshadowed in Activity 7.3: hence the term '*policy*' scenarios.

To be more specific, for each greenhouse gas in turn they constructed four alternative emission scenarios. In each case, one of these amounted to '**Business as Usual**' (**BaU**). Think of it as a plausible — albeit inherently uncertain — answer to the question: 'What if few or no active steps are taken to limit the release of CO_2 (or CH_4, or whatever)? For CO_2, for example, this was taken to mean: 'What if little is done to promote energy-saving measures, *and* world energy supplies remain heavily dependent on fossil fuels (i.e. existing technical, economic or other constraints continue to limit the share taken by all non-fossil fuel alternatives), *and* tropical deforestation continues unchecked throughout the next century?'

The short answer is that global energy demand would rise sharply, doubling by around 2025, and doubling again by 2100 — at which point the share consumed in the developing countries would have increased from 22% today to over 50%. High energy demand would also bring the reserve constraints noted earlier (Figure 7.8) into play, with a trend toward coal as the dominant fossil fuel (see Figure 7.12). And tropical forests would be more or less wiped out. The implications of all this for CO_2 emissions are recorded by the line labelled BaU in Figure 7.13.

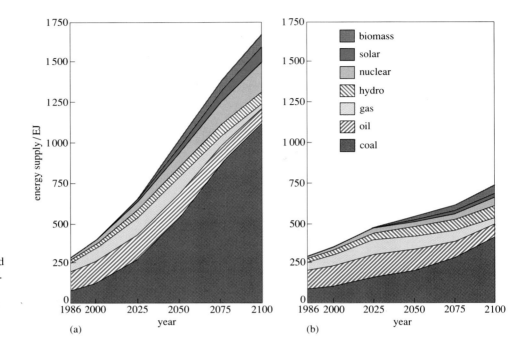

Figure 7.12 Projected global primary energy supply by type according to the IPCC BaU scenario, assuming (a) higher and (b) lower economic growth rates. The BaU emission scenario for CO_2 (Figure 7.13) was based on the average of these two projections. (1 EJ (exajoule) = 10^{18} J.)

Also included in Figure 7.13 are the three alternative emission scenarios for CO_2 (labelled B, C and D). In effect, they provide a spectrum of answers to the question: 'What if, on the other hand, steps to curb the release of CO_2 *are* actively pursued?' As the trend apparent in the figure suggests, the 'controls' thereby achieved become progressively stronger, or they take effect sooner, from B to D. Some brief notes about the broad strategies assumed in constructing these alternative scenarios are included in the caption to Figure 7.13; they were all touched on earlier in this chapter.

A comparable set of scenarios was drawn up for methane, nitrous oxide, the two most important CFCs (CFC-11 and CFC-12), and for HCFC-22 (as a surrogate for all the shorter-lived CFC substitutes). Without dwelling on the detailed assumptions involved, a few key points are worth noting. In particular, methane emissions as projected by the IPCC's four policy scenarios are shown in Figure 7.14.

Figure 7.13 Projected emissions of CO_2 according to the IPCC's four policy scenarios: all of these were based on the average of two assumed economic growth rates, as noted in the caption to Figure 7.12. On the demand side, Scenarios B–D assume (the same) rapid improvements in energy efficiency. In Scenario B, energy supply remains fossil-fuel intensive, but with increased use of natural gas actively encouraged. For the other two cases, constraints that impede the penetration and use of non-fossil fuel sources are relaxed, either in the middle of the next century (Scenario C), or very much earlier (Scenario D). All three scenarios assume that tropical deforestation stops by 2025, with about a billion hectares being reforested by 2100.

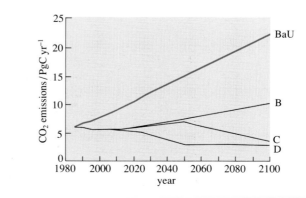

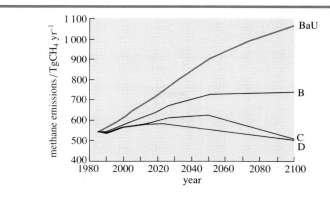

Figure 7.14 Projected emissions of methane according to the IPCC's four policy scenarios (BaU, B, C, D).

Activity 7.4   *You should spend up to 20 minutes on this activity.*

(a) With the major anthropogenic sources of methane in mind (Table 4.3 in Section 4.3.1), explain why a BaU future might be expected to generate the growth in emissions evident in Figure 7.14? (Hint: remember that a BaU future assumes the population growth projected in Figure 7.3.)

(b) Which of the control strategies assumed in the corresponding CO_2 emission scenarios (B–D in Figure 7.13) should act to curb the release of methane as well?

(c) What about curtailing the other anthropogenic sources of methane? (Just note down your immediate thoughts on this.)

In practice, scenarios C and D in Figure 7.14 did assume some controls over methane emissions from the agricultural sector — through changing methods of rice cultivation, for example, or different feed and management practices for livestock. And so did the corresponding scenarios for nitrous oxide, as regards fertilizer use. Bear in mind, however, that *current* emissions of these two gases are poorly characterized as yet — a point stressed in Section 4.4. This inevitably adds another element of uncertainty to *any* assessment of their future releases.

By contrast, one might imagine that the situation would be more clear cut for the 'basket' of infrared-absorbing halocarbons covered by the provisions of the Montreal Protocol. But here the impact of an *evolving* policy-making process (the very factor

I THINK THESE METHANE THEORIES ARE BLOWN UP OUT OF ALL PROPORTION!

that the alternative scenarios for the *other* gases were essentially designed to illustrate!) has already made itself felt. To be more specific, the set of assumptions made by the IPCC in 1990 have now been overtaken by events. Heightened fears for the ozone layer prompted a further strengthening of the Protocol in 1992. As a result, CFCs now look set to be phased out before the end of the century.

We pick up this particular issue again later on. For the moment, we simply adopt the 'package' of emission scenarios put together by the IPCC in 1990 as representing a spectrum of possible futures. We turn now to the projected changes in global-mean surface temperature that then emerge from the 'other end' of the modelling sequence shown schematically in Figure 7.1.

7.2 What might a 'Business as Usual' future be like?

Collected in Figure 7.15 are several of the intermediate results produced by 'taking' the BaU emission scenarios through the successive layers of modelling studies indicated in Figure 7.1. By asking you a series of questions, the following activity aims to draw together what you already know about the key steps in this sequence and the main uncertainties involved — as identified in Chapters 4, 5 and 6. It also invites you to set the model-predicted scale and pace of change in the context of past *natural* variations in climate — thus drawing in material from Chapter 3 as well. The questions include references to salient sections of earlier chapters, but (*if time permits*) it would be a good plan to try doing them *without* referring back.

Activity 7.5   *You should spend up to 1 hour on this activity.*

(a) What are the main deficiencies of the carbon-cycle models (of the type described in Section 4.2.4) used to transform the BaU emission scenario for CO_2 in Figure 7.13 into the projected atmospheric concentrations recorded in Figure 7.15a? (Section 4.2.4 and Answer to Activity 4.4)

(b) What *additional* assumptions — apart from the emission rates labelled BaU in Figure 7.14, that is — must have been fed into the 'chemistry' model used to calculate the projected atmospheric concentrations of methane shown in Figure 7.15b? (Section 4.3.1 and Answer to Activity 4.6)

(c) Figure 7.15c shows the time-evolving *total* radiative forcing of the climate system (the upper blue line) due to the increasing atmospheric burden of CO_2, CH_4, N_2O and the halocarbons, and their separate contributions. According to this figure, when (roughly) does the total radiative forcing become *equivalent* to that induced by doubling the pre-industrial atmospheric concentration of CO_2 (i.e. $4\,W\,m^{-2}$)? How does this compare with the time-scale over which the increased atmospheric burden of CO_2, taken alone, would induce this level of radiative forcing?

(d) What other possible sources of radiative forcing are *not* included in Figure 7.15c? Is it possible, at present, reliably to predict the size of any such contributions and/or whether they would act to enhance or to offset the greenhouse forcing recorded in Figure 7.15c? (Sections 4.3.2 and 6.3.2)

(e) Figure 7.15d effectively takes the model-predicted greenhouse warming over the *past* century (from Figure 6.5), and projects it forward on the basis of the forcing scenario in Figure 7.15c. However, there is one new feature. Here, a climate sensitivity of $2.5\,°C$ is identified as the 'best estimate' — the choice endorsed by the IPCC. Is this choice based on a scientific judgement? (Section 6.4)

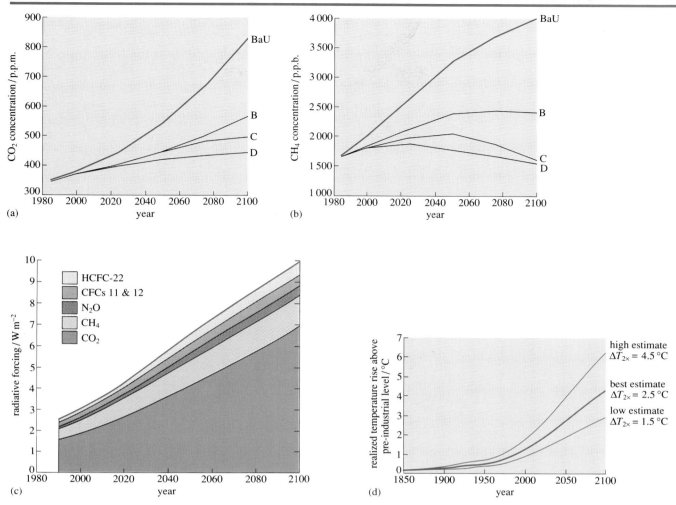

(f) According to Figure 7.15d, what is the 'best estimate' of the model-predicted rise in global-mean surface temperature during the next century? How does this compare with:

(i) the kind of long-term (i.e. century time-scale) temperature fluctuations during the Holocene for which there is evidence in the historical and palaeoclimatic records? (Section 3.4)

(ii) the temperature variations that characterize the 100 000-year glacial–interglacial cycles? (Question 3.1 in Section 3.1)

(g) From part (f), what is the current 'best estimate' of the average *rate* of global warming per decade predicted to occur over the next century? Now use the other two lines in Figure 7.15d to add an upper and lower limit to this estimate. How do these figures compare with the rates of temperature change suggested by your answers to part (f), (i) and (ii)?

(h) Suppose, finally, that greenhouse gases do go on accumulating in the atmosphere, and that this translates into a radiative forcing that follows something like the BaU trajectory in Figure 7.15c — for the next two or three decades, say. Would the globally-averaged temperature record be expected to show a steady upward trend? Explain your answer. (Section 6.3)

Figure 7.15 (a) and (b) Projected atmospheric concentrations of CO_2 and CH_4, according to the IPCC's four policy scenarios (BaU, B, C, D). (c) Contributions to the *total* radiative forcing (the blue line) between 1990 and 2100 due to projected increases in greenhouse gas concentrations, based on the BaU emission scenario for each gas. Values are changes in forcing from the pre-industrial (i.e. 1750–1800) concentrations given in Table 4.1. (d) The model-simu-lated increase in global-mean sur-face temperature above the pre-industrial value, due to observed increases in greenhouse gases from 1850–1990 (compare with Figure 6.5) and thereafter projected on the basis of the radiative forcing in part (c). As before, $\Delta T_{2\times}$ refers to prescribed values of the climate sensitivity within the currently accepted range.

To weave your thoughts on this activity together, it helps to work back from the final results of the whole modelling process — the projections in Figure 7.15d. Given these, the short answer to the question posed as the title to this section was implicit in parts (f) and (g) of Activity 7.5. To quote from the IPCC report, according to the current 'best estimate',

> *The changes predicted to occur by about the middle of the next century ... will make global mean temperatures higher than they have been in the last 150 000 years.*

(Policymakers Summary, *prepared by Science Working Group of the IPCC, 1990*)

And the *pace* of change — averaging 0.3 °C per decade — would be unprecedented since the world emerged from the last glacial period about 10 000 years ago (more on which in Section 7.3).

But is it possible to gauge the reliability of these 'best estimate' predictions — to get a feel for the full 'envelope of uncertainty' as it were, that surrounds them? The short answer is 'no'. Hopefully, the discussion in the previous chapter brought home some of the inherent difficulties involved. Thus, the range of possible climate sensitivities introduces a fairly clear-cut 'factor of two' uncertainty into the model-predicted rate of warming over the next century (from Activity 7.5g). Recall that here an important, perhaps dominant, contribution comes from the unresolved question of *cloud feedback* (as discussed in Section 5.5). But even this envelope of uncertainty has 'fuzzy' edges. Parts (d) and (h) of Activity 7.5 were a reminder that through the combined effects of other forcing factors, together with the 'wild card' of internally-generated natural variability, a range of largely unpredictable temperature variations (of either sign) will inevitably be superimposed on the greenhouse warming signal in the future — just as they have been in the past.

Moving back up the modelling sequence in Figure 7.1 only serves to blur the picture further, as it draws in all of the uncertainties embedded in any emission scenario, and in then 'transforming' those emission rates into atmospheric concentrations — matters that parts (a) and (b) of Activity 7.5 sought to remind you about. In which context, it is important to register (from part b) that emission scenarios also have to cover the gases (notably, CO and NO_x) that have an *indirect* chemical effect on the atmospheric burden of methane (and tropospheric ozone, Activity 7.5d).

As far as emission rates are concerned, the emphasis throughout this chapter has been on the *non*-scientific factors involved — the demographic, economic, social, technological, but above all political forces that may shape future developments. From this perspective, the influence that strategies designed to curb greenhouse gas emissions might have is apparent in Figure 7.16. The message is really self-evident: the more urgent and concerted such control policies, the slower and less marked global warming is likely to be. That is the essence of the precautionary principle.

Figure 7.16 'Best estimate' (i.e. $\Delta T_{2\times} = 2.5$ °C) simulations of the realized warming through to the end of the next century resulting from the IPCC's four policy scenarios for greenhouse gas emissions.

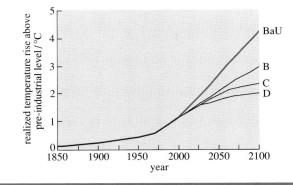

However, working through Section 7.1 (and its activities) should have heightened your awareness of the many barriers to *acting* on this principle — to actually taking out the kind of global insurance policy implicit in Scenario D, say. Greenhouse gas emissions are an intrinsic by-product of basic activities in contemporary human society. Policies to curtail them will inevitably challenge countless established practices (in personal life-styles, in industry and commerce, in agriculture and the exploitation of forests), and powerful interest groups. The potential conflicts of national interest are manifold, especially — if by no means exclusively — between the developed and developing worlds (a dimension touched on in Activities 7.3 and 7.4). In short, the attempt to orchestrate a substantial international response — let alone at the level needed to achieve the stabilized, and then reducing emission rates assumed in Scenario D (Figures 7.13 and 7.14) — is having to address complex, and interwoven, environment and development issues.

That wider political debate about responding to the prospect of climatic change is taken up in Chapter 9 — *after* we have explored some of the possible consequences of choosing to do nothing. To draw up the kind of 'impact assessments' that are fed into the policy-making process, the somewhat abstract, if disturbing, threat crystallized in the quote that followed Activity 7.5 has to be translated into more concrete terms (Figure 7.17). That is the subject of the next chapter. Before we embark on that, however, a brief look at a question raised in Section 6.4.3 is in order.

Figure 7.17 As far as the wider public is concerned, one all-important way of getting the message across is through the media. Since 1991, the UK Department of the Environment's Energy Efficiency Office has been sponsoring a press, television and public relations campaign on energy use in the home, and the link to the threat of global warming. It included a television commercial which was followed up with newspaper advertisements like the one shown here. The emphasis in this public information campaign is on the contribution the individual can make to reducing CO_2 emissions through domestic energy efficiency (its logo is 'Helping the Earth Begins at Home') — a message given emotional force by using children in the television commercial. This campaign to encourage energy efficiency in the home is just one part of a targeted package of programmes aimed at different sectors of the community.

7.3 What about surprises?

For all the reasons identified earlier in this book, and revisited above, the projections of future global warming collected in Figure 7.16 can only be indicative of the risks incurred by following various courses of action. They are 'best estimates' based on the state of knowledge at the time they were drawn up (1990). Such assessments are bound to change, as new facets to the problem are gradually uncovered and incorporated into ever more elaborate and 'complete' computer models. Sometimes new findings will act to mitigate the perceived threat: sometimes the reverse. Clearly, there are echoes here of the debate about CFCs and ozone depletion. Indeed, the first example below — which only came to light in early 1992 — emphasizes the link between the twin problems of ozone depletion and global warming. But more than that, it exemplifies a theme running through this book. The real planetary system is a complex, interconnected whole, 'with threads that reach down into the deepest ocean, and extend up into the stratosphere as well' (a message stressed in the Summary to Chapter 4). If we go on disturbing this system, should we expect it to respond in a gradual, and more or less predictable way, as the results collected in Figures 7.15d and 7.16 would tend to suggest — however uncertain the precise trajectory might be? Or are we really 'playing Russian roulette' with our planet, as Broecker would have it? (Recall his letter to *Science* in Extract 6.1.) It seems appropriate to end our 'crystal ball gazing' on this more speculative note.

7.3.1 A 'wrinkle' in the CFC story

If CFC emissions really do cease much earlier than assumed in the IPCC's BaU scenario, then so too should their continuing buildup in the atmosphere. In other words, the slow process whereby their atmospheric concentrations gradually 'decay' away (recall Section 4.3.3) should start sooner than assumed in 1990. Thus, it seems likely that Figure 7.15c overestimates the *direct* contribution CFCs might make to future greenhouse forcing. But the issue I want to focus on here is an *indirect* effect, linked to CFCs through their role in depleting stratospheric ozone.

There is now good evidence that the ozone layer *is* being eroded at mid- and high latitudes in both hemispheres. In particular, the most recent observations show that the period 1979–1990 saw a significant loss of ozone from the lower stratosphere at these latitudes. New calculations, reported in *Nature* in early 1992[*], indicate that this observed depletion results in a *negative* forcing of the surface climate system (for reasons which are taken up in Box 7.2, *if you are interested*). Further — and this is the point to note — they imply that, averaged around the globe, this cooling effect may be large enough essentially to cancel out the direct (i.e. *positive*) greenhouse forcing of the CFCs themselves. In short, they suggest that the *net* radiative effect of the CFCs (direct greenhouse, plus indirect chemical) may be close to zero.

The calculations referred to here only considered the observed ozone loss, as against the observed increase in CFC concentrations, over the period 1979–1990. At the time of writing, the wider ramifications of these results, especially for projections of greenhouse forcing — and the global warming scenarios derived from them — have yet to

[*] V. Ramaswamy, M. D. Schwarzkopf and K. Shine (1992) Radiative forcing of climate from halocarbon-induced global stratospheric ozone loss, *Nature*, **355**, pp. 810–812.

be explored. But the message I want to emphasize was well expressed by Jeffrey T. Kiehl, in a commentary in the *News and Views* section of the same issue of *Nature* (27 February 1992):

> *The new results show that stratospheric ozone continues to surprise atmospheric scientists. It would be wrong to conclude from them that CFCs are a benign component in global warming.* Indeed, these findings indicate how intimately coupled is the chemistry of the stratosphere to the climate response at the Earth's surface. *From the past 20 years of ozone studies, it seems that the only thing that is not surprising about this facet of the climate is that it will keep surprising us. [Emphasis added.]*

Box 7.2   Stratospheric ozone depletion: why should it have a cooling effect?

To unpick this question, it is vital to recall (from Box 2.2 in Section 2.2.3) that stratospheric ozone absorbs both incoming uv radiation *and* outgoing ir radiation. Both processes warm the stratosphere. The lower stratosphere also contributes to the surface climate by emitting longwave radiation back down into the troposphere. Put in simple terms then, depletion of the ozone layer is predicted to cool the stratosphere itself. But it can also modify the surface climate. The problem is that there are two competing processes.

o   If more uv radiation gets through to the Earth's surface and lower atmosphere (because there is less stratospheric ozone to filter it out) that should contribute to surface warming.

o   On the other hand, a cooler stratosphere would be expected to emit *less* longwave radiation back down towards the surface, which would be a cooling effect.

For reasons I don't plan to go into, it turns out that the balance between these two opposing effects depends critically on the *altitude* at which the ozone loss occurs. Based on the observed loss from the lower stratosphere, it seems that the cooling effect is likely to dominate. ■

7.3.2 Greenhouse gas feedbacks

Kiehl's remarks highlight an important and more general limitation of existing *climate* models (noted in Section 5.3): they do not incorporate in an interactive way the lifecycles of any of the greenhouse gases, natural or unnatural (apart from water vapour of course). At present, those are simulated through the separate carbon-cycle and chemistry models that are used to generate the radiative forcing scenarios. Assessments based on this strategy cannot capture the effect of potential feedbacks, whereby a change in climate could act back on the *natural* sources and sinks of the greenhouse gases (or their precursors).

To again take CO_2 as the leading example, ice-core data (referred to in Section 4.1) reveal that its atmospheric concentration was fairly constant — at around 280 ± 10 p.p.m. — throughout the millenium that preceded the industrial age. This suggests that the natural controls over atmospheric CO_2 are relatively insensitive to minor climatic changes, such as the degree or so temperature fluctuations associated with cool periods like the Little Ice Age. Recent global warming is still within this range of natural variability. But what if the larger changes in climate anticipated in Figure 7.15d did occur?

▷   What evidence have you already met for a close interaction between major natural climate variations and the carbon cycle?

▶   The remarkable correlation between temperature and atmospheric CO_2 over the whole period of the last glacial–interglacial cycle — as revealed by analysis of the Vostock ice core (Figure 3.25).

As discussed in Section 3.3, there is convincing evidence that the Milankovic–Croll orbital effects have set the pace for the repeated glacial and interglacial cycles of the past million or so years. Yet these 'wobbles' in the Earth's orbit and orientation only result in slight changes in the seasonal and geographical pattern of solar radiation. To trigger the onset or the end of glacial periods, these direct effects must be amplified by positive feedbacks *within* the Earth's climate system. Careful analysis of the Vostock data (Section 3.6) points to changes in atmospheric CO_2 as an important contributory factor. Around 200 Pg of carbon disappeared from the atmosphere as the planet cooled, only to return over a few thousand years at the end of the glacial period. Model calculations (of the kind mentioned in Section 5.4) indicate that the greenhouse forcing induced by these changes was large enough to contribute a substantial — albeit not the major — part of the full glacial–interglacial temperature change.

As yet, there is no consensus about the detailed workings of this amplification system. However, there is evidence that carbon lost from the atmosphere went into the deep ocean. The careful analysis and dating of marine sediments have shown that the biological pump was stronger during the last glacial period — i.e. more fixed carbon settled out of surface waters. But the mechanisms driving this enhanced marine productivity are still uncertain. Most suggestions link it to major changes in ocean circulation. By this stage, you should recognize that shifts in ocean currents — or more dramatically, in the large scale thermohaline circulation — could, by themselves, have a significant effect on the climate. Indeed, this *is* one of the factors that probably helps to amplify the climatic response to orbital forcing — a possibility noted in Section 3.3 (more on which in Section 7.3.3). But given the discussion in Section 4.2, there is every reason to suppose that changes in ocean circulation could also influence the behaviour of the oceanic carbon cycle — the complex interplay of physical, chemical and biological processes that control the flux of CO_2 across the air–sea boundary, and the movement of carbon throughout the world's oceans.

As far as the glacial–interglacial cycles are concerned, it appears that shifts in the oceanic carbon system acted to reinforce temperature trends that were already under way. But are the responses that operated then relevant to the present situation? Remember that the oceans are generally thought to have sequestered up to 60% of the CO_2 released by human activities over the last two centuries. Could continued global warming — a temperature rise of a few degrees, say — *reduce* the efficiency of this oceanic sink, and so counter efforts to control anthropogenic emissions? Worse still, could it even trigger release of the vast amount of carbon stored in the oceans, and hence a self-accelerating rise in atmospheric CO_2? Or could it perhaps activate a more efficient uptake of anthropogenic CO_2?

Simplistic arguments point to a wealth of potential feedbacks on the oceanic carbon cycle. The problem is to quantify them, and hence assess what the *net* effect might be. The difficulties involved can be traced back to issues raised in Section 4.2.4 (and revisited in part (a) of Activity 7.5). Put bluntly, scientists do not really understand the mechanisms that drive the ocean–atmosphere carbon system, let alone what might bring about a change in its behaviour. Many of the component processes are still only poorly characterized. In particular, early studies under the JGOFS umbrella have already revealed surprises about the biological components of the system. For example, the spring bloom of different communities of phytoplankton looks to be far more complicated than previously supposed — as does the fate of the carbon fixed by marine photosynthesis. No doubt too the data being gathered by WOCE (Section 5.6) will offer novel, and perhaps telling, insights into how the ocean circulation really functions at all depths — and hence into the physical processes that move dissolved carbon (and important nutrients) around the globe, and govern the exchange between surface and deep waters.

These on-going research programmes should eventually provide the deeper under-standing needed to address the questions posed earlier in a quantitative way. But even then, definitive answers may not be immediately forthcoming (see Section 7.3.3). Fur-thermore, possible oceanic responses to climatic change are not the only issue. There were hints in Section 4.2.4 that higher levels of CO_2, coupled with changes in key environmental factors (temperature, rainfall, soil moisture, and so on) could act back on the terrestrial carbon cycle as well. Since the important scientific questions here are central to the task of making impact assessments, they are taken up, in that con-text, in the next chapter. For now, suffice it to say that the corollary to such studies — the effect that impacts *on* terrestrial ecosystems may, in turn, have on future levels of CO_2 — remains an open question.

To sum up. The palaeoclimatic record suggests that the natural carbon cycle *is* sensi-tive to climatic change. But predicting whether, and if so how and to what extent, the natural controls over atmospheric CO_2 might respond to future global warming is frankly impossible at present.

That conclusion holds with equal — some would say, even greater — force for the other greenhouse gases as well. For a start, the fate of all of these gases is bound up with atmospheric chemistry. The signal failure to predict the Antarctic ozone hole is especially pertinent here. As noted in Section 6.4.2, recent research has revealed that this seasonal phenomenon is produced by a peculiar combination of meteorological and chemical factors; none of these were included in the models being used to forecast ozone depletion in the mid-1980s. Like these 'stratospheric chemistry' models, their tropospheric counterparts currently contain many simplifying assump-tions and approximations (Section 4.4). Undoubtedly, they too are incomplete. Cer-tainly, they cannot capture ways in which a changing climate — a warmer and more humid troposphere, say, or a different pattern of atmospheric circulation — might act back on the chemical balance in general, and the global abundance of OH• radicals in particular. The pivotal role played by this molecular scavenger was stressed in Chapter 4 (and revisited in part (b) of Activity 7.5); if forecasts of future OH• radical concen-trations are highly uncertain, then so too are current assessments of how effectively the atmosphere will 'dispose' of continuing emissions of potent greenhouse gases like methane and the CFC substitutes.

In addition, there are still significant uncertainties about the strength and geographical distribution of the natural *sources* of methane and nitrous oxide — and of other key ingredients in the atmospheric chemistry 'brew', notably NO_x. Further, these emissions are largely biogenic in origin — methane from wetlands, for example — and often sensitive to changes in temperature and other environmental factors. In short, the potential for 'greenhouse gas feedbacks' again arises — with a changing climatic regime triggering responses that could either counter or reinforce efforts to control anthropogenic emissions of these gases. To date, speculation about such feedbacks has focused on methane; *if you are interested* (and if time allows), Activity 7.6 invites you to indulge in that exercise. Suffice it to say that here — as with CO_2 — the 'current state of knowledge' provides little, if any, definitive guidance. But that, in itself, adds to a gathering sense that surprises — unpleasant or otherwise — could well be in store.

Activity 7.6   *You should spend up to 15 minutes on this activity.*

As with CO_2, concern that a shift in the natural methane cycle could act to amplify future global warming was fuelled by publication of the data shown in Figure 7.18. Specifically, careful analysis of the correlation evident in the figure suggests that changes in atmospheric methane also helped to reinforce the climatic changes triggered by the Milankovic–Croll orbital effects. But once again, evidence that a positive feedback apparently operated in the past has to be interpreted with caution.

(a) For example, present wetland sources of methane are mainly concentrated in the tropics and in the tundra regions at high northern latitudes (Figure 2.1). Current understanding of the controlling factors suggests that a warmer *and* wetter regime could enhance the flux of methane from these sources; conversely, warming coupled with drier soils could reduce it. Drawing on the equilibrium scenarios discussed in Section 5.5, explain *briefly* why it is difficult to assess what effect greenhouse gas-induced global warming might have on the *total* flux of methane from wetlands. What about the other *natural* sources of methane identified in Section 4.3.1 (Table 4.3)?

(b) Permafrost persists at high northern latitudes where the annual mean temperature is less than −7 °C. There are known to be large amounts of methane trapped (in various forms) in the permafrost. Why does speculation that this 'store' of methane could provide a positive feedback in a 'Business as Usual' future have a somewhat firmer basis? Note any reservations you might have.

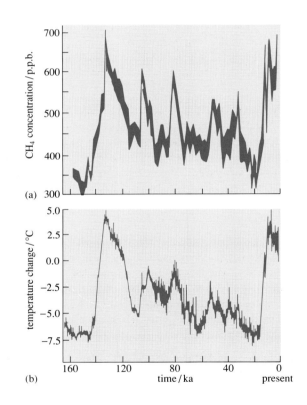

Figure 7.18 (a) Methane concentrations, in p.p.b., as determined from the analysis of air bubbles trapped in the Vostock ice-core. The pattern of change is strikingly similar to that revealed by the corresponding analysis for CO_2 (Figure 3.25): once again it is closely correlated with the estimated deviations from the present temperature (b).

7.3.3 The Younger Dryas: an object lesson for the future?

As outlined above, it seems likely that changes in atmospheric composition (both CO_2 and CH_4) during glacial–interglacial cycles help to amplify the direct climatic effects of orbital 'forcing'. But the palaeoclimatic record also contains evidence of *rapid* changes in climate which cannot be directly related to the combined influence of these factors. The best documented examples come from well-dated records that portray conditions in and around the North Atlantic as the world emerged from the last glacial period.

The disintegration of the great North American and Eurasian ice sheets took roughly 7 000 years, spanning the period from around 15 000 BP to 8 000 BP. By the end of this deglaciation, the world was some 6 °C warmer, on average. But with a growing body of high quality proxy data to draw on, it has become increasingly clear that the transition to a warmer regime was not a simple or gradual affair. The salient points are evident in the record from a North Atlantic sediment core shown in Figure 7.19, and described in its caption: notice how the rapid warming trend that set in about 15 000 years ago was interrupted by brief intervals of renewed cold. Oxygen isotope measurements on ice cores from Greenland reveal a similar picture, with sharp jumps in climate seen throughout the older (i.e. fully-glaciated) part of the record as well.

The last, and most intense, of the cold episodes evident in Figure 7.19 occurred about 11 000 years ago. Known as the **Younger Dryas**, it was an event of global significance: it can just be seen in the Vostock record (Figure 3.11), and it also shows up in palaeoclimatic records from New Zealand. However, the cooling appears to have been strongest in the North Atlantic region: sea-surface temperatures fell by some 7 °C in 700 years. On land, the reversion to glacial conditions is documented in the pollen records of lake and bog sediments from northern Europe and northeastern North America. Forests, which had repopulated these areas after the ice retreated, were destroyed and replaced by the flora typical of the Arctic tundra. Indeed, the Younger Dryas is named after an alpine shrub (Figure 7.20) which colonized Europe during this time. All of the records indicate that this final cold period lasted several hundred years, and ended very abruptly, with radical changes in climate throughout the North Atlantic region. Temperatures in Greenland appear to have risen by about 7 °C in just 50 years!

As yet, there is no consensus about the reasons for the onset, and abrupt end of the Younger Dryas — nor for the series of similar, if less dramatic, climatic 'oscillations' that apparently preceded it. Several hypotheses have been proposed, only to be challenged and discarded, or to re-emerge in modified form. For reasons that will become apparent later on, I plan to look briefly at just one of these, originally put forward as an 'educated hunch' by Wallace Broecker. The central idea revolves around the workings of the ocean's large-scale thermohaline circulation and its influence on the climate, especially that of the North Atlantic region.

In Section 2.3.3, the way this system operates today — and apparently has done since the end of the Younger Dryas — was likened to a gigantic conveyor belt (Figure 2.32), driven by cold, dense water sinking at high latitudes. By stripping away all the detail (the very thing those designing OGCMs are striving to simulate), Broecker has argued that this global circulation both maintains, *and is maintained by*, salt — or to be a bit more precise, by the higher salinity of the surface waters of the North Atlantic as compared with the North Pacific.

Put simply, the argument goes as follows. Because the large-scale circulation functions as it does, sea-surface temperatures in the North Atlantic are on average warmer than those in the North Pacific (a difference evident in Figure 2.16), so there is relatively more evaporation from the ocean's surface there. That goes a long way toward explaining the markedly different salinities noted above. But the enrichment in salt is, in turn, the key reason why North Atlantic waters, cooled by cold winds in winter, become dense enough to sink — thus feeding the deep ocean conveyor, and hence, ultimately, the return flow of warm surface waters shown in Figure 2.32. In short, the whole system is self-reinforcing. In Broecker's words: 'Excess evaporation causes the deep current; the deep current causes excess evaporation'.*

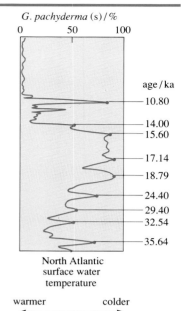

G. pachyderma (s) / %

North Atlantic surface water temperature

warmer ← ~8 °C → colder

Figure 7.19 The palaeoclimatic record derived from a deep-sea sediment core obtained west of the British Isles. The record is based on the abundance of the shells of the planktonic herbivore *Globigerina pachyderma* (s), which currently lives in waters off Greenland — the only species of planktonic foraminifera found in these icy waters. During cold periods this species dominated the entire North Atlantic, providing up to 90% of the shells found in sediments off Britain. (The results of analysing a similar, but much longer, sediment core were shown in Figure 3.9.)

---

* From an article entitled 'Unpleasant surprises in the greenhouse?' in the *Commentary* section of *Nature*, 9 July 1987, pp. 123–126.

Figure 7.20 Dryas octapetala.

Currently, this system has a benign influence on the climate of the North Atlantic region. Evaporation of the warm surface waters — carried northwards by the return part of the Atlantic conveyor — releases a vast amount of heat into the atmosphere at high latitudes. Mostly this works to the benefit of northern Europe, which is downwind of the ocean. Broecker's hunch was that the rapid cooling portrayed in the palaeoclimatic records was triggered by a shutdown of deep-water formation in the North Atlantic. This effectively 'switched off' the ocean conveyor and hence the associated heat flux to the high-latitude atmosphere.

Over the past few years, Broecker and colleagues have elaborated on this core idea, offering possible explanations for a periodic shutdown, and subsequent reactivation, of the thermohaline circulation during the last deglaciation — and perhaps before that as well. A recurrent theme is the salinity of North Atlantic waters. The arguments revolve around mechanisms that might have pushed this *below* the threshold needed for deep-water formation (thus switching off the conveyor) — and some time later, driven it back over that threshold (switching it on again). In one way or another, these mechanisms all presuppose extensive ice cover on the surrounding continents, so the details are not immediately relevant to today's world, much less to the 'super-interglacial' conditions we could be heading towards.

What, then, of the question posed as the title to this section? The climatic oscillations outlined here happened during a time when *external* forcing of the climate system (due to orbital effects) was limited and gradual. Somehow that triggered abrupt — not smooth — changes in climate. That is the important general message. Perhaps a drastic change in the ocean's large-scale circulation was the key factor. Perhaps not. What on-going research reveals, in the way of evidence for or against that hypothesis, remains to be seen. Whatever the outcome of that debate, however, Broecker's analysis of the workings of the ocean conveyor, albeit oversimplified, does touch on a more fundamental issue. Notice that it stresses how interactions *within* the climate system — specifically links between the atmosphere, surface ocean and deep ocean — generate a self-reinforcing mode of operation. Systems like this — even ones far simpler than the thermohaline circulation assuredly is in reality — can, if perturbed in some way, flip abruptly to a quite different mode of operation. Suffice it to say that this is a further manifestation of the 'demon of non-linearity' (Box 6.1), with the feedbacks within the system effectively working to push some key factor (the salinity of the North Atlantic, say) over a critical threshold, and hence trigger an abrupt — *and often inherently unpredictable* — change.

Could continued greenhouse forcing — of the kind envisaged in the IPCC's BaU scenario, say — jolt the ocean–atmosphere system out of its current mode of operation, perhaps provoking an abrupt transition to some radically different climatic regime? Once again, this remains an open question. True, early experiments with coupled AGCM/OGCMs simulate a smooth, time-evolving response to a gradual increase in CO_2. Or at least, they do on the decade to century time-scale. Recall the results produced by the GFDL model (shown in Figure 5.17), and their broad similarity with those computed by the much simpler type of climate model used to generate the IPCC global warming projections (Figure 7.15d, for example). On the other hand, there was one telling feature of the GFDL study. As mentioned in Section 5.6, there were indications that downwelling and deep vertical convection in the North Atlantic was becoming systematically weaker toward the end of the 100-year 'perturbed' run — the physical origin of this change apparently being the combined influence of surface warming and enhanced precipitation. Might an even longer run have seen this feed into the deep ocean circulation cease altogether, as it may have done during the Younger Dryas?

Perhaps. But as yet, most climate modellers warn against attaching too much credance to these findings — based as they are on very early simulations with coupled AGCM/OGCMs. Researchers are only too aware of the deficiencies in the separate atmosphere and ocean models, and of certain difficulties that arise when existing versions are coupled together: the details need not concern us. Suffice it to say that this note of caution does not rule out the *possibility* that continued greenhouse forcing could induce marked and, more importantly, rapid changes in the ocean's large-scale circulation: it simply underlines the difficulty of assessing the likelihood, timing or possible consequences of such changes.

▷ In view of the discussion in Section 7.3.2, what potentially important 'possible consequence' comes to mind — other than a change in climate *per se*, that is?

▶ That a major change in ocean circulation could trigger feedbacks within the oceanic carbon cycle — as it may have done in the past — and hence alter (for good or ill) the efficiency of the oceanic sink for anthropogenic CO_2.

From this perspective, the uncertainties noted above only compound those rehearsed in Section 7.3.2 — making the prospect that modelling studies will provide early answers to the questions posed there a somewhat remote one.

7.3.4 The detection issue revisited

To sum up. The final point above emphasizes only one link between the least certain aspects of the output from even the most sophisticated climate models — possible changes in ocean circulation in this case — and the whole question of greenhouse gas feedbacks. There are countless other examples of such links (witness those in Activity 7.6 if you attempted it). Or to refer back to my opening remarks: crucial areas of uncertainty about the workings of the *total* planetary system — the web of interactions that binds it together, that is — interlock, as it were, around the issues raised in this section. And that, in turn, adds substance to a message spelt out in general terms toward the end of Section 6.4.3; the greater and more numerous the uncertainties, the greater the chance of unexpected changes, 'surprises', occurring in the future — just as they did in the past (and indeed, continue to do so) up in the stratosphere (Section 7.3.1).

Climate, or climate-related, surprises add another element of risk (recall Broecker's 'Russian roulette' metaphor) to the future envisaged in the IPCC's BaU scenario (Figure 7.15d). That has been the underlying theme of this section. But there is another aspect to the kind of changes noted here. Might the possibility of such changes offer further opportunities for *detecting* the enhanced greenhouse effect in action? After all, it was detection of the ozone hole over Antarctica that provided the first unequivocal signal of a real change to stratospheric ozone — however surprising the extent of the damage and its geographical character.

Unfortunately, the difficulties that surround this extension of the detection issue are familiar ones — already touched on over the question of possible changes in the frequency and/or intensity of extreme events like droughts and severe storms (Section 6.4). To be specific, the 1990s will see a major expansion in the observations of key ocean variables (as part of WOCE), thus facilitating the direct detection of any possible changes in ocean circulation. However, existing data suggest that the thermohaline circulation varies naturally on decadal time-scales. So come the turn of the century, the tricky question of attribution — and in particular, of eliminating natural variability as a partial explanation — will again arise. Similar difficulties are likely to attend the early detection of statistically significant trends in the fluxes of CO_2 across the air–sea boundary, for example, or in methane emissions — and more importantly, a convincing demonstration of a causal link with the enhanced greenhouse effect.

In short, it seems unlikely that awareness of these other possible consequences of continued greenhouse forcing will shorten the time-scale for a consensus verdict on the detection issue — probably a decade or more, using the 'unprecedented change' criterion (Section 6.3.3). On the other hand, they do underscore the importance of a *long-term* commitment to monitoring the behaviour of many *different* facets of the total planetary system — not just the more obvious climate parameters, like surface temperature, precipitation, cloudiness and so on. In the meantime, you will be in a better position to judge our ability to cope with the gradual warming projected by the IPCC — let alone any unpleasant surprises — after studying the next chapter.

Summary of Chapter 7

1   Projecting future anthropogenic emissions of greenhouse gases is a difficult and inherently uncertain business. It is tackled by constructing emission scenarios, based on assumptions about the demographic, economic, social, technological and political factors that are likely to influence future release rates. In this context, 'Business as

Usual' (BaU) effectively implies a continuation of past and current trends—i.e. it envisages a future in which few or no *active* steps are taken to curb greenhouse gas emissions.

2   On a BaU basis, the next century will see an ongoing increase in CO_2 emissions from fossil fuel use—the primary driving force being the link between energy consumption and economic development, coupled with continuing population growth (especially in the developing world). Unchecked tropical deforestation would make a significant, but smaller, contribution to future CO_2 emissions.

3   Strategies that would act to slow the growth in CO_2 emissions include: (i) major improvements in the overall energy efficiency of different economies; (ii) a greater reliance on natural gas (which is less 'carbon-intensive' than coal) and all non-fossil fuel energy sources (hydroelectric, nuclear, biomass, solar and other renewables); and to a lesser extent (iii) efforts to slow, halt or even reverse tropical deforestation, and to promote afforestation programmes outside of the tropics. In practice, policies to curtail CO_2 emissions will challenge countless established practices in the industrialized world, and the legitimate aspirations of less economically developed regions. Achieving effective controls will require concerted government action, at both the national and international level.

Important: You should be aware of the key issues involved here, as summarized in Activities 7.1 and 7.3.

4   A BaU future would be expected to generate a continuing increase in anthropogenic emissions of methane, especially those linked to crucial agricultural activities (i.e. rice cultivation and rearing livestock).

Note: Refer to Activity 7.4 for a summary of the key points here.

5   As noted in Section 4.3.3, future emissions of ir-absorbing halocarbons (i.e. the CFCs and their likely substitutes) will be largely determined by the level of international compliance with the evolving provisions of the Montreal Protocol.

6   According to the IPCC's assessment in 1990, a BaU future would subject the planet to sustained—and ever increasing—greenhouse forcing throughout the next century: the *total* forcing could reach a value equivalent to a CO_2-doubling by around 2020. Model simulations indicate that this forcing scenario could induce global warming at an unprecedented rate—the current 'best estimate' being around 0.3 °C per decade (with an uncertainty range of 0.2–0.45 °C). The more urgent and concerted the measures taken to curb greenhouse gas emissions (especially of those gases with long atmospheric lifetimes, notably CO_2 and the CFCs), the slower and less marked anthropogenic greenhouse warming is likely to be: that is the essence of the precautionary principle.

Important: Given a diagram like the one in Figure 7.1, you should be able to put together a critical appraisal of the layers of modelling studies involved—and hence explain briefly why the 'What if?' global warming scenarios generated in this way can only be indicative of the risks incurred by following various courses of action. The key points here were identified in Activity 7.5, and taken up in the text that followed it in Section 7.2.

7   Existing modelling studies (referred to in point 6) do not capture the full 'interconnectedness' of the real planetary system. In particular, they cannot simulate:

o   the possible climatic effects of ozone layer depletion;

o   possible climate-related greenhouse gas feedbacks, comparable to those that apparently operated during major natural climatic changes in the past (i.e. glacial–interglacial transitions);

○ possible interactions within the ocean–atmosphere system that could trigger the kind of abrupt—not smooth—changes in climate for which there is evidence in the palaeoclimatic record (e.g. the onset, and abrupt end, of the Younger Dryas).

More generally, the 'current state of knowledge' cannot rule out the possibility that continued greenhouse forcing could induce presently unsuspected responses within the planetary system. Surprises could well be in store—adding another element of uncertainty to existing assessments of what a BaU future might be like.

8 Potential impacts of climatic change

8.1 Introduction

In previous chapters, you have seen how atmospheric concentrations of carbon dioxide and other greenhouse gases have risen substantially during the 20th century. These concentrations will continue to increase throughout the next century, unless urgent and concerted action is taken to reduce emissions radically. It is certain that such increases will enhance the greenhouse effect, which will result, on average, in extra warming of the Earth's surface. At this point, certainty and unanimity of opinion cease.

By this stage, you should be all too well aware of the uncertainties that surround *any* assessment of the likely scale, pace and geographical distribution of the warming — *and other climatic changes* — induced by a continuing accumulation of greenhouse gases.

Much of this chapter is concerned with the possible consequences of the 'do nothing' choice implicit in the IPCC's 'Business as Usual' (BaU) scenario. On this basis, greenhouse forcing could reach values equivalent to a CO_2-doubling by around 2020, and go on increasing thereafter (Figure 7.15c). As a result, the next century could see global warming at an unprecedented rate, with current estimates in the range 0.2–0.45 °C per decade. For all the reasons stressed in the wake of Activity 7.5, such estimates can only be indicative of the changes in global-mean surface temperature that might occur over the coming decades. When it comes to assessing the likely consequences of such changes, however, further layers of uncertainty come into play.

The key points here (touched on in Activity 7.6) can be traced back to the major deficiencies in existing climate models identified in Chapter 5 — limited spatial resolution, relatively crude treatment of surface processes, and of the oceans in general, and so on. As a result, changes in *regional* climates — in the seasonal pattern of temperature, winds, rain, snow, etc. experienced by different regions — cannot yet be predicted with confidence. Recall the discrepancies between the *equilibrium* scenarios generated by different GCMs that we looked at in Section 5.5 — especially as regards changes in crucial climate parameters like precipitation and soil moisture. Recall too the conclusions we reached in Section 5.6: early studies with coupled AGCM/OGCMs suggest that the geographical distribution of the time-evolving temperature rise — and quite possibly, of changes to other climate parameters as well — could be different from that likely to characterize the eventual equilibrium response to a CO_2-doubling.

Such uncertainty is not a favourable start to a chapter concerned with the likely impacts of greenhouse gas-induced climatic change. Not only do we have low confidence in regional estimates, but uncertainty about the timing of future climatic changes means that their severity is impossible to establish. However, there is agreement that the range of *potential* impacts is very wide. Agriculture is very likely to be affected, with the most vulnerable countries being those seemingly least able to adjust. A decline in the quality and quantity of forests is envisaged, and natural ecosystems will be affected because of alterations in the distribution and abundance of animal and plant species. Some species could thrive, insect pests for example; other rare species, more sensitive to environmental change, could face extinction. Even small climatic changes would alter the availability of water in many vulnerable areas of Africa, for example. Expensive irrigation schemes would be a prerequisite for successful crop growth. Natural catastrophes such as drought, flooding and severe cyclones may increase in frequency. Major diseases of humans may become more frequent; parasites and pests may become more prevalent. Increased ultraviolet radiation (due to depletion of stratospheric ozone) may increase rates of skin cancer and disrupt marine ecosystems, especially the planktonic components that form the essential lowest tier of food chains. Changes in the course of ocean currents could have dramatic effects on the distribution of marine species. Ice contained in glaciers and ice-sheets is likely to diminish. Of particular concern is an acceleration of the rise in sea-level, which threatens productive coastal fisheries and may displace tens of millions of people from land that is productive at present.

Space does not allow us to attempt a comprehensive review of such possible impacts here. Instead, this chapter aims to look critically at a few important aspects of the potential impacts of climatic change, explaining our current level of scientific knowledge and indicating the complexities, uncertainties and risks. Section 8.2 examines the consequences of global warming for changes in sea-level, while Sections 8.3 and 8.4 discuss some of the potential impacts on plants and animals. Each of these sections briefly indicates some of the implications for different human societies. The chapter ends with a short discussion of the potential *economic and political* impacts of climatic change.

8.2 Changes in sea-level

The term 'sea-level' sounds as if it should represent a fixed level. Nothing could be further from the truth. In reality, sea-level is constantly changing on local, regional and global spatial scales, and on different time-scales, from the daily, due to tides and weather, to millions of years, due to geological changes.

Today, sea-levels are recorded by tide gauges that measure variations in relation to a fixed benchmark on land, and so record changes not just in seawater level, but also those caused by vertical land movements. It is the vertical land movements that cause sea-level changes on the local or regional scale. These result from various natural phenomena (such as a change in ice cover, sedimentation on land causing subsidence, or other geological changes) and from human activities (such as the extraction of oil or groundwater). In parts of Scandinavia, for example, the sea-level is falling by up to 1 cm a year, as the land is still rising after the melting of a glacial ice-cap: the mass of the ice-cap caused the land to sink and it is still returning to its equilibrium position. Such local and regional changes will not be examined further in this section; instead we shall concentrate on the *global-mean sea-level*, which is affected by climatic change. For the rest of this section, 'sea-level' will be used to mean 'the global-mean sea-level'.

In the past, sea-level has varied by hundreds of metres from its present position. About 20 ka ago, during the last glacial period, it was up to 130 metres lower than at present, making, for example, a Channel tunnel irrelevant: you could have walked to France as the English Channel would have been dry land at the time. This sea-level change was caused by a change in the *volume of seawater* in the oceans.

Longer ago, there were even greater changes in sea-level: 100 Ma ago, sea-levels were about 300 metres higher than at present. This longer-term difference is caused by a change in the *volume of the ocean basins*, due to plate tectonics. For example, ocean ridges are amongst the shallowest parts of the ocean basins, and if the length or width of the ridges increases, the mean depth of the oceans decreases, so the volume of the ocean basins also decreases (Figures 8.1a and b). Also, if plate tectonics causes an increase in the rate of weathering on land, so that more sediment is transported into the oceans by rivers, the extra sediment reduces the volume of the ocean basins (Figure 8.1c).

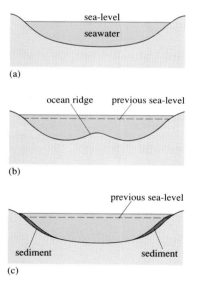

Figure 8.1 Plate tectonics can cause changes in the volume of the ocean basins, and hence in the sea-level. (a) An ocean basin without a ridge. (b) An ocean basin with an ocean ridge, which is shallower than the surrounding ocean floor. An increase in height or width of the ridge has caused the sea-level to rise (the previous sea-level is shown by the dashed line). (c) Sedimentation in the ocean reduces the volume of the ocean basin and causes a rise in the sea-level.

These longer-term sea-level changes caused by plate tectonics are unaffected by climatic change, so we will not consider them further: you just have to be aware that they exist, and can cause very large (although slow) changes in sea-level. Instead, this section will concentrate on the sea-level changes caused by climatic change, in particular those that have occurred over the last 100 years, or which may occur in the near future.

Four questions will be considered.

o Has sea-level been rising over the last 100 years, and if so, by how much, and is the rate increasing?

o What caused sea-level to rise during this time?

o What increases in sea-level can be expected in the near future?

o What are the consequences of a higher sea-level?

8.2.1 Sea-level during the last 100 years

There are many problems in establishing how sea-level has varied in the last 100 years, and these are similar to the problems of establishing the global warming trend (Section 6.2). Obtaining a global picture requires records from tide gauges throughout the world, but unfortunately the distribution of gauging stations is patchy; many more records are available from the Northern Hemisphere than from the Southern Hemisphere. The length of many records is limited; only 420, out of a data set of about 1 300 tide gauges, extend for 20 years or more. Also, many stations are not ideally sited, being in geologically unstable areas with vertical land movements, so the records must be adjusted for these local variations.

The results of two of the most thorough recent studies of changes in sea-level are given in Figure 8.2.

▷ What is the major difference between the records shown in Figures 8.2a and b?

▶ Gornitz and Lebedeff's record appears to increase generally over most of the time period, from 1890 to the present, but Barnett's suggests a slight fall until around 1907, after which it increases.

▷ Can Figure 8.2 be used to answer the question in Section 8.2: 'Has sea-level been rising over the last 100 years?'

▶ It can. Sea-level does appear to have risen over the past 100 years according to (a) and the past 80 years according to (b).

The answers to the remaining parts of that question — by how much, and is the rate increasing — are less obvious from Figure 8.2. The records have a large variability between years, shown by the dashed lines, which is caused by meteorological and oceanographic effects. This illustrates the need for long periods of data collection in order to determine accurate trends. The two records, although among the best available, also have significant differences.

▷ How is the *rate* of sea-level rise determined from these records?

▶ From the gradient of the graph, which is the change in sea-level (cm)/time (yr).

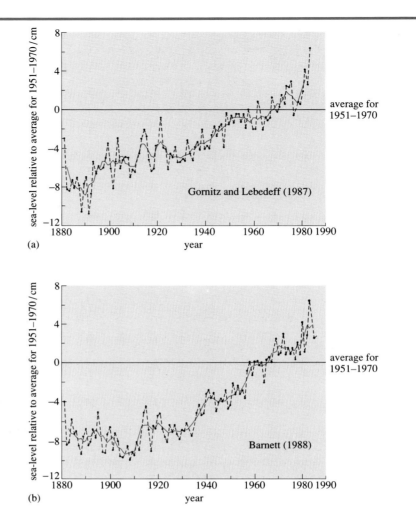

Figure 8.2 Changes in the sea-level over the last century. (a) From V. Gornitz and S. Lebedeff (1987), using data from 130 tide gauge stations with a minimum record length of 20 years. (b) From T. P. Barnett (1988), using data from 155 stations. Positive values represent sea-level above the base-line (which is the average for 1951–1970). Dashed lines join up annual means, and solid blue lines represent 5-year running means (averages over the current year and the two previous and two following years, e.g. the 5-year running mean for 1960 averages over the years 1958–1962).

Calculation of the rate of sea-level rise from records such as these gives a value that is dependent on the statistical method used, and also has a large uncertainty: we shall look at this in more detail in Activity 8.1.

Activity 8.1

(a) Calculate the mean rate of sea-level rise over the last 100 years from Figure 8.2a. Give your answer in $mm\,yr^{-1}$, and estimate the uncertainty in your result.

(b) Why is it not sensible to use the method you used in (a) on Figure 8.2b? How could the method be adapted?

Careful analysis of record (a) by Gornitz and Lebedeff gave values for the rise in sea-level of $1.2 \pm 0.3\,mm\,yr^{-1}$ or $1.0 \pm 0.1\,mm\,yr^{-1}$, depending on the method of analysis used. Analysis by Barnett of record (b) gave a rise of $1.15\,mm\,yr^{-1}$ over 100 years, or $1.7\,mm\,yr^{-1}$ over 1910–1980 (Barnett does not give an estimate of the uncertainty). Estimates by other investigators since 1980 give values of between $1.0 \pm 0.1\,mm\,yr^{-1}$ and $2.4 \pm 0.9\,mm\,yr^{-1}$, with most estimates between 1.0 and $2.0\,mm\,yr^{-1}$. These rates imply that the sea-level has risen 9–33 cm over the last century (with most estimates in the range of 10–20 cm).

The fact that a straight line can be 'fitted' to Figure 8.2a shows that the *rate* of the rise in sea-level does not appear to have changed over the last century; or, as the 1990 IPCC report authors put it more cautiously, 'there is no convincing evidence of an acceleration in global sea-level rise during the 20th century'.

However, is the rise in sea-level *linked* to climatic changes alone? There is no independent evidence of this: all we can do is to *estimate* the sea-level rise that would be caused by the observed temperature rise, and see whether this matches the *observed* sea-level rise. If it does, it is reasonable to suggest that the recent rise in sea-level could be caused by rising temperatures.

8.2.2 Causes of the change in sea-level

In this subsection we consider only those causes that might be affected by changing climate, i.e. causes that change the *volume* of water in the oceans. These are:

o thermal expansion of seawater,
o melting of land-ice.

The effect of land-ice melting and adding to the volume of water in the oceans is considered here under three headings, with different climatic settings and different **response times** (the time between the temperature change and the effect on sea-level) to temperature changes; that of the ice melt from (i) glaciers (such as in the Alps) and small ice-caps (such as Scandinavia and Iceland), (ii) the Greenland ice-sheet, and (iii) the Antarctic ice-sheet.

Thermal expansion of the oceans

If the oceans warm, the density of the seawater decreases and the oceans expand (a thermal expansion), giving a rise in sea-level. This sounds straightforward, but estimating how *much* expansion will be produced, and particularly how much the sea-level will rise for a given rise in global-mean surface temperature (called the sensitivity) is not easy. There are two distinct problems; the lack of sufficient data on ocean temperature, salinity and hence density at various depths on a global scale, and the limitations of the present OGCMs for predicting how these values vary with changes in global-mean surface temperature. Large-scale and long-term oceanographic experiments are taking place to obtain the data needed (WOCE, Section 5.6), and better models are being developed to use these data. However, as you will see shortly, current estimates of the rise in sea-level due to thermal expansion of the oceans still have a large uncertainty.

Land-ice

Land-ice volume does not necessarily decrease with rising temperature. Whether an ice-sheet gets larger or smaller, as the temperature rises, depends on the balance of two factors: the **accumulation** of snow onto the ice-sheet, and the **ablation** (melting, runoff and evaporation) of ice from it. The variation of these factors with temperature is shown in Figure 8.3.

▷ How does accumulation vary as ice-sheet temperature increases?

▶ At low temperatures, accumulation generally increases as the temperature increases, until it reaches a maximum near the freezing point of 0 °C; it then decreases with a further temperature rise.

▷ How does ablation vary as temperature increases?

▶ Ablation occurs at mean annual surface temperatures above about −12 °C, and increases rapidly at higher temperatures.

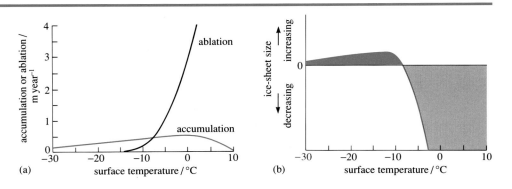

Figure 8.3 (a) The variation of accumulation (snowfall) and ablation (melting, runoff and evaporation) with the mean annual surface temperature of ice-sheets. (b) The size of the ice-sheet depends on the balance of accumulation and ablation, increasing in size (blue shaded area) or decreasing in size (grey shaded area) with temperature. The diagram is schematic and will vary slightly from place to place.

▷ How does the size of the ice-sheet vary as temperature increases?

▶ At low temperatures, below about −8 °C, accumulation is greater than ablation and the ice-sheet increases in size. At higher temperatures, ablation is greater than accumulation and the size of the ice-sheet decreases.

This makes the response of ice-sheets to changes in temperature *dependent on the surface temperature of the ice-sheet*. At low temperatures, the ice-sheet will increase in size with a rise in temperature (blue shaded area on Figure 8.3), but at temperatures above about −8 °C the situation is reversed (grey shaded area). Most glaciers, small ice-caps, and the Greenland ice-sheet have high enough surface temperatures to lie in the grey area, but the Antarctic ice-sheet is much colder (in the blue area), where an increase in temperature increases the size of the ice-sheet, contributing to a lowering of the sea-level.

(i) Ice melt from glaciers and small ice-caps

Most valley glaciers (such as in the Alps) and small ice-caps (such as Scandinavia and Iceland) have decreased in size over the last 100 years (Figure 8.4). The response time is relatively short, about 50 years or so, and the decrease probably started as a response to the warming at the end of the Little Ice Age about 150 years ago.

▷ Has the rate of retreat (decrease in glacier length) been continuous over the last 100 years?

▶ No. Retreat was generally fastest in the middle of this century (the graphs have steep negative gradients), but seems to have slowed since then, with some glaciers (e.g. D'Argentiere) slowly advancing (the gradient is positive).

As with the 'thermal expansion of seawater' story, measuring the retreat or advance of glaciers and ice-caps is the easy part. What is more difficult is estimating the degree of melting, and hence the rise in sea-level for the observed global-mean surface temperature increase. Although a warmer climate is judged to cause melting of ice, there is considerable uncertainty about the amount of ice that would melt, and thus in the estimated rise in the sea-level caused by the melting of glaciers and small ice-caps (Table 8.1).

(ii) Melting of the Greenland ice-sheet

The Greenland ice-sheet is considered separately from the small ice-caps because of its enormous size of about $3 \times 10^6 \, \text{km}^3$, 30 times larger than all the glaciers and small ice-caps combined, and because it has a longer response time.

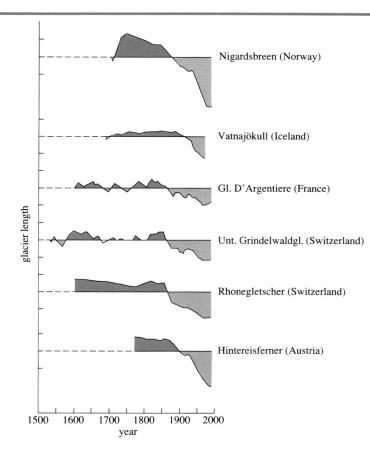

Figure 8.4 Variations in length of some European glaciers and ice-caps. The vertical scale shows an increase (upwards) or decrease (downwards) in length. Each unit on the vertical scale is a change in length of 1 km. The horizontal line is the average length of the glacier/ice-cap over the time it has been measured, so that the blue areas represent times when the glacier/ice-cap was larger than average, and the grey areas times when it was smaller than average. The response time for each glacier or ice-cap varies slightly, due to differences in surface area, thickness, the range of temperatures from summer to winter, and other factors.

We know less about how the Greenland ice-sheet has changed in the last 100 years than we do about glaciers, as fewer direct measurements have been made. However, the summer temperatures on Greenland over this time are known fairly well, and can be used to estimate rates of melting.

(iii) Changes in the Antarctic ice-sheet

The amount of ice in the Antarctic ice-sheet is enormous — about ten times as much as the Greenland ice-sheet and sufficient to cause a rise in the sea-level of around 65 m, if it all melted. Luckily, this is unlikely, at least on a short time-scale, as it has a long response time (being considered to have not finally adjusted even to the last glacial–interglacial transition that ended around 10 ka ago). However, its enormous potential for raising the sea-level makes climatologists consider the Antarctic ice-sheet with particular care.

The climatic situation of the Antarctic ice-sheet differs from most other ice-sheets in one major respect — it is much colder. As noted earlier, this has a significant effect on the response of the ice-sheet to global warming, and leads to the possibility that global warming could *increase* the size of the Antarctic ice-sheet, contributing to a *fall* in sea-level (Figure 8.3).

One part of the Antarctic ice-sheet, the West Antarctic ice-sheet needs separate consideration, as it is thought to be less stable, having a much faster response time to climatic change. Most ice-sheets (e.g. the Greenland ice-sheet and most of the Antarctic ice-sheet) are on land, but parts of the base of the West Antarctic ice-sheet are below sea-level and may be very sensitive to changes in sea-level or melting rates. Under an extra mass of snow, the ice-sheet could become unstable and release enormous numbers of icebergs into the ocean. However, recent estimates suggest that although the West

Antarctic ice-sheet is potentially unstable it should not melt or disintegrate significantly in the next 100 years, but could cause a large rise in sea-level after this time.

In general, the contribution of the Antarctic ice-sheet to the rise in sea-level over the past 100 years is difficult to estimate and has a large uncertainty; there is no good direct evidence of changes in its size.

The estimated contribution of each of the four causes considered in this section to sea-level rise over the last 100 years, calculated from the sensitivities of each source and the observed change in global-mean surface temperature, is given in Table 8.1.

Table 8.1   Estimated contributions to the rise in sea-level over the last 100 years, in cm. A negative value represents a fall in sea-level. The estimates of the *observed* rises in sea-level are shown for comparison.

	low	best estimate	high	uncertainty of best estimate
thermal expansion of oceans	2	4	6	
glaciers/small ice-caps	1.5	4	7	
Greenland ice-sheet	1	2.5	4	
Antarctic ice-sheet	−5	0	5	
total estimated	−0.5	10.5	22	
observed	10	15	20	

Question 8.1

(a) Complete Table 8.1 by filling in the last column.

(b) Which of the four causes has the lowest uncertainty, and which has the highest?

(c) Why has the melting of glaciers and small ice-caps believed to have had a much larger effect than melting of the Greenland ice-sheet?

You may have been surprised at the relatively large size of the total uncertainty (±11.5 cm), but if you consider the lack of data on which the estimates are based it is possibly less surprising. The best estimate (10.5 cm) is just within the range of the observed rise in sea-level (10–20 cm, Section 8.2.1).

8.2.3 Future changes in sea-level

The same sensitivity values that produced the estimates in Table 8.1 can be used to predict future changes in sea-level, based on predicted values for future temperature rises. Table 8.2 gives estimates based on the IPCC BaU policy scenario, in which few or no active steps are taken to limit the release of greenhouse gases (Section 7.1.3). On that basis, the best estimate is that the sea-level would be 18 cm higher in 2030 than in 1985, but could be as little as 9 cm or as much as 29 cm higher.

Table 8.2   Estimates of future contributions to a rise in sea-level, from 1985 to 2030, in cm, based on the BaU policy scenario. A negative value represents a fall in the sea-level.

	low	best estimate	high
thermal expansion of oceans	6.8	10.1	14.9
glaciers/small ice-caps	2.3	7.0	10.3
Greenland ice-sheet	0.5	1.8	3.7
Antarctic ice-sheet	−0.8	−0.6	0.0
total	8.8	18.3	28.9

▷   Are the estimates of major contributors to the rise in sea-level over the last 100 years (Table 8.1) the same as those estimated until 2030 (Table 8.2)?

▸   Yes, the major contributions to the rise in sea-level up to 2030 are estimated to come from thermal expansion of the oceans and melting of glaciers and small ice-caps; contributions from the Greenland and Antarctic ice-sheets are minor.

Figure 8.5 shows the extension of these predictions to 2100. By 2070 the best estimate is 44 cm (with a range of 21–71 cm), and by 2100 the best estimate is 66 cm (with a range of 31–110 cm). Figure 8.6 shows predictions for the alternative scenarios B, C and D (Section 7.1.3). These lower forcing scenarios show rises that are about one-third less than the BaU scenario, with best estimates of 33–57 cm by 2100. Even under these scenarios of strict emissions reduction, the sea-level continues to rise throughout the 21st century, because of delays in the climatic response to greenhouse forcing (the 'unrealized' warming discussed in Section 5.6), and in the thermal expansion of the oceans and the melting of land-ice. This creates an inevitable 'commitment' to a continuing sea-level rise, even if greenhouse forcing was stabilized (Figure 8.7).

Question 8.2   According to the BaU scenario shown in Figure 8.5, what is the best estimate for the rise in sea-level from 2000 to 2100, and how does this compare with the observed sea-level rise over the past 100 years?

In the next 100 years the sea-level may, therefore, rise four times faster than over the last 100 years. It is this possibility of a rapid *rate* of global-mean sea-level rise, as

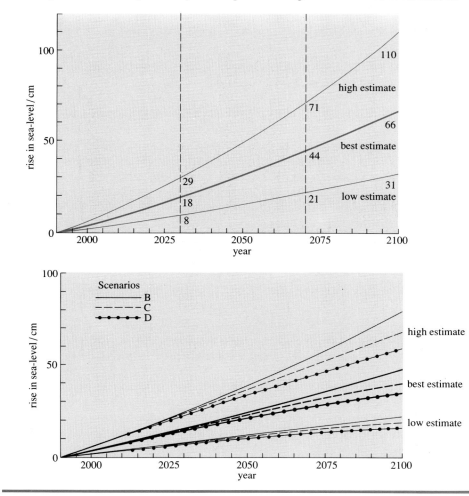

Figure 8.5   Predictions for the rise in sea-level for 1990–2100, using the IPCC BaU policy scenario.

Figure 8.6   Predictions for the rise in sea-level for 1990–2100, using the IPCC policy scenarios B, C and D.

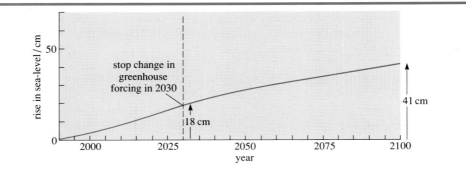

Figure 8.7 Prediction for the rise in sea-level for 2030–2100, based on the BaU scenario to 2030, but assuming that greenhouse forcing was stabilized in 2030. The rise continues for the remainder of the century.

well as the size of rise, that is causing concern. Of even greater concern in some areas is that the sea-level may not rise uniformly around the world: it is likely to be influenced by local and regional land movements, which may be large, and could exacerbate climate-related global changes.

8.2.4 Consequences of changes in sea-level

The rise in sea-level predicted over the next century is a very real danger, capable of destroying cities, croplands, coastal environments and even nations.

Most of the world's major cities are situated on coasts, and many of these are built on land less than a few metres above sea-level. Cities such as New York, Hong Kong, London, Tokyo, Rio de Janeiro, Alexandria, Bangkok, Shanghai, Canton, Venice, New Orleans and Miami are threatened by the predicted rise in sea-level. Cities where there is also local subsidence, such as Bangkok (which is already sinking due to the excessive extraction of groundwater from beneath the city), are particularly in danger.

The world's more productive croplands are often on low-lying coastal plains, which would be flooded by the sea. China would be particularly affected, with the displacement of about 30 million people, and so would Bangladesh and Egypt. Bangladesh is a country built on the world's largest deltaic plain — the Bengal delta is 80% of the area of Bangladesh — which is close to sea-level, and already subsiding. River deltas continually subside naturally, but are usually maintained above sea-level by the addition of sediment carried down by the river. In Bangladesh, this sediment supply has been decreased by irrigation schemes, which trap sediment upstream behind dams. In addition, the over-extraction of groundwater has led to increased subsidence. These factors, together with a globally rising sea-level, put even the existence of Bangladesh as a nation in doubt; at the least, much of its population could become environmental refugees. Egypt is a country that is desert except for a strip along the River Nile and its delta, where almost the entire population live. This delta is subsiding and being eroded, as the sediment that once supplied it is now trapped upstream behind the Aswan dam. One-fifth of this delta area may be submerged by 2050 due to the combination of subsidence and a rising sea-level.

Coastal environments are among the most biologically productive areas on Earth: the Louisiana coastal wetlands, for example, supply a quarter of the US seafood catch; the coastal mangrove zone of Bangladesh supports about a third of the nation's population. These are also important wildlife habitats and areas of recreation and tourism. In some regions the coastal environment may be able to re-establish further inland, but the rate of sea-level rise may make this difficult in other areas, and impossible where wetlands are backed by coastal development. On the north coast of Brazil, for example, mangroves may be able to retreat inland, but further south, especially near Rio de Janeiro, they are restricted by urban growth.

How about Britain? Some beaches would disappear, wetlands would be drowned, and cities, power stations and low-lying land would be flooded. Much of Britain's most valuable industry is situated near sea-level on vulnerable estuaries (e.g. the Tees), and productive farmland is on low-lying land near the coast (e.g. East Anglia). Some cities and areas of coastline, especially the east coast, which has regional subsidence, could be flooded (Figure 8.8). This flooding would be exacerbated by **storm surges** on top of a rising sea-level; storm surges are rises in sea-level lasting a day or so that are caused by the low-pressure areas of strong cyclonic wind systems (Section 2.3.2), and they have already caused floods in Britain (this was the reason for the construction of the Thames Flood Barrier). It is possible to build sea defences to keep out the sea; for example, without its system of dykes and sea walls, half the present area of the Netherlands would be under water, but the cost is enormous, taking about 6% of the country's gross national product. For Britain, sea defences are only likely to be built to protect the more valuable cities and installations such as power stations; farmland and wetland are unlikely to be saved. Is retiring to a bungalow by the sea really such a good idea?

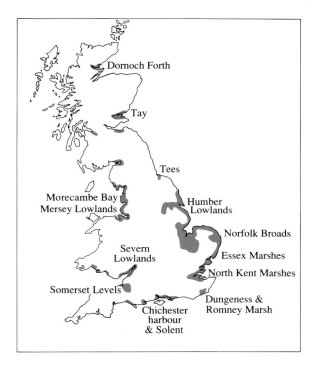

Figure 8.8 Areas of Britain vulnerable to rising sea-levels.

Other nations may have even greater problems — they may completely cease to exist. Bangladesh is in partial danger, but the future existence of some island nations is even more threatened. The Maldives, a group of 1 196 seamounts and coral atolls in the Indian Ocean are only just above sea-level today. The Maldives president has called his country 'an endangered nation' as there is a real chance that it would be submerged and washed away. Also in danger are other Indian Ocean and Pacific Ocean island nations, such as the Cocos Islands, Tuvalu, Tokelau, Kiribati, the Marshall Islands and the Line Islands. A notice on the Maldives protesting against global warming says it all: 'DOWN WITH SEA-LEVEL RISE'.

Summary of Section 8.2

1   There are many problems involved in estimating whether, and by how much, global-mean sea-level has risen over the last 100 years. The best estimate is that the average rate of sea-level rise over the last 100 years is 1.0–2.0 mm yr^{-1} (10–20 cm in 100 years). There is no firm evidence for an acceleration in the rate of sea-level rise over the last century.

2   Causes of the rise in the sea-level in the last 100 years are the thermal expansion of the oceans, melting of glaciers and small ice-caps, melting of the Greenland ice-sheet, and changes in the Antarctic ice-sheet. There are large uncertainties in the estimated contributions of each to the rise in sea-level. Most of the rise is caused by thermal expansion of the oceans and melting of glaciers and small ice-caps.

3   Future changes to the sea-level can be modelled using the IPCC scenarios. For the Business as Usual scenario, the best estimate for 2100 is a rise of 66 cm. Most of this comes from thermal expansion of the oceans, and melting of glaciers and small ice-caps. The West Antarctica ice-sheet is potentially unstable, but is unlikely to disintegrate and contribute to the rise in sea-level within the next century. The IPCC policy scenarios B, C and D project rises in the sea-level about one-third lower than the BaU scenario.

4   Even with a substantial stabilization or decrease in the emission of greenhouse gases, there will inevitably be future increases of temperature and, consequently, a further rise in sea-level due to slow response times to the causes of sea-level rise.

5   The rate of the rise in sea-level predicted for the next 100 years on the BaU scenario is about four times faster than over the last 100 years.

6   The predicted rise in sea-level would have major global consequences; cities, croplands, coastal environments and even entire nations would be flooded.

8.3 Effects on living organisms

This section considers the likely impacts of future climatic change on plants and animals. The questions we ask include: What kind of ecological changes are predicted? Why might such changes come about? What effects might they have on human affairs? If we assume for the moment that a particular set of climatic changes will occur (itself a problematic exercise, as you are now all too well aware), how *confident* can we be of predictions of the effects of these changes on living organisms?

To make some inroads into answers to these questions we need to think more about the life of individual plants, about communities of plants, and about more complex communities (such as forests) which contain a wide variety of animals and plants, and where the entire ecosystem is maintained by complex interactions between the constituent species. Our attention is largely confined to the likely impacts on terrestrial species, where our understanding is greatest; for reasons of space, we are obliged to neglect some significant issues such the potential effects of climatic change on human health.

You are probably already familiar with the idea that the global distribution and abundance of plants and animals is determined in part by the regional variations in climate. 'Good' and 'bad' years for grain harvests reveal the sensitivity of cereal crops to the vagaries of temperature and rainfall. Unwelcome swarms of insect pests such as aphids are a consequence of particular climatic conditions.

It is not surprising therefore that the significant changes in global-mean surface temperature that have taken place in the recent historical past have had a major impact on plants and animals, and therefore on humans. Between 900 and 1200 AD, during the earliest phase of the so-called Medieval Climatic Optimum (see Figure 3.3c), temperatures in much of Northern Canada were about 1 °C warmer than at present, and forests covered areas much further north than the current tree line. In the same period, farmers in Iceland, Scotland and Scandinavia were able to grow wheat in areas where modern descendants have to farm less ambitiously. By 1400 AD, climatic conditions in

Europe had worsened, with an apparent increased frequency of severe winters and exceptionally hot or wet summers causing disastrous harvests; by 1500 AD, summers were on average about 0.7 °C cooler than during the Medieval Optimum. These changes heralded the onset of the 'Little Ice Age' from about 1400 to 1850 AD (see Section 3.1), which had dramatic effects on population levels and on general economic activity, especially on farming. For example, most cereal farming was abandoned in Iceland, and much Scandinavian farmland was damaged by increased rainfall, causing frequent avalanches and landslides.

The changes in surface temperature just mentioned are within the range predicted for the near future, but historically the *rate* of change was generally slow. Changes in temperature envisaged for the next 100 years are so rapid as to be without parallel in human history — perhaps as great as 4 °C by the end of the next century. This makes firm prediction all the more difficult. But if we are to assess the likely impacts of climatic change, the best place to start is to look at the climatic factors that at present exert the greatest influence on the growth and success of organisms, especially of plants.

8.3.1 Influence of CO_2 levels on plants

As you may remember from Box 4.1, plants require CO_2 as a vital raw material to fuel *photosynthesis*, the process of synthesizing the complex organic constituents of plant cells (notably carbohydrates), using the energy of sunlight. Remember too that the utilization of CO_2 in this way is often referred to as CO_2 *fixation*, because carbon from CO_2 becomes incorporated (i.e. fixed) within complex organic molecules. Not surprisingly, the rate of plant photosynthesis — measured for example as the rate of production of carbohydrates or the rate of fixation of CO_2 — increases when the level of CO_2 in the atmosphere surrounding the plant is raised. Thus, when CO_2 levels are doubled the rate of photosynthesis can increase in the short-term by 30–100%, the precise figure depending on the particular species involved and other factors, such as the temperature and moisture content of the air.

▷ Will all the carbohydrate formed by photosynthesis contribute to the production of new plant tissue, i.e. contribute to plant growth?

▶ No, some will be used in the process of *respiration* to generate the chemical energy that the plant needs to stay alive.

Remember that respiration (which we can abbreviate to R) *releases* CO_2, so the best indicator of the rate at which plants are growing is not the total amount of CO_2 absorbed per unit time (sometimes termed the rate of **gross photosynthesis, GP**) but the difference between the total CO_2 absorbed and the amount released via respiration — the rate of **net photosynthesis, NP**. Measuring NP in a photosynthesizing plant over time enables the net amount of carbon gained by the plant or, in the terminology of Box 4.1, the *net primary production*, to be estimated. Healthy plants in good growing conditions have a GP:R ratio of up to 9:1, but over a full growing season (remember photosynthesis occurs only in the light) the ratio is usually only about 2:1 or 3:1.

Figure 8.9 shows how NP changes in two different plant species — maize and wheat — in response to changes in CO_2 levels.

▷ From Figure 8.9, which species achieves the higher rate of net photosynthesis?

▶ Wheat, which achieves about $65 \, \text{mg} \, CO_2 \, \text{dm}^{-2} \, \text{h}^{-1}$ at CO_2 concentrations of about 800 p.p.m.

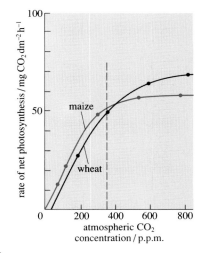

Figure 8.9 Changes in the rate of net photosynthesis in maize (blue) and wheat (black) in response to changes in atmospheric CO_2 levels. Photosynthesis is measured in terms of the mass of CO_2 fixed in relation to the leaf area (dm^2) per hour. The vertical dashed line indicates the current average atmospheric CO_2 level.

▷ Do the species achieve their maximum rate of photosynthesis at similar CO_2 concentrations?

▶ No; the rate of net photosynthesis in maize is highest at CO_2 concentrations of about 500 p.p.m. and above (note how this curve 'flattens out' here), whereas in wheat the maximum rate is not achieved until 800 p.p.m. CO_2 or more.

Wheat and maize are representatives of two distinct types of plant species that differ in responsiveness to CO_2. They are examples of what are known as 'three carbon' (i.e. C3) and 'four carbon' (C4) plants, respectively, and are distinguished by the biochemical details of how they conduct photosynthesis. The great majority of the Earth's plant species, including many of the staple food crops of the world such as wheat and rice, synthesize an intermediate compound with three carbon atoms as the first step in photosynthesis. To simplify a very complex issue, such C3 plant species are biochemically equipped to work well in cool climates with moderate light levels and tend to respond vigorously to raised CO_2 levels. This may be because such plants evolved in the distant past when natural levels of CO_2 in the atmosphere were much higher than they are today; their photosynthesis is markedly held back or 'limited' by present-day, sub-optimal CO_2 levels.

By contrast, C4 plant species, which include many tropical grasses and important crops such as maize and sugar-cane, grow in warmer conditions, where the light levels are usually higher. Such plants have an ability to concentrate CO_2 at high levels close to the sites of photosynthesis; their initial photosynthetic product has four carbon atoms. Such plants photosynthesize more efficiently than C3 plants at current CO_2 levels (probably reflecting their more recent origin), but respond less enthusiastically to raised CO_2 levels. (Figure 8.9 shows that the difference in photosynthetic rate between the two plant types is not always very significant at current atmospheric CO_2 levels.)

▷ On this basis, which crops are likely to benefit most significantly from any future increase in CO_2 levels?

▶ C3 crops such as wheat, grown in temperate regions, may be invigorated by raised CO_2; C4 crops such as maize (especially if grown in stressful semi-arid regions) may benefit less.

This implies that an increase in atmospheric CO_2 levels could provide some welcome benefits, especially for C3 plants. Growth rates might be boosted, with the extra CO_2 acting rather like a fertilizer — hence the term *CO_2 fertilization effect* mentioned in Section 4.2.4. Experimental findings appear to support such a view; for example, in glasshouse conditions, the yield from 38 important crops increases by an average of 32 ($\pm$ 5) % when CO_2 levels in the surrounding air are raised from 330 to 660 p.p.m. Growth of both the roots and shoots of most experimental plants is substantially enhanced, much more in some species than others. For example, in 30-cm tall specimens of sour orange trees, the mass of the stem and branches was on average 2.8 times greater in saplings grown in an atmosphere of 660 p.p.m. CO_2 than in controls grown at a 'present-day' CO_2 level. There are some notable exceptions to the CO_2 fertilization effect; the runner bean and the beach pine, for example, *reduce* photosynthesis in response to elevated CO_2. This variability between species makes generalizations very difficult, especially when, as here, we don't know *why* species behave so differently.

The broad implication is that agricultural productivity would be raised in a CO_2-richer world, as rates of net photosynthesis increased. Indeed, such a view has prompted some optimists to look forward to a 'greenhouse world' with equanimity, even enthusiasm. They are consoled by calculations showing that if the effect of raising CO_2 levels in future was to *double* the growth rates of the world's existing forests, and if such an accelerated growth was maintained for at least 30 years, this would fix all the carbon that had been released to the atmosphere over the past 200 years.

▷ What assumptions in this calculation would you challenge?

▶ That overall growth rates would be doubled and that enhanced growth could be maintained for 30 years — and that the existing forests would be conserved over that period.

In fact, the *long-term* effects of raised CO_2 levels are largely unknown — many C3 species show increased photosynthesis for only a few days or weeks in such an atmosphere. Furthermore, there is great uncertainty about extrapolating data obtained under carefully controlled laboratory or glasshouse environments to the harsher reality of 'field conditions', where a range of variables is likely to change. Experimental plants in glasshouses enjoy comparatively idyllic conditions during their brief lives.

Question 8.3 Young specimens of Monterey pine, grown under glasshouse conditions, increase their gross photosynthetic rate by 221% in response to a doubling of the CO_2 concentration. However, when such trees are grown in the same CO_2-doubled atmosphere but in soil deficient in the mineral phosphorus, photosynthesis *decreases* by 21%. What general implications are there here for predicting the effects of a CO_2-rich atmosphere on plants 'in the field'?

▷ What major *climatic* variables are also likely to influence plant growth?

▶ Changes in the temperature and moisture content of the atmosphere and soil are all likely to exert a powerful influence on plant growth.

Reference back to Figure 5.14 will remind you of the scale of changes in soil moisture envisaged in the event of global warming. This raises a crucial question; it is one thing to find that a doubling of CO_2 concentrations increases the yield of well-watered crops as diverse as wheat, orange trees, barley and sunflowers, but would the same increase be apparent if raised CO_2 concentrations occurred in combination with higher air temperatures and reduced soil moisture? We can get a little nearer an answer by looking at how other variables such as temperature and moisture influence plants.

8.3.2 Effects of increased temperature

In most plants, temperatures have to exceed 0 °C before gross photosynthesis occurs: thereafter, GP rises very rapidly as temperature increases.

▷ Is it likely that plant growth (i.e. an increase in biomass) will vary with temperature in exactly the same way?

▶ Not necessarily — remember from Box 4.1 that changes in plant biomass will reflect the *net* rate of photosynthesis. In practice, respiration also increases with temperature.

Figure 8.10 shows that, up to about 20 °C, the rate of GP increases rapidly in response to rising temperature. Over the same temperature range, the change in respiration rate is relatively small, but at higher temperatures, respiration is increasingly sensitive to temperature changes.

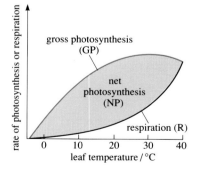

Figure 8.10 A schematic representation of how the rates of gross photosynthesis (blue line), net photosynthesis (blue shaded area) and respiration (black line) of plants are all influenced by leaf temperature, in glasshouse conditions.

▷ Why is the change in *net* photosynthesis with temperature shown as an *area* rather than a line on Figure 8.10?

▶ Remember that net photosynthesis is the difference between GP and R; at any one temperature, NP is the difference between them. So the overall change in NP with temperature is represented by the area shaded blue.

▷ What would a line graph of rate of net photosynthesis vs leaf temperature look like?

▶ It would be a 'bell-shaped' curve, with an maximum NP at a temperature of about 18–24 °C. The precise value and range of this optimum temperature for plant growth varies between species — some species have broad optima — and it depends on a range of other environmental factors as well.

▷ What are the implications of Figure 8.10 as far as the consequences of any future global warming are concerned?

▶ Where existing average leaf temperatures are *below* the optimum for a particular species, global warming would (theoretically) increase growth. Where temperatures are already at or near the optimum, any future warming is likely to have the opposite effect.

In general, since most plants are well adapted to their environment, they currently operate close to their optimum temperatures. Any future global warming is likely to reduce net photosynthesis and so probably reduce plant growth for the present plant communities. Once again, however, when we try to relate this 'laboratory phenomenon', based on the response of individual plants grown under controlled conditions, to the more complex world of say, grasslands and forests 'in the wild', complications and uncertainties abound. Here we can consider only a few representative examples.

o Some plants may be able to *adapt* to changes in temperature, so that an initial reduction in plant growth might be gradually offset by improved photosynthetic efficiency at the 'new' temperature.

o As well as influencing plant growth, temperature affects many aspects of the development of the plant, e.g. seed production, leaf growth and leaf loss. Two examples illustrate the point:

1 In the UK, the small-leafed lime (*Tilia cordata*) is mainly confined to the south of England at present. When young saplings are transplanted to the central Highlands of Scotland, they thrive. So, in this species, lower temperatures do not restrict the growth of young trees — rather they appear to restrict their reproduction as their seeds cannot be formed at temperatures below 15 °C. Future warming would probably permit the species gradually to extend its range.

2 In the spruce (*Picea sitchensis*), buds burst into life only after a winter of at least 140 days with a temperature of *less* than 5 °C, followed by warm spring weather. If global warming leads to higher winter temperatures, bud burst is much less likely to occur. This would probably lead to a change in the geographical distribution of the species, so that it would be confined to higher latitudes and/or higher altitudes.

o The growth of spring wheat in the Canadian prairies is likely to benefit from global warming; it is estimated that the length of the **growing season** (between the last frosts in spring and the first frost of autumn) is likely to increase by 10 days per 1 °C increase in the mean annual surface temperature. Moreover, an increase in this mean temperature would decrease the amount of time required by the grain to mature to ripeness; the likelihood of any immature grain being damaged by the first frosts of autumn is therefore reduced.

However, although raised temperatures cause maturation to occur more quickly, the *amount* of new organic matter being added to the grain during maturation is reduced. Thus, for spring wheat in the Canadian prairies, future warming is likely to reduce the amount of grain damaged by frost, but any benefit would probably be outweighed by reduced yields of grain. This example shows just how complex the full effects of raised temperatures on cereals are likely to be, particularly because such effects are likely to vary from crop to crop and from location to location.

o   Interactions between plants and animals will change in the event of global warming. At present, the life-cycles of many plants and animals are closely synchronized — animals such as butterflies and bees are active when the flowers of particular species are ready for pollination. To ensure the effective dispersal of seeds, birds have to be feeding at a time when the fruit becomes mature. Plant development, flowering and maturation are all likely to change with small increases in temperature, and with no guarantee that the habits and life-cycles of the associated animals, notably insects, could change in synchrony.

There is particular concern about how future temperature changes may influence animal and plant **pests**. Insect pests warrant special attention; because they are 'cold-blooded' they are particularly strongly influenced by the temperature of their environment. Sensitivity to temperature change varies from species to species in ways that are not fully understood. Other factors such as relative humidity and rainfall also have major influences on population size. In general, however, raised temperatures are likely to allow insect pests to extend their geographical range and to boost their population size, for example by increasing the number of generations of offspring produced per season, coupled with better survival in milder winters. Bear in mind too that climatic change may weaken the resistance of plants to attack by pests. So in this respect, as in so many others, precise prediction about the effect of any future global warming is impossible, but significant economic loss is envisaged.

Three specific examples show the general nature of the threat.

o   The horn fly has caused an estimated loss of about $730 million in recent years to the beef and dairy cattle industries of the USA; raised temperatures might extend the range of this pest, resulting in even greater economic loss.

o   The potato hopper is a significant insect pest on soya beans, and currently over-winters in a narrow band along the coast of the Gulf of Mexico. If winter temperatures were to be warmer, its over-wintering areas might increase by as much as two or three times, with a consequent increase in the destructive potential the following year.

o   Our final example concerns another type of pest of great economic importance — a fungus. At present, potato blight causes relatively little damage to potato stocks in Iceland, because temperatures are currently too low. According to model predictions, the equilibrium warming induced by a doubling of CO_2 levels could increase mean temperatures in Iceland by as much as 4 °C. Although this could increase yields of potato, losses due to blight would probably increase by about 15%.

8.3.3 Plants and moisture

Plants need water. Since most plants expose a substantial surface area to the atmosphere (to ensure uptake of CO_2), these same surfaces ensure a substantial loss of water by evaporation, especially in bright, warm and windy conditions. Thus, actively photosynthesizing leaves can readily lose their own weight of water every hour. Water lost by this process of *transpiration* (see Section 2.3.4) has to be replaced by uptake from the soil via the roots; if the water content of the soil is reduced, plants suffer from **water stress** and the rate of photosynthesis diminishes.

▷ Is it possible to predict the effects on net photosynthesis of an increase in air temperature, accompanied by a decrease in soil moisture content?

▶ Not definitively; any increase in net photosynthesis (caused by temperature increase) may be offset by a fall in photosynthesis due to water stress.

We can begin to see how complex the picture is when several variables have an effect in different directions: in this example, the response of the plant will depend upon which of two variables exerts the strongest influence on photosynthesis, i.e. which is the key **limiting factor**. If we add possible changes in availability of nutrients and light, the overall picture becomes yet more uncertain. But knowing how such variables influence plant growth is just what is required to make precise predictions about future impacts; not surprisingly therefore, the present lack of understanding leads to occasional confusion and controversy. For example, some scientists have argued that elevated levels of CO_2 alone would be unlikely to affect forests, because other factors limit growth, notably availability of water and nutrients (recall Question 8.3). In order to pursue the matter further, we need to take a closer look at how water is lost from plants.

Most of the evaporation of water from plants occurs from the leaves; Figure 8.11 illustrates the structure of a typical leaf. Most of the surface is covered with a waxy layer, called a cuticle, which protects the delicate tissue within and also has a beneficial effect in reducing water loss. Because the cuticle is a barrier to the diffusion of gases, it restricts movement of CO_2 into the inner tissue, which is the site of photosynthesis. Movement of CO_2 (and of water vapour) therefore depends mainly on **stomata** (a single such pore is called a stoma) on the lower leaf surface. The cells that immediately surround the stomatal opening (the guard cells, see Figure 8.11) are sensitive to changes in light. In sunny conditions during the daytime, they ensure that stomata are usually open, allowing maximum photosynthesis; at

Figure 8.11 The structure of a typical leaf, as revealed by a vertical section through a single leaf blade. The upper and lower surfaces each consist of an epidermis, which is only one cell thick. Between them are collections of photosynthesizing cells, with an upper layer more densely packed and regularly arranged than that below. The round inclusions within cells are the chloroplasts, the sites of photosynthesis. Because healthy plant cells have a high water content, their surfaces tend to be moist, which means that water evaporates into air pockets and then via stomata to the outside. Thus a stream of water continuously enters the leaf from the rest of the plant (along its visible veins) to replace that lost by transpiration.

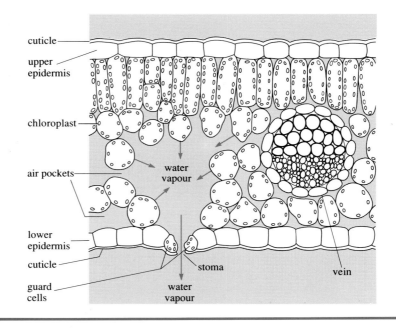

night-time, stomatal apertures usually close, though some movement of gases such as oxygen can still occur into and out of the leaf. However, in many situations closure of stomata may be partial and is often short-lived.

The opening and closing of the stomata reflects the varying levels of demand for CO_2 as the raw material for photosynthesis. When stomata are open, loss of water from the plant by transpiration increases sharply. Thus, on a moment by moment basis, plants have to strike a compromise between the conflicting demands of maximizing photosynthesis (requiring open stomata) and avoiding an excessive loss of water (which requires that stomata are occasionally closed). How this stomatal control is achieved in plants is a complex story that need not concern us here, except to say that a variety of external factors other than light intensity have an effect, notably the relative humidity of the air. Plants in dry air tend to partially close their stomata, even in bright conditions, thereby avoiding excessive water loss.

The partial closure of stomata is also triggered when CO_2 levels are increased in the air outside (or inside) a photosynthesizing leaf. This may immediately strike you as rather odd, because Section 8.3.1 explained how raised levels of atmospheric CO_2 *increase* photosynthesis, i.e. the CO_2 fertilization effect. But because external levels of CO_2 are increased, there will be enough CO_2 to meet the increased demands of photosynthesis, even if the stomata are partially closed. The advantage of stomatal closure to the plant is that precious water is conserved (which would clearly be important if the soil moisture content was low) *without* compromising photosynthesis. Thus, in a CO_2-rich environment, plants would tend to use water more efficiently.

In the context of future global warming, this means that we now have to think in terms of the combined effect of both changes in CO_2 and water availability. Imagine transplanting a typical, temperate, present-day plant into a future environment which is warmer and richer in CO_2, but with a *lower* soil moisture content. One response is likely to be partial stomatal closure, thereby avoiding excessive water loss without restricting photosynthesis; growth rate is likely to be maintained, or, on the evidence of Section 8.3.1, increased. If soil moisture levels are at a very low level, however, growth (and crop yields) will be compromised as the plant becomes increasingly water-stressed.

So, in these conditions, lack of water may well become the dominant factor that restricts photosynthesis, despite the CO_2-rich atmosphere. There is some experimental evidence to support the idea that, in the long term, such plants (and their descendants) would probably adapt to a drier, CO_2-richer environment. They would probably grow many more roots, which would improve the plant's supply of water and may grow more leaves, perhaps with an altered number of stomata per unit area. Again, firm predictions and generalizations are difficult, largely because of our incomplete knowledge of how different plants would react under such novel 'field conditions'.

Which climatic factor exerts the stronger influence on the growth and productivity of today's crop plants — low temperatures or low soil moisture? The answer — yet another answer less clear-cut than we would wish — is both. Some crops, especially those at higher latitudes, appear to be constrained by temperature — when the mean surface temperature increases so does the yield — though, as we saw in the last section, with crops such as wheat the full effects are usually more complex. However, for many other crops, and not just those crops of semi-arid conditions, soil moisture is thought to be a major limiting factor. For example, consider Table 8.3; this shows predictions of the change in the wheat yield in the Volvograd region of the former USSR, in response to changes in temperature and precipitation during the growing season.

Table 8.3 Changes in the yield of spring wheat in the Volvograd region of the former USSR that are likely to accompany variations in air temperature (ΔT) and precipitation (ΔP) during the growing season. Existing mean yields, with the current climatic regime, are expressed as 100: the other values in the table show predicted yields as percentages of current values.

ΔP/mm	ΔT /°C				
	−1.0	−0.5	0	+0.5	+1.0
−40	79	79	76	76	76
−20	92	92	89	89	89
0	104	103	100	100	99
+20	115	114	110	109	108
+40	125	124	120	118	117

▷ What effect would an increase in air temperature alone of 1 °C have on yields?

▶ The yield would be virtually unchanged — 99% of the existing mean value.

▷ What would be the effect on yields of a 1 °C increase in temperature combined with a fall in precipitation of 40 mm?

▶ From these predictions, yields would be only 76% of those at present.

Data such as these suggest that future climatic change will have a particularly serious effect on vegetation *where it leads to a reduction in the availability of soil moisture*. As you may recall from Chapter 5, *all* GCMs indicate that CO_2-induced warming will intensify the global hydrological cycle, with consequent increases in average global precipitation *and* evaporation. However, there is much less agreement at the regional level, where simulated changes in the spatial pattern of precipitation—and its seasonal distribution—are markedly model-dependent (recall Plate 5.3). The influence of changes in precipitation *and* temperature on the availability of soil moisture is even less clear cut—a point stressed in Section 5.5, and evident in the equilibrium scenarios (Figure 5.14) we examined at that stage. Nevertheless, the IPCC did make a preliminary identification of regions where there is some agreement among such scenarios, concerning the regional implications for soil moisture availability under a warmer (CO_2-doubled) climatic regime. The regions where soil moisture may be reduced—with possibly serious consequences for plant growth and agriculture—are collected in Table 8.4: more on this shortly.

Table 8.4 Regions where soil moisture may be reduced by greenhouse gas-induced climatic change, identified by comparing the CO_2-doubled equilibrium scenarios generated by different GCMs.

	Decreases of soil moisture in Dec, Jan, Feb	Decreases of soil moisture in June, July, Aug
Africa	northeast Africa southern Africa	north Africa west Africa
Europe		parts of southern and eastern Europe
Asia	western Arabian peninsula southeast Asia	north and central China parts of Soviet and central Asia and Siberia
Australasia	eastern Australia	western Australia
North America	southern USA	southern USA and central America
South America	Argentine pampas	eastern Brazil

One final point is worth noting at this stage: enhanced precipitation is not *necessarily* beneficial to plant growth. On the contrary, heavy rainfall over a long period can increase the risk of soil erosion and the loss of important minerals and essential nitrate (by leaching); for crops this could well lead to significant reductions in yield.

Summary of Section 8.3

1 Raised CO_2 levels increase net photosynthesis, most noticeably in C3 plants. Many tropical crops of economic importance to developing countries, e.g. maize and sugar cane, are C4 plants, which are less affected by raised CO_2 levels.

2 A CO_2-fertilization effect is usually evident in most plants grown in high CO_2 under ideal conditions, but such increased photosynthesis is (i) not universal, (ii) often transitory, and (iii) often outweighed by reductions in soil moisture content or mineral nutrients.

3 Increased temperatures may or may not increase net photosynthesis, depending on the species. Changes in temperature have diverse and far-reaching effects on plant growth and reproduction, and therefore on the yields of important crops such as wheat. The success and geographical range of plants are strongly influenced by mean surface temperature.

4 Future increases in temperature are likely to benefit insect and fungal pests, with detrimental effects on crops, farm animals and humans.

5 Stomatal closure, triggered by high CO_2 levels, restricts transpiration and thereby conserves water. The ability of some plants to withstand semi-arid conditions is therefore enhanced by a CO_2-rich atmosphere, because water is used more efficiently, at least temporarily. However, the long-term effects are likely to be detrimental.

6 Growth (and yield) of some important crops is limited by temperature. At low latitudes, the major constraint is more likely to be soil moisture, suggesting that any future changes in temperature or in precipitation at the regional level will strongly influence productivity.

Activity 8.2

Read the following brief extract from an imaginary tabloid newspaper, which attempts to show why the threat of global warming on plant life is unreal. (The extract is invented but such views are occasionally aired in the media, in a similar swashbuckling style, with scant regard for the truth.)

> *Come off it, you gloomy scientists — CO_2 is an essential raw material for plants, so if the air in the future has more CO_2, then I say that's good news for plants. All plants make more food in a CO_2-rich world — and in greenhouses with lots of CO_2 in the air, scientists have shown irrefutably that orange trees grow more than twice as fast as usual. So, in a greenhouse world, there will be more trees and more fruit — enough to mop up all the extra CO_2 that society has been pumping into the atmosphere from our motor cars and nuclear power stations. Higher temperatures — more growth — isn't that the message of spring after all? And scientists have now found that plants growing in lots of CO_2 can cope very nicely, thank you, with desert drought: they shut down cells that scientists call the 'cuticle' and so avoid losing any water.*

First, briefly list about five errors of fact made in the extract. Then, in a couple of sentences, mention two important points that the author has ignored in reaching these biased conclusions.

8.4 Impacts on natural communities and agriculture

Up to now our attention has been focused on the different factors — increased CO_2 concentrations, higher temperatures, alterations in soil moisture — that might well form a part of future climatic change. Now we need to speculate on what implications as a whole these interacting factors might have for natural communities of plants and animals, and for agriculture. Note the use of the word 'speculate'; we have already touched on two major reasons for uncertainty.

The first reflects the uncertainty of future projections using climate models. We have repeatedly mentioned the difficulty of assessing future climatic change at the regional level, for example with respect to precipitation, where there are significant differences between the various GCMs. Furthermore, although the projections we looked at in Chapter 7 suggest a gradual, smooth increase in global temperature, it is possible that there could be periods of sudden, rapid warming in some areas, and perhaps short-term cooling in others.

Most assessments of the possible biological impacts of future climatic change are based on model simulations of the equilibrium response to a CO_2-doubling, i.e. on the kind of equilibrium scenarios we looked at in Chapter 5. A standard question to ask might then be: If the climate was to change in this way, e.g. a 3 °C increase in the global-mean surface temperature, what would be its impact on particular species? This has been a useful approach, but it has a number of drawbacks, such as depending on making the 'right' choice of climatic factor, e.g. that the yield of a crop will be more influenced by temperature change than by changes in soil moisture content. Further, in the real world, the severity of the impact will be strongly influenced by the *rate* of change, which is impossible to establish with certainty. It is also impossible to say with certainty how *likely* it is that any given change in a climatic factor will occur. Imperfect though the approach is, we shall see in this section that it has been routinely adopted.

You should already be aware of the second problem of prediction from Section 8.3 — the incompleteness of our knowledge of how plants and animals are likely to respond to alterations in climate. We have seen already that individual species react differently to the same environmental change — recall what we said earlier about the CO_2 fertilization effect. It is therefore very difficult to generalize from one circumstance, or from one species to another. As you know, much of the limited knowledge that we do have emanates from artificial 'glasshouse' conditions. Confident predictions of impacts on natural communities and agriculture would require a depth of biological understanding that we are unlikely to acquire on the time-scale required. But as we shall see, the limited information we do have provides cause for concern.

8.4.1 Impacts on natural communities

Societies of animals and plants, for example those within a woodland, may appear long established and stable, but in reality such communities are in a constant state of change. Different species compete, with varying success. As we have seen in previous sections, minor changes in external conditions, e.g. in the amount of rainfall and sunlight, will affect different species to varying degrees, allowing some to flourish at the expense of others. When any changes are rapid and on a large scale, the resulting responses are correspondingly dramatic.

Ecosystems such as woodlands are not likely to respond 'as a whole' to any future climatic change; individual species are likely to react differently. New assemblages of plants and animals will arise, just as they did in the geological past during periods of major climatic change. Indeed, most of our modern plant and animal communities in the UK are relatively recent in origin — perhaps less than 10 000 years old — and have been established in their present complex form since the last major glacial period in Britain.

We have already highlighted the idea that the success and geographical distribution of particular plant species is determined very largely by climatic variables, such as summer temperature, hours of sunshine, length of growing season, rainfall and available soil moisture. Of course, non-climatic factors such as soil type and competition from other species have an important influence too, but as a broad generalization the dominant influence of climate on plant species holds true. The distribution of many animals also reflects features of the climate. For example, Figure 8.12a shows the distribution of dragonfly species in Great Britain, while (b) shows mean temperatures over the same area in April. (This is a particularly significant month for larval dragonflies, which start to feed in the spring after a winter spent dormant at the bottom of ponds and water-courses.)

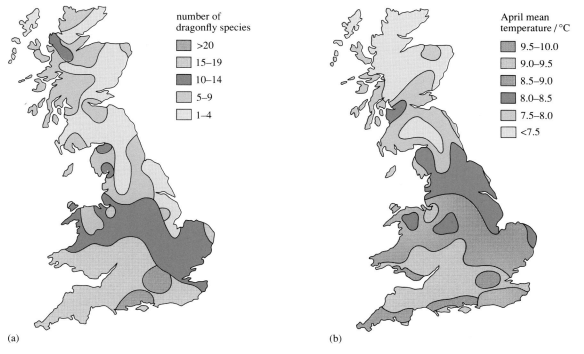

number of
dragonfly species

- >20
- 15–19
- 10–14
- 5–9
- 1–4

April mean
temperature / °C

- 9.5–10.0
- 9.0–9.5
- 8.5–9.0
- 8.0–8.5
- 7.5–8.0
- <7.5

(a)

(b)

Figure 8.12 (a) The numbers of different species of dragonfly in Great Britain, and (b) the distribution of mean surface temperature for April.

▷ What is striking about a comparison of Figures 8.12a and b?

▶ In general, locations with the greatest number of dragonfly species (a) have the highest April mean temperatures (b).

▷ Do the data suggest that factors other than mean April temperatures influence the number of dragonfly species?

▶ Yes, the correlation is far from perfect. For example, east Norfolk is a dragonfly hot spot, though it has a lower April temperature than the rest of East Anglia. (This is probably due to the historical land use pattern in the area, which overrides the climatic trend.)

The distribution of butterflies in the UK also illustrates the importance of climatic variables. Of the 58 native butterfly species, only eight are present throughout mainland Britain; 45 have a northern limit (probably determined by summer and winter temperature), while 5 have a southern limit, which is probably related to competition from other species and/or availability of food plants. 'Cold-blooded' species are not the only ones to be strongly influenced by climate — 19 of the UK's 52 mammalian species have a northern limit, including bats, the muntjac deer and the fat or edible dormouse.

All this suggests that future changes in climate are very likely to alter both the distribution of species and the composition of communities. Predictions have been made of the effect of an average temperature rise of 1.5 °C, by 2030, on UK wildlife. Mountain breeding birds such as the ptarmigan and snow bunting would decline, along with mountain plants such as saxifrages and dwarf willows. Some freshwater fish such as the temperature-sensitive trout would suffer; others like the more resistant carp would probably benefit. Otters would be advantaged because their shallow water habitats are likely to become warmer. Most butterflies would benefit, for reasons we have mentioned; insect-feeding birds such as willow warblers would decline if their insect food supply suffered because of increased drought. Early flowering plants such as snowdrops and bluebells would probably suffer, as they are physiologically adapted to start their growth very early in the year, when temperatures are still low. In a warmer climate, more adaptable plants, including grasses, will start their growth earlier in the season and out-compete the spring flowers.

The net effect is that plants and animals that are well adapted to warmth and that are currently restricted to the south of England would be likely to increase their range northward. This would be both easy and advantageous for mobile species such as butterflies and birds and for those plants that have relatively lightweight seeds, such as orchids, many of which have seeds normally dispersed by the wind. It would suit other species much less well, e.g. the less mobile insects and those plants, such as the cowslip, which have heavier seeds. For much the same reasons, continental species are likely to be drawn into Britain: some welcome, such as birds like the golden oriel and butterflies and moths such as the hummingbird hawkmoth, but others less so, such as the desert locust.

In many cases, established species would be obliged to expand into new locations because their existing environments may become hostile. So, a key point (especially for plant species) is the *rate* of any future climatic change; will species be able to move out of less suitable environments and into new ones fast enough to avoid a reduction in overall numbers? This is an enormously difficult question to answer, partly because the rate of future change is so uncertain, but also because different species will migrate at different rates. There are a few examples from the past to help the predictions, notably from records of tree pollen deposited during earlier periods of major climatic change. For example, at the end of the last glacial period it appears that forest trees migrated 25–40 km a century, on average. Exceptionally, migration rates for particular species, notably spruce, approached 200 km a century. The rate of warming envisaged in the future threatens to be much greater than at the end of the last ice age — an increase of 3 °C in the next 100 years (Activity 7.5g) would be about 25 times as fast — so trees are very unlikely to change their geographical distribution fast enough to avoid loss of numbers.

One of the few examples where good information on past distribution and rates of migration is available is for the eastern hemlock (*Tsuga canadensis*) in North America. Figure 8.13a shows the very restricted distribution of this species about 10 000 years ago at the end of the last ice age. Over the following thousands of years, as the temperature increased, hemlock slowly migrated northwards along the line of the Appalachian mountains, and subsequently along the Great Lakes and thereafter into the northeast coast of Canada. Estimates have recently been made of the likely distribution of hemlock in the event of a doubling of CO_2 levels from pre-industrial values. New potential habitats for the species open up approximately 500–1 000 km to the north of the present range — these are represented as the mid-blue area in Figures 8.13b and c.

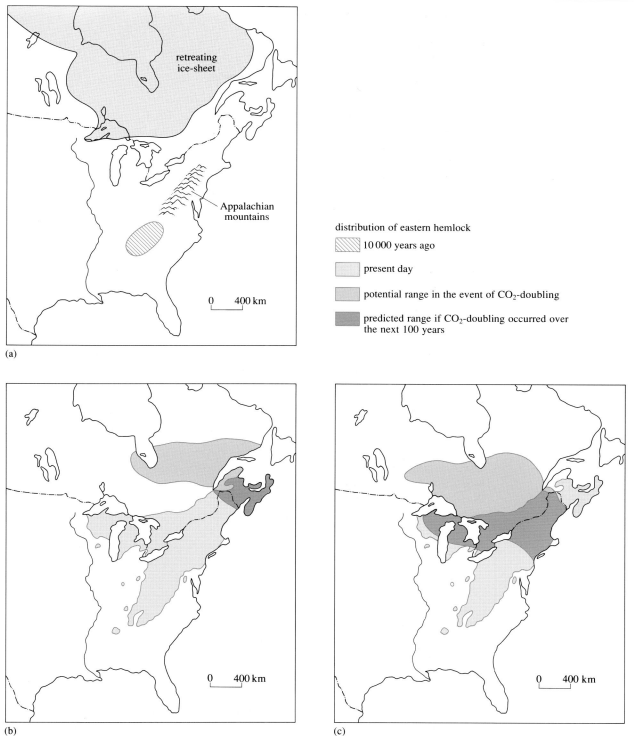

(a)

distribution of eastern hemlock

10 000 years ago

present day

potential range in the event of CO_2-doubling

predicted range if CO_2-doubling occurred over the next 100 years

(b)

(c)

Figure 8.13 Past, present and possible future distribution of eastern hemlock (*Tsuga canadensis*). (a) The distribution 10 000 years ago (the cross-hatched area). The grey shaded area to the north shows the retreating ice-sheet. The extent of the Appalachian mountains are shown, together with the Great Lakes. The present-day distribution is given in (b) and (c) as a pale blue tone. The mid-blue tone shows the possible future *potential* distribution, subject to two different CO_2-doubling climate projections. The darkest blue areas are regions where the present distribution and the future potential distribution of the species overlap, showing the *predicted* range in the event of rapid CO_2-doubling.

These potential new habitats are shown for two different CO_2-doubling scenarios; they differ largely because, as you know, projecting future climatic change at a regional level is difficult — as indeed is establishing the precise climatic variable to which hemlock is most sensitive. Each projection suggests that much of the area that currently supports hemlock growth would become unsuitable in the event of global warming, in one case (Figure 8.13b), markedly so. However, could the species shift its geographical distribution fast enough by migrating into new potential habitats? It seems not; a migration rate of several hundred kilometres per century would be required of a species that in the past has migrated less than 50 km a century. Once again the *rate* of future warming is critical. If the climatic changes envisaged in these scenarios were to happen rapidly (say over the next 100 years), the species is likely to become restricted almost exclusively to areas where the present and projected distributions overlap (i.e. in the areas of darkest blue in Figure 8.13b and c).

The general picture that emerges from examples of this type is of great change in natural ecosystems. There is uncertainty and controversy about the magnitude and effects of such changes, particularly because today's flora and fauna have never before encountered changes at the rate envisaged for the future. Remember that the rate of change threatens to be many, many times greater than that after the last ice age (Activity 7.5g) — when amongst the mammals alone, 32 major types (i.e. genera) became extinct. Rare species are likely to be particularly at risk of extinction. Other vulnerable species are those ill-equipped for migration or those which face natural or artificial barriers (e.g. farmland, lakes and roads). Other species could thrive. Faced with the prospect of change, some ecologists take a positive view and see the altered communities of the future as a welcome novelty, reflecting the adaptability of natural ecosystems. Others are more fearful of the wholesale loss of species and disturbance of the fragile ecosystems that are the objects of so much existing conservation effort. It is possible that whole habitats may be at risk. There are likely to be changes in the boundaries that presently divide major biomes (recall Figure 2.1). Decreased soil moisture within major land masses could well increase the areas of deserts and semi-arid scrub. Note from Figure 2.1 the current boundary in the far north between the boreal forests and the tundra; it is apparent (in North America for instance) that this boundary correlates reasonably well with minimum annual temperatures. Remember that, in the event of CO_2-doubling, GCMs consistently predict greater warming at higher latitudes. All this suggests that coniferous trees are likely to flourish in areas much further north than at present; one likely outcome might then be the virtual disappearance of the tundra zone, at least with its present characteristic flora and fauna.

8.4.2 Impacts on agriculture

In the UK, there is a superficial attraction about the novelty and opportunities that may arise in the event of future warming of a couple of degrees or so over the next 30–50 years. If warmer winters and longer growing seasons were to become a reality, yields of many existing crops might increase and the changed conditions might suit many new crops, especially those that are currently grown in the UK close to their northern limit of cold tolerance. Maize is a good example. At present, grain maize can be grown only in the extreme southeast parts of England (see Figure 8.14a), and even then only with a relatively high risk of failure. This is because fairly high, sustained temperatures are needed to ensure successful ripening of grain maize. With a warmer UK climate, the growing limit would shift, as shown in Figure 8.14a, to an extent that would depend on the magnitude of warming. Maize is grown for silage over a much wider area of the UK, and here too the evidence of recent unusually warm years suggests the crop could be grown much further north in the event of global warming (see Figure 8.14b).

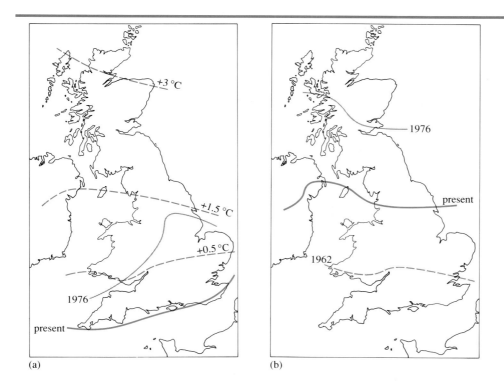

(a)   (b)

Figure 8.14   (a) The likely northern limits for the ripening of grain maize. The present limit is shown (in solid blue), along with the suggested future limits for a range of degrees of warming. 1976 was a particularly warm summer in the UK and the limit for grain maize ripening shifted accordingly. (b) Maize is also produced in the UK for silage, and because the conditions for its growth are less demanding than those for grain maize (the grain need not mature) it is currently grown well up into the north of England (blue line). This northern boundary would also shift in the event of global warming, much as happened in 1976. In cool years such as 1962, the existing boundary shifts south.

> Which other factors are likely to influence growing limits besides temperature?

▶   Soil moisture level, which will itself be influenced by temperature, and probably soil quality.

Maize provides just one example of a number of '**spatial shifts**' in the potential for growing crops that are likely to be associated with a CO_2-richer climate. It is these opportunities that have prompted headline writers to predict a 'Mediterranean' face for UK agriculture in the future, with continental crops decorating the south of England. For example, sunflowers can at present be grown only in the extreme south of England, where the high hours of sunshine and low air humidity are just about sufficient to allow ripening of the seedhead. It has been estimated that with a climate 1.5 °C warmer than at present, their temperature limit could be shifted about 500 km further north.

The general European picture of the future 'greenhouse' environment is of a significant northward spatial shift in agricultural potential. Because crops are so sensitive to climatic variables, even modest warming will have far-reaching effects. For example, it has been estimated that every 1 °C warming would shift the northern limits of grain maize by between 200 and 400 km, with the shift greatest in Eastern Europe, although here soil quality is often too poor to support new crops. Agricultural benefits will probably be greatest in regions that are currently cool and temperate. For example, the effects of a doubling of CO_2 on Finland's climate would probably increase yields of barley and oats by an average of 9–18%. One equilibrium scenario (produced by the GCM developed at the GISS) predicts that the changed climate of Iceland would resemble that of northern Britain today. The raised productivity of Icelandic-managed grassland is likely to increase its present capacity to support sheep by about two and a half times.

By contrast, in southern Europe, where soil moisture levels are more likely to limit growth, crop yields may be reduced and the growing season is likely to decrease because of drier conditions. Thus, areas close to the Mediterranean may well become less productive. Whether such a northward spatial shift of European crop growing actually occurs will, of course, depend on the response made by the agricultural industry to such opportunities. The economic cost of the necessary adjustments in agriculture will be considerable.

Agriculture is also likely to be strongly influenced if, as is predicted, future climate involves much more than gradual changes in mean surface temperature; an increased frequency of *extreme* climatic events is likely, e.g. hot, dry spells or cyclones. We have already mentioned briefly in Section 8.3.2 the importance of temperatures during grain maturation. In Iowa, in the US corn belt, it has been estimated that an increase in mean temperature of just 1.7 °C is likely to produce a threefold increase in the probability of a 'very hot' spell — defined in this instance as five consecutive days with a maximum temperature over 35 °C. A correlation has been established between crop yield and the number of days with temperatures above 35 °C, especially at the time when the grain is maturing; the greater the number of such hot days, the lower the maize and wheat yield. Maize and wheat in the USA are currently grown in many areas, especially those towards the south of the 'corn belt', where the crops are already near the upper limit of temperature tolerance, suggesting that an increase in very hot spells will have a particularly deleterious effect on yield.

In many tropical and subtropical regions, temperate cereals are currently grown near the limit of their heat tolerance. In northern India, if the mean annual temperature increased by about 4 °C, with an increased frequency of extremely hot spells, it is unlikely that wheat production would be viable. If the increased incidence of extreme events such as cyclones occurs alongside the sustained, large-scale rise in sea-level predicted in Section 8.2, the effects are likely to be devastating. Bangladesh is one area likely to suffer such twin threats in the event of global warming. In general, the effects of extreme climatic events would be most severe in those areas that for reasons of economics and/or ecology are least able to cope.

So, on a global scale, the 'lottery' of future global warming would produce both winners and losers. In certain locations, the shifts of agricultural potential are wholly beneficial. Figure 8.15a shows the present-day area of northern Japan that is suitable for irrigated rice; the crop can be grown only where there is no significant loss because of frost. In the event of a warming of 3.5 °C, potential growing regions for the crop increase substantially (see Figure 8.15b). In other situations, climatic changes would open up new regions for cultivation, but only at the expense of the loss of

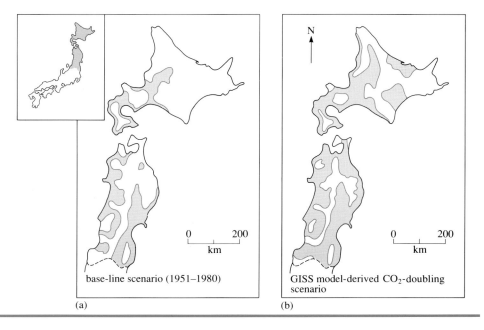

Figure 8.15 Areas in northern Japan that currently have the potential to grow irrigated rice are shown in (a). (b) shows likely suitable areas assuming a 3.5 °C increase in temperature, consistent with the prediction of the GISS CO_2-doubling equilibrium scenario.

base-line scenario (1951–1980)

GISS model-derived CO_2-doubling scenario

(a)

(b)

areas currently suitable. This is probably true of the corn belt of the USA where a displacement of 175 km in a northeasterly direction for the belt is predicted per 1 °C increase. Here one farmer's gain is matched by another's loss, and adjustments will require changes in agricultural practice and the application of new technology. For relatively affluent countries, such change is probably both feasible and affordable, but in the developing world, future prospects are much more alarming.

Remember that the majority of GCMs predict significant alterations in regional precipitation (see Plate 5.3) and soil moisture (Figure 5.14). In particular, substantial decreases in soil moisture are envisaged in a wide variety of global sites, as Table 8.4 indicated. They range from the Horn of Africa (i.e. Ethiopia and Somalia), major parts of Australia, central Asia and the southwest USA. Figure 8.16 shows a composite of several GCM predictions for Africa in the event of CO_2-doubling. Ignore for the moment the variations in blue shading on the map and concentrate on the blue lines. The dotted blue lines indicate areas where there is a 50% probability of a future decrease in precipitation; the major areas so affected are likely to be part of North Africa, much of the Horn of Africa and a sizeable strip along the Atlantic Coast. The dashed blue lines indicate regions where increases in mean temperature of 3–5 °C are predicted with a CO_2-doubled environment.

Now look at the shading on Figure 8.16. Where appropriate data are available, each African country has been assigned an '**index of food security**'. The precise details of how this index was calculated need not concern us, other than to say that each nation is assigned a value that reflects its self-sufficiency and the extent of the availability of 'household foods'. Countries are grouped into one of the six broad categories according to this index, as shown in the key to the figure; a low index indicates nations with low food security. Thus, countries such as Somalia and Mozambique have the lowest food security index, which implies they are particularly vulnerable to hunger.

▷ Identify areas that are both highly vulnerable to hunger and may suffer major changes in climate in the event of global warming.

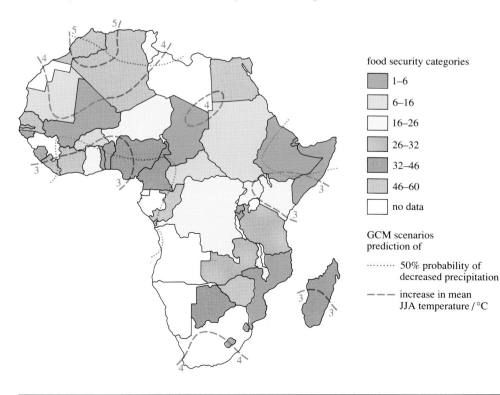

food security categories

1–6
6–16
16–26
26–32
32–46
46–60
no data

GCM scenarios
prediction of

········· 50% probability of
decreased precipitation

– – – increase in mean
JJA temperature / °C

Figure 8.16 Vulnerability to hunger (as measured by an index of food security) and locations most likely to suffer significant future climatic change. Each country has been assigned to one of six 'food security' categories. The dashed blue lines show predicted increases for mean June, July and August temperatures of 3–5 °C; the dotted blue lines show the most likely regions of decreased precipitation in the event of CO_2-doubling.

> ▶ The Horn of Africa looks especially at risk, because of the effects of temperature increase and decreased precipitation. Other areas at high risk include parts of the Atlantic Coast, for example Ghana, and major parts of central and northern Africa, where temperature changes of about 4 °C are predicted.

In such areas, climatic change is likely to have a devastating effect, with great loss of life and yet more civil strife. Nor is such a gloomy prediction confined to Africa. GCM predictions have been applied to southeast Asia, estimating the consequences for agriculture of increased mean annual temperatures of about 3–4 °C by 2050. Reduced water availability in many regions would be likely to diminish yields of rice, maize and soya bean. Higher temperatures would shorten the maturation period for such crops; requirements for irrigation would increase. In regions of Java, the increase in rainfall would probably be sufficient to raise rates of soil erosion, by 14–40%. A rise in sea-level of 10–30 cm in coastal regions throughout southeast Asia would cause extensive damage to the fish and prawn industry, which provides a major source of protein in local diets.

So, the world-wide implications for agriculture of possible future climatic change are profound. The most authoritative present projections of trends for the middle of the next century are:

o a 10–15% decline in grain yields in Africa, tropical Latin America and much of India and southeast Asia,

o a significant decline in harvests in North America, which is likely to raise grain prices by between 25 and 150%,

o a 7% reduction in world food production, and

o food prices rising by more than 20%.

Between 60 and 360 million *extra* people within the developing nations are likely to face starvation as a consequence. By this time, more than one in eight of the world's population may be at risk from hunger. Of course, human population growth will itself create the pressure to divert more land for agricultural use. As Section 4.2.3 revealed, continuing deforestation will itself cause further perturbations to the natural carbon cycle, risking an accelerated movement to a CO_2-richer world.

In the face of such dire warnings, many optimists stress the ingenuity of humans and the adaptability of agriculture. If CO_2 emissions were soon sharply reduced, if reforestation was a priority, if trade was liberalized and population growth reduced, the crisis might be manageable. Breakthroughs in genetic engineering might create crops with yet higher yields, better adapted to drier soils and higher temperatures. The more pessimistic agricultural view points to the present global trends of habitat degradation, to the increased uniformity of the world's food crops, to the recent reductions in world harvests, and the limited success of sustainable agricultural practices, and sees the prospect of modest global warming in the future tipping the balance towards catastrophe. As with so many other aspects of science, the proponents from both camps claim scientific evidence and a growing consensus in their favour. Unfortunately, the 'do-nothing' prospect of waiting until passing time and unequivocal evidence points to a clearer view of the future is an inherently risky strategy for humankind.

Summary of Section 8.4

1 Because of uncertainty about the scale, pace and geographical distribution of any future changes in climate, predictions about impacts upon plants and animals are difficult, both in natural ecosystems and in agriculture.

2 Present-day natural communities of plants and animals are in a constant state of change and their composition is often strongly influenced by climatic factors. The

geographical limits of many plants and animals are determined by temperature, for example the northern boundary of many insects in the UK. Such species are likely to expand their range in the event of global warming.

3   In a warmer climate, some species would fare better than others: species able to migrate only slowly into new territories would be disadvantaged as existing locations became unsuitable.

4   A northward spatial shift in European agricultural potential is predicted. For example, the northern boundary for successful grain maize cultivation is likely to shift by between 200 and 400 km for each 1 °C warming. Southern areas of Europe may become less productive, largely because of lower soil moisture. In the UK, a warmer climate would provide opportunities for novel crops (in part because of the longer growing season), and yields would increase for some existing crops.

5   Equilibrium GCMs suggest that a doubling of CO_2 would, at the regional level, result in expansions and/or shifts in suitable growing zones and there would be very significant dislocation of existing agricultural practices.

6   The most authoritative estimates of the impact of global warming on a global scale foresee an overall reduction in food production and an increase in food costs, increasing the risk of major famines in the developing countries, and substantial economic damage to the developed world.

Activity 8.3

(a) 'Skim read' through Sections 8.3 and 8.4 and quickly identify and list about 15–20 examples of significant impacts of possible future climatic change on plants and animals, summarizing each in a brief phrase, e.g. 'CO_2 fertilization effect'.

(b) Classify each of the items on your list as an *adverse* or a *beneficial* effect. What conclusions, if any, can you draw from this exercise?

8.5 Economic and political impacts

It is clear that the economic consequences of climatic change *could* be enormous. The effects of rising sea-levels alone are sufficient for economic costs in the range of hundreds of thousands of billions of dollars to seem plausible, even without taking into account the ecological and human costs. The loss of farmland and wetlands would reduce agricultural production and seafood resources. The contamination of water resources and disruption of transport systems and lines of communication would need to be considered, as would the consequences for recreation and tourism. Human populations and industry would have to move to higher ground, or to ground preserved by sea defences that are expensive to build and maintain.

Some economists have attempted to quantify the overall costs of climatic change. For example, estimates can be made of the costs of improving sea defences around vulnerable towns and industrial centres, or of relocating people or facilities. The value of agricultural production from farmlands threatened with inundation or salination can be measured, as can that of the tourist industry at risk. However, the uncertainties about the timing and rate of the rise in sea-levels, particularly on a local scale, mean that each such estimate can only be very unreliable. Moreover, overall assessments would have to make many assumptions about links or synergies between these factors; about any adaptations, technological innovations or alternative new productive activities; and about the overall patterns of trade and production. Moreover, proper account would need to be taken of the consequences of all the other impacts of climatic change besides the rise in sea-level, as listed in Section 8.1, and discussed in Sections 8.3 and 8.4.

Such economic modelling can have important heuristic value, but the quantitative estimates of the potential economic costs of climatic change should probably be accorded little credibility for the foreseeable future. Plausible models can be constructed that predict devastatingly high economic costs assuming the IPCC climatic change scenarios discussed in Chapter 7, but other models can indicate costs on a scale that many societies could reasonably hope to absorb.

What can be usefully said is that the *slower* the rate of climatic change, the lower the risks and costs are likely to be. Societies are in any case continually involved in upgrading facilities or engaged in new investments. If trends in regional climatic change and sea-level rise were predictable and gradual, they could be taken into account in planning decisions. The economic, social and political costs of possible adaptation could be spread over a long period.

However, even assuming that substantial international measures are taken to limit greenhouse gas emissions, the rate at which global climatic change might occur over the next century could be unprecedentedly fast. At local or regional levels, changes could well occur over time-scales that are short compared with existing investment cycles. Moreover, trends in regional climatic change will tend to be hard to identify reliably: both the rates and the character of the changes can be expected to vary unpredictably, as can the consequences of these changes for the overall environment.

In this context, the costs of coping with and adapting to changes as they occur will be high. In general, economically developed countries and communities will be in a much better position than poorer ones to bear these costs. They have greater financial and technical resources available for necessary adaptive measures, a more fully developed infrastructure for implementing them effectively, and reductions in their standards of living are possible without threatening the survival of their people. As mentioned in Sections 8.2 and 8.4, it is in the developing countries that significant climatic change would first cause large-scale human suffering, particularly in those regions where substantial proportions of the population are particularly poor, or live in semi-arid or coastal regions, or depend on seasonal rainfall for water.

By intensifying social, environmental and economic stress, the impacts of climatic change would be expected to increase political instability and the frequency and intensity of conflicts within and between states. Political, social and ethnic divisions are particularly dangerous during periods of declining living standards. The prospects for democratic or tolerant government may consequently be reduced, particularly since the stresses would be prolonged as climatic changes proceeded throughout the next century. The loss of use of much of the Bengal delta is bound to increase the risk of conflict within Bangladesh. The instability caused by mass migrations could also have consequences for neighbouring states such as India. India would itself be suffering from the consequences of climatic change, with implications for example, for its capacity to avoid fragmentation and large scale secession. Similarly, China's economic and political development would be profoundly affected if climatic change particularly damaged the relatively rich and highly populated coastal cities and southern coastal regions. Interstate competition for freshwater is already great in many areas, for example over the waters of the Jordan, Tigris, and Euphrates, which cross international borders in the Middle East. Climatic change could increase water shortages, and increase the likelihood of war.

More generally, climatic change would inevitably alter relative levels of power and prosperity within and between states and regions. Agricultural production in some areas would decline due to adverse climatic conditions and increasing costs, whereas the productive potential of other regions would improve. Not only would patterns of trade and migration change, but so would patterns of economic, political and, ultimately, military power.

The impacts of climatic change on human societies as well as for the natural or managed environment are thus highly uncertain, but they are likely to be profound. The risks of massive disruption and damage are high. As this has become apparent, the question of how states and societies should respond to the risk of anthropogenic climatic change has moved towards the top of political and scientific agendas. This issue is the topic of the final chapter.

9 Responding to the challenge

By 1990, there was a virtual scientific consensus that greenhouse gas-induced climatic changes could result in major social, economic and environmental changes, with possibly disastrous effects for some nations during the 21st century and beyond. A broad political consensus was emerging that urgent action was required, culminating in the Second World Climate Conference held in Geneva in November 1990, where representatives of 137 countries agreed to start work on formulating effective international responses to the risk of climatic change.

However, there is a big difference between agreeing in principle that co-ordinated action is needed to reduce the risk of climatic change, and actually establishing an effective international regime to achieve that aim. This closing chapter examines the progress towards such a regime in the early 1990s. It discusses the challenges and obstacles (political and technical) to taking effective action in the future, and considers in particular the continuing role of science and technology in the formulation and implementation of international policy.

9.1 Response strategies

There are broadly three ways of responding to the threats posed by anthropogenic climatic change. These are technical fixes, adaptation, and preventive action.

9.1.1 Technical fixes

A **technical fix** would aim to counteract the effects of greenhouse gas emissions on climate by deliberately engineering modifications to the environment. One proposal in this category would be to disperse large quantities of reflective dust into the stratosphere.

▷ What effect would this have?

▶ Such dust would be expected to reflect solar radiation back into space, thus cooling the lower atmosphere and counteracting the warming effects of greenhouse gases.

This should thus produce artificially a similar cooling effect to that produced naturally by the injection of debris into the stratosphere from volcanic eruptions (Section 3.5).

However, most scientists regard such schemes as extremely risky. The effects of such a deliberate assault on the environment are uncertain and poorly understood. There may be damaging side-effects. We might well end up worse off. Moreover, it could lead to difficult legal claims or political conflicts: peoples and states might blame any adverse weather or climatic conditions on those who engineered or supported the well-intentioned dust dispersal. Other technically ingenious schemes for environmental intervention meet with the same types of objection.

One technical fix that seems to present relatively low risks would be to 'scrub-out' the carbon dioxide from emissions from burning fossil fuels, at power stations for example, in much the same way as is presently done with the sulphur dioxide (a prime cause of acid rain). The 'carbon' could then be buried in the form of solidified carbonates. However, major practical problems arise with such an approach. Though technically feasible, the carbon dioxide scrubbing process is expensive, and itself requires substantial amounts of energy — reducing the *overall* energy efficiency of the power stations or other fuel-burning facilities involved. Moreover, in order to reduce CO_2 emissions significantly (and thus the predicted climatic change) this process would have to be carried out on a massive scale. The solid or liquid carbonates thus generated would have little commercial value. Burying or otherwise disposing of the enormous quantities of such materials that would be generated in an environmentally acceptable way would pose a great and expensive challenge, but it would reduce CO_2 emissions *without* requiring the measures to reduce consumption of fossil fuels discussed in Chapter 7. Nevertheless, proposals to limit climatic change mainly through technical fixes have little serious scientific, political or economic support.

9.1.2 Adaptation

Adaptive strategies for coping with the risks of climatic change have broader appeal. For example, policies for adapting to possible rises in sea-level can roughly be divided into three categories: *retreat*, *accommodation*, and *protection*. Retreat would involve progressive abandonment of coastal areas at risk — with settlements, ecosystems and communication links shifting inland. *Accommodation* would involve continuing to use the land at risk, while taking measures such as erecting emergency flood shelters, elevating buildings on piles; or converting agriculture to fish-farming or growing flood or salt-tolerant crops. *Protection* would involve building coastal defences (sea walls, dunes or dykes) to protect the land from the sea so that existing land uses could continue.

Similarly, there is a range of potential strategies to adapt agricultural production to changing (or more unpredictable) rainfall patterns, growing seasons and other weather conditions. Some regions may plan to reduce their economic reliance on agriculture, investing instead in manufacturing or services to pay for food imports from more favoured regions. Measures to accommodate possible climatic changes may include: changing types of crop, farm animal, or farming methods to those that are adapted to the new conditions; developing water reservoirs and distribution and irrigation systems to ensure against drought and to allow water to be channelled towards areas of scarcity; or developing (through conventional breeding techniques or genetic engineering) new crop varieties that are less vulnerable to climatic change or weather extremes than the current widely-used varieties.

In terms of economic efficiency, it may be better to aim for adaptation to environmental changes as they occur, rather than to engage in expensive projects designed to cope with predicted changes that may not actually take place. Even if global-mean changes could be predicted with reasonable confidence, the scientific uncertainties about the scale and character of predicted climatic changes at the regional or local level will remain very great for the foreseeable future. For example, Britain could become colder and dryer or hotter and wetter in future decades, depending on a wide range of poorly understood factors (including the effects of global warming on the Gulf Stream, for example). Since, for instance, coastal defences and water distribution systems are constantly being maintained or replaced anyway, it may be less expensive to modify on-going investment plans in these systems as required.

Investment in adaptive measures is likely to be most efficient if it increases the capability to adapt to climatic change without making assumptions about the precise nature of such changes. For example, monocultures (with their heavy reliance on one crop or crop strain) are particularly vulnerable to changes in their environment. Thus *agricultural diversification* is an appropriate adaptive policy. So is improved environmental protection (such as measures to reduce pollution or prevent degradation) to reduce the overall stresses on vulnerable ecosystems. It may also be possible to enhance the flexibility of water distribution systems so that water can be stored and channelled to wherever it may be needed.

In practice, societies in the 21st century will probably have no alternative than to take adaptive measures to cope with climatic changes. According to present scientific understanding, significant anthropogenic climatic change is expected unless immediate and radical reductions in global greenhouse gas emissions are achieved (such as the 60% reduction in present global CO_2 emissions needed to stabilize atmospheric CO_2 concentrations). There is no prospect of achieving emission reductions on this scale during the 1990s. For the foreseeable future, then, the most realistic aim would be to slow down the *rate* of climatic change (by reducing greenhouse gas emissions) rather than prevent it altogether. Societies will be obliged to cope with the changes that do occur.

As the discussion in Chapter 8 indicates, the potential consequences of climatic change are so great that effective adaptive strategies are likely to be very costly. They would probably be unable to prevent large-scale ecological damage and species loss. Developed countries may, nevertheless, have the capital resources to be able to absorb the costs of the infrastructure improvements necessary to cope with the impacts on coastal defences, water distribution and agriculture. Developing countries would find it much harder to find adequate resources for such investment: for them the human suffering involved in adapting to climatic change promises to be enormous. For some poor island and coastal communities and states, their very survival may be at risk. The mass migrations, political instabilities and conflicts that may result could affect all states.

9.1.3 Preventive action

For these reasons the international community has declared itself in favour of focusing on **preventive strategies**. Following from the Second World Climate Conference in 1990, some 18 months of negotiations led to the signing of a **Framework Convention on Climate Change (FCCC)** at the UN Conference on Environment and Development (UNCED) in Rio de Janeiro in June 1992. The declared ultimate objective of this convention is:

> *to achieve ... stabilization of greenhouse gas concentrations in the atmosphere at a level that would prevent dangerous anthropogenic interference with the climate system. Such a level should be achieved within a time frame sufficient to allow ecosystems to adapt naturally to climatic change, to ensure that food production is not threatened and to enable economic development to proceed in a sustainable manner.*

(Framework Convention on Climate Change, Article 2)

This is indeed an ambitious goal, as previous chapters make clear. The following sections examine the prospects for effective preventive measures to limit climatic change, beginning in the next section with an examination of the FCCC. This will involve discussion of international politics and the processes affecting the ways in which the international community may respond to the threat of climatic change. Unlike most of the previous chapters, the focus is thus on *political* rather than *natural* science, an emphasis which may be unfamiliar to many of you. However, before proceeding to the next section, try the following activity.

Activity 9.1

On the basis of information in previous chapters (particularly Chapters 4 and 7), what measures could be taken to limit or reduce greenhouse gas emissions arising from each of the following sectors of human activity: energy production and use; industrial production; forestry; agricultural practices; and waste management?

9.2 The Framework Convention on Climate Change

9.2.1 The 'framework' convention approach

The FCCC was signed by representatives of 153 states at UNCED in June 1992. It is due to come into force when it has been ratified (that is, endorsed) by the national legislatures of 50 states, a process expected to take about two years. Compared with its ambitious goal (quoted above), the shortcomings of the Convention seem manifest. The FCCC contains no specific obligations on countries to reduce their greenhouse gas emissions. Nevertheless, it provides the 'framework' within which any effective international regime to limit climatic change will now be developed.

In fact, the FCCC was specifically designed to *be* a **'framework' convention**. As such, it aims mainly to establish basic principles and objectives for an international regime to limit climatic change, and also to establish an agreed framework within which *subsequent* agreements detailing specific and more substantial obligations can be negotiated and reviewed. These subsequent agreements would be incorporated as *protocols* to the FCCC.

The 'framework' approach disappointed many of those who were promoting urgent international action to limit climatic change. To them it seemed a weak and unpromising approach: agreement on most of the important decisions and obligations had been deferred to the indefinite future.

An alternative approach to establishing an effective international regime would have been to aim to achieve an **'umbrella' convention**. Negotiators for an 'umbrella' convention would have aimed to establish a fully-fledged regulatory structure (treaty) defining states' obligations relating to all key aspects of the problem. If successful, global limits for anthropogenic emissions of each greenhouse gas would have been agreed, and the burden of achieving them would have been explicitly distributed amongst the states that were party to the treaty. Thus, each such state would have been allocated a specific limit on its emissions. Methodologies for monitoring or calculating each states' emissions of each greenhouse gas for each sector (such as energy use, waste management, agriculture or forestry) would have been internationally established, and rules for comparing actions in different areas would have been agreed.

The characteristic problem with the 'umbrella' convention approach is that the negotiations can become hopelessly bogged down; the combination of technical complexity and the aim of establishing strong obligations on states provides enormous scope for dispute and delay. By 1992, many governments still lacked the political will to commit themselves to substantial global limits on greenhouse gas emissions. Still less was there agreement about how the costs of achieving such limits should be distributed amongst states. Moreover, the task of limiting climatic change is so complex, involving sources of several types of greenhouse gas from a wide range of human activities and a range of sinks for CO_2 (notably the oceans and forests) that there seemed to be little hope of tackling all important aspects of the problem in a single treaty.

The flexibility of a framework convention allows an agreement to be achieved at a stage where negotiations for an umbrella convention would have been blocked or endlessly protracted. A well-designed framework convention establishes regular reviews of scientific developments and policy responses. It can thereby help to increase international and domestic political pressures for action, and promote progress towards achieving binding and substantial commitment in subsequent protocols.

International negotiations to limit stratospheric ozone depletion (see Section 6.4.2) offer a good example of this framework approach. The 1985 Vienna Convention specified no detailed targets or regulations concerning CFC emissions. Rather it established the destruction of the ozone layer as an issue of international concern, confirmed that halocarbon (especially CFC) emissions were primarily responsible, and established general goals for reducing those emissions. Subsequent reviews of the scientific 'case' against the halocarbons, and of the technical and economic feasibility of phasing out the most destructive CFCs, led to an agreement on the specific obligations of the 1987 Montreal Protocol. These were then tightened considerably at the review meetings in London in June 1990 and Copenhagen in November 1992. By establishing a review process and helping to create a general expectation that CFC production would soon be limited, the Vienna Convention encouraged large corporations and bureaucracies to plan for a future in which CFCs would be phased out. Moreover, states proved to be more willing to take unilateral actions as they became confident that other states would probably have to follow in due course. The process has resulted in CFC production being phased out much more rapidly than seemed possible in 1985.

In principle, therefore, the lack of substantial commitments in the FCCC is not necessarily a substantial set-back to the establishment of an effective international regime that will limit climatic change. Undoubtedly, the regime-building process in the case of climatic change will be much more complex and difficult than that designed to protect the ozone layer. Nevertheless, the international community has agreed that preventive action to limit global warming is necessary. For better or worse it is now clear that a 'framework' convention approach has been adopted as the basis upon which international preventive action will be developed.

Question 9.1 Why is the establishment of an effective regime to limit climatic change likely to be much more difficult than in the case of protection of stratospheric ozone?

9.2.2 The details of the FCCC

The FCCC contains 26 articles, several of which are standard for any well-drafted treaty. The declared objective of the Convention has already been quoted earlier (Section 9.1.3). Broad principles guiding how this objective should be achieved are set out in Article 3. It accepts the 'precautionary principle' (Section 6.4.2): precautionary measures should be taken even though scientific understanding is incomplete. Developed countries should take a lead in combating climatic change. All parties have a right to, and should, promote sustainable development (that is, development that provides growth and progress to meet humankind's present needs without damaging the environment in ways that compromise the ability of future generations to meet their own needs). The special needs of developing countries should be taken into account, particularly those that are especially vulnerable to the effects of climatic change or that bear a disproportionate burden under the Convention. Finally, parties should promote an open international economy, and thus unilateral or other measures to combat climatic change 'should not constitute a means of arbitrary or unjustifiable discrimination or disguised restriction on international trade'.

Article 4 deals with commitments, and was the object of most controversy during the negotiations before UNCED. No specific commitments to reduce or limit greenhouse gas emissions of countries survived the negotiating process. The initial aim, that developed states should return 'individually or jointly to their 1990 levels of … anthropogenic emisions of carbon dioxide and other greenhouse gases not controlled by the Montreal Protocol' did remain, but it was highly qualified and non-binding.

Instead of regulating greenhouse gas emissions, the Convention allows each country to adopt whatever national obligations and commitments it deems appropriate. Article 4 obliges parties to the Convention to formulate, implement, publish and regularly update national or regional programmes to limit greenhouse gas emissions, and cooperate in and promote a range of beneficial activities (such as technology transfer, forest management, public education and scientific research). Under these broad headings, states are free under the FCCC to choose which measures to adopt.

However, under Articles 4 and 12, all parties to the FCCC must report on the programmes they have adopted, and on their progress towards implementing them. Developed states must regularly provide a detailed description of the measures they have taken, and a specific estimate of the effects that these will have on greenhouse gas emissions (or absorption of CO_2 through sinks such as forests), starting within 6 months of the Convention coming into force. Moreover, using comparable methodologies, all parties are specifically obliged to 'develop, periodically update, publish and make available to the Conference of the Parties … national inventories of anthropogenic emissions by sources and removals by sinks of all greenhouse gases not controlled by the Montreal Protocol, using comparable methodologies to be agreed by the Conference of the Parties' (Article 4). Developed countries must meet the agreed full costs of compiling the national inventories of developing states.

It is therefore a key element of the FCCC that states can choose (within broad guidelines) what measures to adopt, but that the substance and implementation of these measures will be reviewed internationally. The hope of the negotiators was that the flexibility about commitments would make it possible for all key states to sign and ratify the Convention, while the international review process would increase political pressures on governments both to make substantial commitments and to honour them.

The review process is thus central to the development of the FCCC. Developments in scientific and technological understanding will be regularly reported to meetings of the Conference of the Parties — the supreme body of the Convention. At the same time, reviews of how states are implementing their commitments not only encourage full implementation, but also provide lessons for future actions and help to identify areas where international help may best be directed.

Both the scientific reviews and the implementation reviews provide a basis for decisions by the Conference of the Parties on whether to adopt amendments or new protocols to the Convention. More broadly, such review processes inform policy-making by all the groups involved, be they international organizations, states, regional groupings such as the EC, multinational companies or pressure groups.

The FCCC established a number of institutions relevant to the review processes. There is provision for a permanent secretariat to service and support the Conference of the Parties and to manage the Convention on a day-to-day basis. In addition, a Subsidiary Body for Scientific and Technological Advice is to be established to provide timely information and advice on scientific and technological matters relating to the Convention. This will be multidisciplinary and open to all relevant experts, as nominated by their governments. A similar Subsidiary Body for Implementation will also be established to provide assessments of the overall aggregated effect of the measures taken to limit climatic change; to review the implementation by states of their commitments (focusing mostly on developed states at first); and to assist the Conference of the Parties in the preparation and implementation of its decisions.

Thus, procedures for feeding scientific and technical advice to the Conference of the Parties are central to the process established to develop the Convention on Climate Change. The Scientific Committee will in many ways be a continuation of the IPCC, which has played such a major role since 1988 in developing and reporting an international consensus on scientific and technical issues relevant to evaluating the risks of climatic change. To facilitate its work, all parties to the FCCC are obliged to promote and cooperate in research, systematic observation, the open exchange of relevant information, the development of data archives related to the climate system, and potential measures to limit climatic change.

9.3 Science and the international review process

9.3.1 Science and policy-making

To appreciate the policy significance of the scientific review procedures discussed in relation to the FCCC Scientific Committee, it is useful at this point to reflect upon the characteristic ways in which science and 'expert knowledge' enters and shapes policy-making processes. One widely-held image is that scientists carry out research in their specialist areas independently of policy debates. Once they have established a reasonably reliable scientific understanding of a phenomenon relevant to policy, they communicate it to policy-makers. The policy-makers then take decisions, weighing risks and allocating resources according to their political and value judgements, on the basis of objective scientific advice.

Research into the relationship between science and policy-making indicates that this image is usually misleading or wrong. Scientists are typically aware of the potential policy implications of their research, and shape their work accordingly. Often such research is stimulated or funded by organizations with an interest in the outcome of the policy debate. Scientists will seek to influence the policy debates, frequently by promoting or interpreting their research findings before there is scientific consensus about their reliability. Interest groups and policy-makers tend to promote scientific research that reinforces their existing arguments and beliefs, and to neglect or criticize more uncomfortable findings.

For issues or phenomena on which there is no firm scientific consensus, the influence of experts tends to depend more on their access to decision-makers or the media than to the reliablility of their knowledge. For example, the political impact of the US scientist James Hanson's statement to the media and the US Senate Energy Committee that 'with a high degree of confidence we could associate the warming [of the hot summer of 1988] with the greenhouse effect' was discussed in Chapter 6. Its impact can be better explained in terms of the timing and Hanson's access to the Senate hearings (and thus to the US press covering them) than of its (dubious) scientific validity.

Moreover, even where a consensus exists among the scientists specializing in an area, it is by no means automatic that policy-makers will accept their scientific findings. Until their scientific advisors are obliged systematically to engage with the evidence, governments can continue to operate on the basis of ideas that have long been disproved. For example, the assessment, by the US administration of President Bush, of the risks of climatic change was long dominated by the sceptical scientific assessment of the President's Chief of Staff and the scientists he chose to consult, although their views were not at all representative of the expert scientific community at that time.

This is where prestigious scientific institutions and learned societies often play an important political role. A report by a National Academy of Science (USA) or the Royal Society (UK) is relatively hard to dismiss. This is even more true of international scientific organizations, such as the International Council of Scientific Unions (ICSU), of which most states' national academies of science are members. As we mentioned briefly in Chapter 4, the publication in 1986 by ICSU's Scientific Committee on Problems of the Environment (SCOPE) of a major report on climatic change did much to legitimize and reinforce concerns about global warming in the late 1980s. Aware of the prestige of science and the political value of a reputation for objective knowledge, leading scientists in the scientific academies have become sophisticated in their approach to the production of reports on policy-relevant science — using them to consolidate a scientific consensus among the broad scientific community, and phrase their conclusions in ways that are not only compatible with scientific understanding but also sensitive to the political situation.

In this context, the IPCC working groups were much more than international gatherings of scientific specialists. IPCC experts were nominated by governments. They included not only the leading scientific specialists, but also scientific advisors who sometimes had little initial expertise in the areas under review but who were trusted by their governments. Within the IPCC, such advisors would be obliged systematically to engage with the available evidence. As reports were being drafted, they were obliged either to align themselves with the scientific consensus or to substantiate their scepticism and sustain it in scientific debate with specialists. In this sense, the IPCC functioned as an international education and consensus-building process.

9.3.2 Science and the FCCC review process

The FCCC has institutionalized the IPCC international scientific education and consensus-building process. Its scientific review process will ensure that governments become aware of developments in scientific understanding, and make it difficult for them not to accept such understanding as a basis for future international measures to limit climatic change. Thus, scientific politics related to the development of the climatic change convention will increasingly focus on informing and shaping the reports of the scientific and implementation advisory committees established by the FCCC.

The FCCC has also inaugurated an 'era of methodologies'. The requirement that states prepare and regularly update national inventories of their greenhouse gas emissions (and removals) according to agreed methodologies is both scientifically and politically important. Cooperation in the open exchange of relevant information is of limited value if the information provided by governments is incompatible or compiled using dubious or unknown methodologies. Such difficulties have plagued scientific attempts to assess global or regional emissions and other phenomena relevant to climatic change. Even statistics which governments have a strong incentive to collect accurately, such as data on national energy use or agricultural production, are notoriously unreliable or difficult to compare between countries. The development of national inventories compiled according to agreed methodologies will greatly facilitate scientific work, although it will be a long and complex task.

The task is not made easier by the political significance of such inventories and methodologies. They will not only be used for scientific work on global climatic change, but also in reviewing the implementation by states of their commitments. The methodologies will inform future negotiations aimed at imposing limits on the greenhouse gas emissions of countries. This makes some states nervous about providing relevant information. It also tends to politicize technical debates about methodologies. Where there is scientific uncertainty, governments will want to shape the methodologies in ways that they believe may further their own interests. For example, the government of a country that emits relatively large amounts of methane may advocate methods that tend to underestimate methane emissions and their contribution to climatic change.

9.3.3 Verification

The FCCC encourages states to make unilateral commitments on measures to limit their contribution to emissions that might lead to climatic change. Developed states in particular are also obliged to produce estimates of the effect of these measures on their greenhouse gas emissions. However, the guidelines for these commitments are very broad. Each party shall take 'measures on the mitigation of climatic change, by limiting its anthropogenic emissions of greenhouse gases and protecting and enhancing its greenhouse gas sinks and reservoirs' (Article 2). Up to a point, it makes sense to allow states maximum flexibility to contribute in ways that they find most cost effective and acceptable. But it does nothing to reduce the risk that some states will meet their FCCC obligations by reporting a collection of programmes that are ambiguously specified, for which it is difficult to assess their significance or to monitor their implementation.

Experience from arms control, for example, indicates that unilateral pledges can invite resentment or suspicion unless they are clear, substantial and verifiable. If governments believe that they can fail to implement their commitments without serious risk of discovery, they may be tempted to do so. The development of agreed methodologies will help to clarify implementation but, unless a measure is amenable to independent checks on its implementation, suspicions may grow. In this context, the prospect of other states making substantial unilateral commitments will be reduced.

Thus, verification issues are important even for the effectiveness of the FCCC. They will become even more important in relation to future protocols that impose substantial limits on states' greenhouse gas emissions. Verification issues tend to become politically important as soon as governments start to consider seriously how to share the burden of achieving constraints that involve them accepting significant costs or risks.

Any arrangements for distributing amongst states the burden of achieving substantial limits on global greenhouse gas emissions would certainly involve tough and controversial compromises, and will impose unequal costs on signatories. In this context, governments would have incentives to cheat, either in order to achieve competitive economic advantage or to avoid offending powerful domestic interest groups. Fossil fuel use, forestry, and agriculture are central economic activities, and there would be fears that implementing commitments to limit greenhouse gas emissions could threaten many established life-styles and industries. At the least there would be temptations for governments to turn a blind eye to misreporting of activities by companies or other groups within their territory. Without an effective verification system, suspicions of non-compliance by some states would tend to undermine the whole climatic change regime.

Effective verification builds mutual confidence, deters cheating, and provides timely detection of non-compliance. It involves a number of stages. First, within each country activities relevant to its commitments are monitored, using (for example) collected statistics, inspectors, and aerial or satellite observations. These data are then analysed by technical experts. Finally, on the basis of such technical analyses, appropriate political authorities assess whether or not obligations are being met. No monitoring system can provide absolute certainty that non-compliance would be quickly detected. In practice, the aim is to provide adequate confidence that significant non-compliance with key commitments would be detected in time to take corrective action.

Technical constraints on monitoring capabilities mean that some commitments are more amenable to verification than others. For example, statistics on the use of commercial fossil fuels are much more reliable than those for non-commercial burning of firewood. Nitrous oxide emissions arising from fertilizer use depend on local conditions and practices in ways that make them inherently difficult to estimate. The amount of carbon dioxide emitted from burning forests likewise depends on a wide range of factors, such as the biomass burned and the precise burning conditions. Thus, treaty commitments defined in terms of, for example, carbon dioxide emissions from deforestation or nitrous oxide emissions from fertilizer use would be relatively unverifiable. Similarly, if a country's carbon dioxide emissions from burning coal can be monitored only with inaccuracies of about 10%, a commitment to reduce such emissions by 2% would be unverifiable. Thus treaty commitments should be designed not only to contribute substantially to limiting climatic change, but also to be adequately verifiable using monitoring and other resources available.

9.3.4 Identifying verifiable commitments

Devices on satellites and aircraft can be used to measure atmospheric concentrations of greenhouse gases. However, such measurements would be of little value for verification purposes, since it would be impossible to identify the source. Instead, direct monitoring of greenhouse gas emissions would involve measuring the mass flow of gas emitted from each source — for example the amounts of carbon dioxide flowing from a chimney or car exhaust pipe. There are no fundamental technical obstacles to carrying out such measurements: existing technologies permit this to be done fairly easily on static sources with errors of less than 5%, and substantially greater accuracies can be achieved.

Table 9.1 summarizes relevant information about the sources of the main greenhouse gas emissions. Within the major sectors, such as energy, the sources are further subdivided (e.g. power stations, industry and business) and the characteristics of each source are classified as, for example, big or small, many or few, etc. Sometimes an emission source has features of both categories (e.g. power stations); some are continuous, others intermittent.

Activity 9.2

Spend no more than about 5 minutes studying Table 9.1. Do not worry about the details of each individual entry; concentrate more on the *problems* posed for the monitoring of greenhouse gas emissions. In particular, which characteristics pose the greatest problems for effective monitoring by direct measurement? As a clue, compare the entries for power stations and for selective forest clearances.

In practice, direct measurements on greenhouse gas emissions may be appropriate only for large point sources such as large power stations. For the remaining sources, methods for *indirect* monitoring of greenhouse gas emissions are required. In such cases, direct measurements would be needed only to provide data that can be used in standardized calculations of emissions, or for random inspections.

Carbon dioxide emissions from burning fossil fuels are amongst the most amenable to reliable indirect monitoring at a national level. National energy production and con-

Table 9.1 Some characteristics of the main greenhouse gas emission sources.

Source	Characteristics of sources of greenhouse gases									
	big	small	many	few	continuous	intermittent	mobile	stationary	point source	diffuse
Energy sector: mainly CO_2, but also other trace gases, e.g. CH_4, N_2O and NO_x										
power stations	*		*	*	*			*	*	
industry and business	*	*	*		*			*	*	
domestic		*	*		*			*	*	
transport		*	*		*	*			*	
Waste sector: CH_4										
drilling for oil and gas	*	*		*	*	*		*	*	
mining	*	*		*		*		*		*
landfill	*		*		*			*		*
Forestry sector: mainly CO_2, but also nitrogen oxides and CH_4										
selective		*	*			*	*			*
clearing	*			*		*	*			*
Agriculture sector: CH_4 and nitrogen oxides										
rice paddies		*	*			*		*		*
ruminants		*	*			*	*		*	
fertilizer		*	*			*	*			*

sumption statistics could provide a reliable guide to how much of each fuel was consumed and in what way. Then the carbon content of each type of fuel could be determined, together with the 'oxidation value' (i.e. $C \rightarrow CO_2$) of each energy conversion process — recall Figure 7.6 and the associated discussion. Using such data, the total annual emissions of carbon dioxide from fossil fuel consumption could be calculated for each country.

In practice there would be substantial problems. Even amongst developed western states, energy statistics can be incomplete or inaccurate. Elsewhere they are often fragmentary and very unreliable (and some states regard the details to be a state secret). The statistics for non-commercial fuel or energy consumption are particularly unreliable. There are great problems with the international comparability of national statistics. Moreover, the carbon content of fuels (particularly coal and petroleum) can vary considerably: even within an individual coal type, the variation may be 10%. For each type of consumption process, the 'oxidation values' may vary significantly within and between states.

Nevertheless, if methodologies can be agreed for the collection of accurate statistics for each country (and for international trade), national emissions of carbon dioxide from burning commercial fossil fuels could probably be calculated to within 10%, provided that governments were prepared to permit appropriate and periodic measurements of carbon contents and oxidation values. In contrast, methane emissions released during fossil fuel production or from gas leaks are intrinsically difficult to estimate: overall estimates for a state are unlikely to be accurate to better than within a factor of two. In relation to the energy sector, national commitments to limit carbon dioxide emissions from fossil fuel burning appear to be most verifiable. Fortunately they also represent the biggest single factor driving anthropogenic climatic change.

Apart from CFCs, which are limited by the Montreal Protocol, the next biggest factor contributing to anthropogenic climatic change is probably deforestation. Limits on net greenhouse gas emissions from forestry and deforestation are intrinsically hard to define or verify. The gases emitted as a result of deforestation over a given area would depend greatly on a wide range of factors, including the biomass affected, the conditions of burning, and the proportion of materials burned, stored or left to decay. Estimates of these can be made for the purposes of scientific review, but the uncertainties in indirect estimates would be too great to allow the implementation of commitments on emissions to be reliably assessed.

However, as Plate 4.2 vividly reveals, forest areas can be reliably monitored using remote sensing devices on satellites and aircraft, supplemented, where appropriate, with ground observations. There are several commercial satellite systems using sensors with spatial resolutions in the range of 10–50 metres: some of these (such as Landsat) operate in the visible or near infrared and others (such as ERS) use microwave sensors. Using such detectors, it would be possible to measure forest areas quite accurately, and also to some extent to monitor changes in forest density or type. Commitments defined in terms of forest areas within states could therefore be reliably monitored, and could indirectly limit greenhouse gas emissions from deforestation or encourage carbon absorption through afforestation programmes.

At present, methane emissions from waste sites, ruminants and rice paddies can only be crudely estimated. In time, however, estimates could be made more reliable. For example, satellite observations of the areas of wet rice paddies could be combined with ground observations and agricultural statistics to produce an estimate of methane emissions due to rice production in a country. However, not all potentially verifiable commitments are necessarily an appropriate focus for international constraints.

▷   Why might endeavouring to obtain commitments on limiting rice paddy production not be a promising approach to limiting climatic change, even though they could be significant and verifiable?

▶   It seems rather unlikely that most countries in which there is large scale wet-rice production would agree to limits on rice production in the interests of limiting climatic change. They are mainly developing countries, such as in southeast Asia, where food production is a priority for survival. Similar arguments may apply to ruminant farming and other agricultural practices in much of the world.

In such cases, it may be better to focus on encouraging 'climate-friendly' agricultural practices. For example, changes in rice paddy management or the feeding of ruminants can reduce methane emissions by up to about 20% without reducing agricultural production. Such reductions are probably not monitorable in themselves. However, national commitments might be expressed in terms of agricultural education or investment programmes, the implementation of which could be monitored using procedures in which institutions such as the World Bank and development aid agencies are experienced.

In summary, commitments by states to limit their carbon dioxide emissions from fossil fuel burning and to regulate the areas and types of forest in their territory appear to be the most immediately promising areas for international action to limit climatic change. Together, these two factors probably account for the majority of anthropogenic climatic change. The implementation by states of such commitments is amenable to reasonably reliable monitoring and verification: an important consideration if an effective and long-lasting international agreement to limit climatic change is to be developed.

Unilateral commitments to such limits should therefore be encouraged within the FCCC. By 1992, limited progress had been made along these lines. Japan, Canada, Australia, New Zealand, the European Community and six other western Europe countries had made unilateral commitments to stabilize or somewhat reduce their carbon dioxide emissions by the end of the century. However, in comparison with the scale of reductions required to limit climatic change significantly, such commitments were modest indeed. Moreover, the unwillingness of the USA to make a similar commitment encouraged other developed states to hesitate even in such measures. In the medium term, effective action to limit climatic change depends upon the negotiation of further protocols to the FCCC that impose substantial limits on all countries' carbon dioxide emissions and forestry programmes. The next section examines some of the challenges that would be involved in negotiating such protocols.

9.4 Negotiating limits

9.4.1 Problems of equity and negotiability

Suppose that the international community could agree upon appropriate global targets for limiting carbon dioxide emissions from fossil fuel burning. The next task would be to negotiate an arrangement for dividing the burden of achieving this target that all or most states would find acceptable and fair.

One superficially equitable proposal would be for each country to make equal percentage reductions in its carbon dioxide emissions, compared (say) to 1990 levels.

Activity 9.3

Referring to previous chapters (and particularly Figures 7.4 and 7.10), spend a few minutes 'jotting down' reasons why many states would find such a proposal unacceptable. The answer is discussed in the following text.

Equal percentage reductions would 'freeze-in' existing gross inequalities in the emissions of states. For example, the USA would retain a quota of permitted carbon dioxide emissions that was roughly double that allowed to China and India combined (despite the fact that these latter countries contain almost ten times more people than the USA). Since carbon dioxide emissions from burning fossil fuels are intimately linked to standards of living and levels of economic activity, such an approach would threaten to perpetuate unequal levels of economic development.

Moreover, equal percentage reductions would impose unequal burdens on states. For example, the Soviet Union used energy so inefficiently in 1990 that ex-Soviet states (such as Russia) could achieve substantial reductions in carbon dioxide emissions from 1990 levels relatively cheaply: indeed, industrial closures in the early 1990s probably mean that Russia has already achieved such reductions. Similarly, traditional energy inefficiency in the USA could allow that country to accommodate reductions in its carbon dioxide emissions at comparatively modest cost. In contrast, Japan has already gone further than most developed states in improving its energy efficiency. Further substantial percentage reductions would be relatively costly for Japan to achieve, since it has already taken many of the relatively inexpensive energy efficiency measures available to it.

Finally, proposals for equal percentage reductions ignore questions of responsibility for the risk of climatic change. Historically, developing countries have contributed relatively little to atmospheric concentrations of carbon dioxide. Such states regard as unjust any arrangement by which they must bear disproportionate burdens for tackling a problem caused largely by others. The 'polluter pays' is increasingly an established principle for other more localized environmental problems. Developing states argue that it should also apply in the case of climatic change.

As mentioned in Section 9.3, the FCCC recognizes that developing states have special needs and that developed states have a particular responsibility to take the lead in limiting climatic change. The combination of population growth and the need for economic development means that developing states are almost certain to insist that they be allowed some scope for increasing their carbon dioxide emissions above 1990 levels.

A modified approach would be to try to negotiate separate limits for developed and developing countries. For example, developing countries could be allowed to increase their greenhouse gas emissions by 1% per year until 2020, say, while emission reductions of some 40% below 1990 levels would be required in developed countries over the same time-scale (such limits would be roughly consistent with a global target of 20% reductions in carbon dioxide emissions from fossil fuels).

It would be hard to persuade many states to accept such limits, however fair they seemed to be, and this approach would still be widely regarded as inequitable. There are wide variations in the burdens such arrangements would impose *within* the developed and developing groups of states. For example, very poor countries such as Bangladesh and Zaire might object to being subject to the same constraints as relatively wealthy states such as Argentina or Thailand. Similarly, Greece may object to being treated in the same way as Sweden or the USA. The 'freezing-in' of inequities within each group of states is likely to be almost as unacceptable as freezing-in inequities between the groups. Moreover, the classification of developing and developed states could prove controversial.

A radically different basis for negotiations would be to allocate carbon dioxide emission quotas on a per capita basis — allowing each country a given amount of annual emissions according to its population. Referring to Figure 7.4, it is clear that this would favour developing states. For any substantial global limit on carbon dioxide emissions, this would imply radical reductions in emissions for all developed states (particularly relatively rich and energy-inefficient countries such as the USA) while allowing ample scope for increases in emissions by developing states. Such an approach would be more consistent with the 'polluter pays' principle, and with the development needs of the developing world. However, it would almost certainly be unacceptable to developed states.

Confronted with the fundamental problems of negotiating an agreement according to any of the principles discussed above, it would be tempting to aim to negotiate separate emissions quotas for each country. The different factors affecting each country would somehow be taken into account, and an equitable target agreed according to criteria related to the costs the country would have to bear to meet a given emissions target, its degree of responsibility for the problem, and its level of development.

The problem with this strategy, however, is that every country would find reasons why it is a special case and should be allocated relatively generous limits. States such as Canada and Russia would argue for a special allowance for heating relative to warmer countries. China might argue that it is more dependent on coal for energy than countries like France, Norway or Israel, which can generate much of their energy from nuclear, hydroelectric, tidal and solar power schemes (power sources that do not give rise to carbon dioxide emissions). Every country is a special case. The negotiations would be enormously complex and prone to dispute and delay. Worse still, to bolster its negotiating position, every country would have a strong incentive to concentrate on finding reasons why it could not feasibly reduce its carbon dioxide emissions instead of looking for oppportunities to make such cuts.

Similar problems of equity and complexity would apply to negotiations to halt and reverse deforestation. Preparations for a forestry convention to be signed at UNCED in 1992 had to be abandoned. States such as Malaysia objected to a convention designed to limit the extent to which developing countries could exploit their forest resources, claiming that it would hamper Third World development, and that it was unjust to limit tropical deforestation when developed countries had cleared much of their temperate forests during earlier stages of their industrial development. The force of arguments by the USA that Brazil should halt deforestation in the Amazon was undermined when it became clear in 1989 that the US Government was itself subsidizing the clearance of its last remaining primeval forest in its Pacific northwest.

In the case of deforestation, however, there are persuasive arguments that tropical deforestation is not even in the medium-term economic interests of the host states. Moreover, the developed states are increasingly committed to reforestation programmes and to providing aid as an incentive to developing countries to curb deforestation and protect natural habitats and biodiversity. The prospects of achieving a substantial international agreement in this area therefore seem relatively promising.

However, there is a strong possibility that some states may insist upon a linkage between a forestry convention and protocols to limit carbon dioxide emissions from the burning of fossil fuels. Governments of developed countries may argue that they are unwilling to take a substantial lead in reducing emissions from the burning of fossil fuels unless developing states with tropical forests are willing to act to limit their own major emissions due to deforestation. Moreover, even if a forestry convention is agreed, there is a significant problem in ensuring compliance with it. For example, several southeast Asian states have declared policies limiting deforestation, but their governments turn a blind eye to illegal logging.

9.4.2 Developing an effective climatic change convention

In view of the problems discussed in the previous section, it is perhaps not surprising that governments opted in 1992 for the flexibility of a framework convention approach. Protocols imposing specific obligations on states will need to start modestly in order to be negotiable. As the process develops they can subsequently be strengthened. Even modest actions implemented quickly would have a long-term beneficial effect. For example, as you will have appreciated from Chapter 4, carbon dioxide has a long atmospheric lifetime (over 100 years), so the effect of emissions is essentially cumulative.

The development of an effective regime to limit climatic change must be a long term process, lasting throughout the next century and beyond. Thus, any protocols negotiated in the 1990s should be based on principles that can be maintained over this time-scale. Deals that simply reflect existing relations between states will not provide a strong foundation in the future, if these relations change.

Ultimately, national emission quotas allocated on a per capita basis may provide the most enduringly acceptable basis for an effective global regime to limit climatic change. In order to avoid creating incentives to increase national populations, this might be amended to a system based on states' adult populations. However, in the short term, quotas will probably have to be based largely on existing emission levels in order to be negotiable. Thus, a long term transition needs to be devised to move from a system based predominantly on equity of burden to one based on the polluter pays principle. Obligations established in protocols to the FCCC need to be expressly related to this transition.

Although constraints on countries' forest areas and carbon dioxide emissions from the burning of fossil fuels are the most appropriate and verifiable focus for negotiated emission limits in the foreseeable future, it is important to encourage an international process that tackles all significant sources of greenhouse gas emissions. This implies formulating and promoting a 'climate friendly' good practice relating to agriculture, land use, waste management, and all aspects of energy use, as well as ensuring the full and rapid phase-out of CFC production. This requires changes in life-styles and long established practices throughout the world. The developed world has the wealth and access to capital to take the lead in this process. Less developed societies must also play their part, but require massive transfer of 'know-how', technology and capital to enable them to do so quickly enough to prevent potentially catastrophic climatic change in the 21st century.

The development of an international response to the risks of climatic change had begun in earnest by 1992. It is probably impossible to build a strong international regime in time to prevent further increases in the *atmospheric concentrations* of greenhouse gases during the next few decades. However, reductions in global *emissions* are feasible, which would substantially limit the rate of climatic change and reduce the scale of the associated damage. Such reductions would allow human societies and natural ecosystems more opportunity to adapt, and make it at least possible that future generations may return atmospheric concentrations of greenhouse gases to present levels by the end of the 21st century.

If this is to be achieved, it will require changes throughout human society. Everybody is involved in generating greenhouse gas emissions, through energy use, industry, agriculture, forestry and waste. Every individual can contribute to the task of limiting climatic change. They can seek to influence government policies and promote the development of an effective climatic change convention. As managers, workers, farmers or consumers, they can influence policies in the companies, farms and organizations with which they come into contact. By changing their own activities at home or at work they can directly contribute by reducing consequent greenhouse gas emissions.

A good understanding of the scientific and policy issues associated with the risk of climatic change helps people to contribute more effectively to the process of limiting this risk. You should now be well-equipped to follow and participate in the continuing debates around the issue of climatic change; to understand the significance of further developments in scientific knowledge; and to detect the appropriate or misleading use of science in policy debates.

One last word. We opened this book with a quote that celebrates the 'interconnectedness' of life and its natural support systems on Earth. It seems appropriate to close it with one that brings humankind and the 'maps of geopolitics' back into sharper focus.

> *If you come away from this volume with one understanding, it should be of the importance of linkages: the interconnections between the risks of rapid climate change and so many other problems of central concern to national governments, corporate leaders, non-governmental organizations, and individual citizens. Climate change is inexorably linked to ozone depletion, acid deposition and urban pollution, deforestation and loss of biological diversity, and desertification. It is intimately tied to the most vital economic undertakings of our time — energy production and use, transportation, agriculture, forestry, building construction,*

industry and manufacturing, and so on. It affects (and is affected by) the fundamental concerns of human society: population growth, urban density and planning, management (and mismanagement) of institutions, and the quality of life for individuals and families. It is no accident that environmental matters, and particularly global warming, have captured the attention of schoolchildren around the planet. What we decide now is shaping their world.

Finally, consideration of climate change is necessarily involved in the great policy negotiations of our time — not only through new environmental treaties, but also through trade negotiations, water rights disputes, and international security debates. The implementation of a framework convention on climate change could affect all these issues ...

In conclusion, we want to emphasize that the international process of managing the risks of rapid climate change is not just an exercise in damage control. It offers an important — and in some ways unique — opportunity: to use the threat of global environmental change as a vehicle for expanding international cooperation — on scientific as well as trade issues — and as an incentive for the development of the advanced, more efficient, and less polluting technologies that can propel humankind forward into the 21st century. If the human race embraces the challenges which this opportunity presents — enthusiastically, energetically and with good courage — then we may truly be on the path to a sustainable world.

(Irving M Mintzer (ed.) (1992) Confronting Climate Change: Risks, Implications and Responses*).*

Summary of Chapter 9

1   There are broadly three different ways of responding to the threat of climatic change: technical fixes, adaptation, and preventive action.

2   A technical fix would aim to counteract climatic change by deliberately engineering modifications to the environment, but those proposed are typically either impractical or very risky, with uncertain side-effects, and are likely to lead to legal or political conflicts.

3   Most adaptive responses are expensive and unable to prevent serious economic, human and environmental costs. The most efficient strategies probably involve early investment to increase adaptability and reduce vulnerability to uncertain climatic changes. Many developing states would not have the capital resources to adapt to most changes, and are therefore vulnerable. Resulting mass migration, political instabilities and conflicts would affect all states.

4   For these reasons, the international community has declared itself in favour of concentrating on preventive strategies. The Framework Convention on Climate Change (FCCC) established basic principles and objectives, and agreed a legal and institutional framework within which subsequent agreements detailing specific and substantial obligations can be negotiated and reviewed. The flexibility and relatively weak commitments of the FCCC allowed an agreement to be reached; more ambitious negotiations would probably have been blocked.

5   A key element of the FCCC is that states can choose what measures to adopt in order to limit greenhouse gas emissions. However, they must not only provide annual national inventories of their emissions, but also regularly report on and develop the substance and implementation of these measures. An international review process would monitor implementation and hopefully would increase political pressures on governments to make substantial commitments and to honour them.

6   Science and 'expert knowledge' enters and shapes international policy-making through this review process, as well as through its influence on individual governments, companies, interest groups and public opinion. The relationship between science and policy-making is complex, and popular images of it are typically misleading or wrong.

7   Verification issues are important for the effectiveness of the developing climate convention. Unless national commitments are adequately verifiable, states may be tempted to set vague objectives or to implement them inadequately, and suspicions of non-compliance by some states could undermine the climate convention. Technical constraints on monitoring capabilities, and the varying availability of appropriate reliable statistics, mean that some commitments are more amenable to verification than others. States' carbon dioxide emissions from the burning of fossil fuels could be reasonably accurately calculated, using national energy statistics and data on the fuels and the combustion process. Limits on emissions due to deforestation or changes in land use would be hard to verify, whereas commitments relating to areas of forest of a given type could be monitored using a combination of remote sensing and ground observation.

8   Once global targets for limiting greenhouse gas emissions are agreed, it will be necessary to negotiate an arrangement for dividing the burden of achieving these targets that all states would find acceptable. Potential approaches include: requiring each state to make equal percentage reductions (perhaps with different reductions for developed and developing states); allocating emission quotas on a per capita of population basis; or negotiating different limits for each state on the basis of equality of burden, levels of development or degrees of responsibility for the problem.

9   There are strong arguments in favour of each of these approaches, but each would pose great negotiating challenges. Nevertheless, initial substantial constraints will have to be agreed soon at least to limit the rate of climatic change and to reduce the scale of the damage associated with it. Such measures could give human societies and natural ecosystems more time to adapt, and make it possible for future generations to return atmospheric concentrations of greenhouse gases to present levels by the end of the 21st century. This will require sustained and profound change throughout human society.

Further Reading

Barry, R. G. and Chorley, R. J. (1987) 5th edn. *Atmosphere, Weather and Climate*, Methuen.
A reasonably non-technical account of how the atmosphere works, as a basis for understanding weather phenomena and regional climates.

Benedick, R. E. (1991) *Ozone Diplomacy: New Directions in Safeguarding the Planet*, Harvard University Press.
A fascinating insider's view of the background to, and significance of, the Montreal Protocol, by the chief US negotiator. Supports part of Chapter 6 and Chapter 9.

Frakes, L. A., Francis, J. E. and Syktus, J. I. (1992) *Climate Modes of the Phanerozoic*, Cambridge University Press.
This looks at the changes in the Earth's climate over the past 600 million years. It relates to Chapter 3, but is a specialist book and includes much more detail than required in *Science Matters*.

Henderson-Sellers, A. and McGuffie, K. (1987) *A Climate Modelling Primer*, Wiley.
A specialist text, parts of which are reasonably accessible to the non-specialist. Supports Chapter 5.

Intergovernmental Panel on Climate Change (IPCC).
Sponsored by the World Meteorological Organization (WMO) and the United Nations Environment Programme (UNEP), the IPCC prepared a three-volume assessment in 1990 summarizing the 'state of the art' on climate modelling, climate impacts, and response strategies. The first part of that assessment was later published as:

Houghton, J., Jenkins, J. and Ephraums, J. (eds) (1990) *Climate Change: The IPCC Scientific Assessment*, Cambridge University Press.

An updated report was completed in 1992, and published as:

Houghton, J., Callander, B. and Varney, S. (eds) (1992) *Climate Change 1992: The Supplementary Report to the IPCC Scientific Assessment*, Cambridge University Press.
Although going well beyond the requirements of *Science Matters*, these two volumes provide the most authoritative assessment of the 'current state of knowledge' about the science of greenhouse gas-induced climatic change. An interesting feature is that each volume is preceded by a short (and very accessible) 'Policymakers Summary' designed to highlight the key points in the main body of the report.

Mintzer, I. M. (ed.) (1992) *Confronting Climate Change: Risks, Implications and Responses*, Cambridge University Press.
Written by a renowned group of scientists, political analysts and economists, the papers collected in this book focus mainly on the potential impacts of climatic change, and the challenge that poses to national and international planners and policy-makers — and to industry, commerce and all elements of the local or wider community, as well. Supports Chapters 7–9.

Nisbet, E. G. (1991) *Leaving Eden*, Cambridge University Press.
This discusses the primary physical, chemical and biological controls on the natural environment, focusing on the complex interplay between the atmosphere and the land from an Earth science point of view. It looks at the different aspects of climatic change, and is very accessible.

Parry, M. (1990) *Climate Change and World Agriculture*, Earthscan Publications, London.
Written by the lead author of the IPCC assessment of the potential impacts of climatic change on agriculture, and essentially a much expanded and more detailed version of that assessment. Supports Chapter 8.

Schneider, S. H. (1990) *Global Warming*, Vintage Books.
The early chapters give a clear, if brief, summary of the science underlying our current understanding of past climates and possible futures. Beyond that, however, the book is rich with insights into the issues behind the public and political debates of the late 1980s.

Smith, P. M. and Warr, K. (1991) *Global Environmental Issues*, Hodder and Stoughton/The Open University.
Book 4 of the Open University Course U206 *Environment*. Covers the science of climatic change more briefly, and at a somewhat lower level, than *Science Matters* — but contains a more detailed analysis of the socioeconomic and political factors that are bound up with the ongoing debates about responding to the prospect of climatic change. Also includes a very readable account of the science and politics of the long debate about CFCs and damage to the ozone layer.

In addition to the above, the following volumes of the Open University Course S330 *Oceanography* contain material relevant to Chapters 2 and 4 of this book:

Ocean Circulation (Volume 3 of S330) (1989) Pergamon Press/The Open University.

Ocean Chemistry and Deep-Sea Sediments (Volume 5 of S330) (1989) Pergamon Press/The Open University.

Skills

In this section we list skills that have, in some sense, been explicitly taught and/or revised in this book. You should find that most of them are special instances of the general skills categories given in the *Course Study Guide*, although some, such as 10–12, are deeply rooted in the particular content of this book. After each one, there is a list of questions and activities where that skill is practised.

1   Convert scientific quantities from one set of units to another. (*Activities 2.1, 4.1, 4.2, 7.3 and 8.1*)

2   Manipulate mathematical formulae to obtain the value of a variable in the formula, when the other variables take given values. (*Questions 3.2, 4.2, 4.5 and 5.1; Activities 2.1, 2.3 and 4.1*)

3   Manipulate, interpret, and draw logical conclusions and inferences from, data presented in various forms (text, tables, graphs, diagrams and maps), or make a critical assessment of a given interpretation of such data. (*Questions 2.2–2.4, 3.1, 3.2, 4.1, 5.1, 5.3, 6.1 and 8.1–8.3; Activities 2.1–2.6, 3.2–3.3, 4.1–4.5, 5.3, 5.4, 6.1, 7.3–7.6, 8.1 and 9.2*)

4   Balance chemical equations. (*Question 4.6; Activity 7.2*)

5   Use a scientific model to draw conclusions. (*Activity 2.2*)

6   Summarize, in writing, the main points from a section of text that you have studied. (*Activities 3.1, 3.4, 4.6, 5.5 and 8.3*)

7   Extract from one or more section(s) of teaching text that you have studied, information that is relevant to a particular question, and then use your understanding of the text to synthesize that information to frame an answer to the question, which you then write out in your own words. (*Questions 4.3, 4.4, 4.6, 5.2, 5.3, 6.2 and 8.3; Activities 2.3, 2.4, 2.6, 4.4, 5.1, 5.2, 5.4, 6.2, 6.4, 7.2–7.6, 8.2, 8.3, 9.1 and 9.3*)

8   Use information obtained from one source to comment on, or criticize, views expressed in another. (*Activities 4.3, 6.2, 6.3, 7.3 and 8.2*)

9   Appreciate the difficulties associated with making objectively quantified judgements about the evidence for or against a particular causal relationship, and recognize that this can give rise to legitimate disputes over interpretation within the scientific community. (*Activity 6.3*)

10 Show familiarity with the main anthropogenic sources of greenhouse gases, or of other trace gases that can influence their atmospheric concentrations, and appreciate the non-scientific factors (demographic, economic, social, technological and political) that are likely to influence future emissions. (*Activities 4.6, 7.1–7.4, 9.1 and 9.2*)

11 Demonstrate an understanding of the nature, strengths and limitations of the set of mathematical models that is used to generate projections of the possible scale, pace and geographical distribution of greenhouse-gas induced climatic change, and appreciate the different kinds of uncertainties associated with such projections. (*Activities 4.4, 5.2–5.4, 7.5 and 7.6*)

12 Appreciate the interactions between scientific evidence (and the uncertainties associated with it) and the many other factors (political, economic, etc.) that are involved in achieving international agreement to tackle a global environmental problem. (*Question 9.1; Activities 6.4, 7.3, 7.4, 9.2 and 9.3*)

Answers to questions

Question 2.1

Much the same argument applies here as it does to the transfer of sensible heat by conduction/convection. Air above the surface may become saturated with water vapour as the result of evaporation, which would tend to stop or reduce that process. But convection causes 'saturated' air to be quickly replaced by new, drier air, which can absorb more moisture, promoting further evaporation. (For much the same reasons, it's a lot easier to get the washing dry on a windy day. There is more on this kind of air 'turbulence' in Section 2.3.)

Question 2.2

The atmosphere transports more heat than the ocean. This is given by the area below each curve: the area beneath the atmosphere curve is greater than that below the ocean curve. (Unlike in Figure 2.21b, the latitude scale does not need to be in proportion to area, as the heat transport, unlike radiation, is not per square metre.)

Question 2.3

(a) North America has a temperature of around 20 °C and the Pacific Ocean 10–15 °C in summer.

(b) In winter, North America is at around −15 °C and the Pacific Ocean about 0 °C.

Question 2.4

According to the globally-averaged estimates in Figure 2.14, 46 units of solar radiation are absorbed by the surface. This is balanced by the transfer of sensible heat (7 units), latent heat (24 units) and the *net* emission of longwave radiation, i.e. the *difference* between that emitted (115 units) and absorbed (100 units). Of these 15 units, only 6 are actually absorbed by the atmosphere: the other 9 go directly out to space through the atmospheric window. Clearly the loss of latent heat, i.e. energy used in evaporating water, is the dominant mechanism, accounting for over 50% of the total transfer.

Question 3.1

(a) The interglacial maximum is about 16 °C and the glacial minimum is about 11 °C, so the temperature change is about 5 °C.

(b) This is more difficult to measure, but the most straightforward way is to count how many glacials/interglacials there have been in the last 400 ka (4 of each), which suggests that they occur about every 100 ka. Measuring the time between glacial minima or interglacial maxima should give a similar result, but with a wider range of values as the minima/maxima do not always occur at similar times during a glacial/interglacial.

Question 3.2

$$\text{Time} = \frac{\text{distance}}{\text{rate of movement}}$$

Distance = 3 000 km.

$$\text{Rate} = 2.0\,\text{cm}\,\text{yr}^{-1} = 2.0 \times 10^{-5}\,\text{km}\,\text{yr}^{-1}.$$

$$\text{Thus, time} = \frac{3\,000\,\text{km}}{2.0 \times 10^{-5}\,\text{km}\,\text{yr}^{-1}}$$

$$= 1.5 \times 10^{8}\,\text{yr} = (1.5 \times 10^{8} \times 10^{-6}\,\text{Ma}) = 150\,\text{Ma}.$$

Question 3.3

From Figure 3.19, the range = $(1\,368.2 - 1\,367.0)\,\text{W}\,\text{m}^{-2} = 1.2\,\text{W}\,\text{m}^{-2}$.

The average value over the period is about $1\,367.5\,\text{W}\,\text{m}^{-2}$ (as this is much larger than the range, it is not necessary to have an accurate value). Thus the percentage change in the solar constant is:

$$\frac{1.2}{1\,367.5} \times 100\% = 0.09\%$$

Question 4.1

From the values collected in Figure 4.6, the global annual NPP = $(100 - 50) = 50\,\text{PgC}$, i.e. the difference between the CO_2 taken up during photosynthesis and that released by plant respiration (Equation 4.3). Notice that in the 'balanced' world captured in Figure 4.6, this is also the annual transfer of carbon to and from (via the decomposers) the reservoir of 'dead' organic matter in soil and detritus, i.e. overall, carbon flows around a closed cycle like the one in Figure 4.5.

Question 4.2

Equation 2.5 defined the residence time in the reservoirs or 'compartments' of a steady-state cycle like this as:

$$\text{residence time} = \frac{\text{reservoir size}}{\text{rate of input (or output)}}$$

Taking the estimates from Figure 4.6, gives:

atmosphere: $[750\,\text{PgC}/(100 + 90)\,\text{PgC}\,\text{yr}^{-1}] = 4\,\text{yr}$

land biomass: $[550\,\text{PgC}/100\,\text{PgC}\,\text{yr}^{-1}] = 5.5\,\text{yr}$

dead organic matter: $[1\,500\,\text{PgC}/50\,\text{PgC}\,\text{yr}^{-1}] = 30\,\text{yr}$

surface ocean: $[1\,000\,\text{PgC}/90\,\text{PgC}\,\text{yr}^{-1}] = 11$ yr.

Note: In fact, Figure 4.6 does *not* incorporate *all* of the fluxes of carbon to and from the surface ocean. This issue is taken up in Section 4.2.2.

Question 4.3

(a) The most telling evidence is that the atmospheric concentration of CO_2 appears to have been pretty constant (at around 280 p.p.m.) for 800 years before the industrial age. The implicit assumption here is that both the oceanic and land-based carbon cycles were in balance during that period, i.e. that some net imbalance in one cycle was not fortuitously cancelled out by an equal and opposite imbalance in the other.

(b) According to point 1, CO_2 is more soluble in cold water. Thus, one might expect to find a net flux of CO_2 *into* the ocean in regions where surface waters are subjected to cooling — at high northern latitudes in winter, for example — and a net transfer in the other direction where they warm up, at low latitudes. Broadly, this is the observed pattern, although the details are complicated by other factors: more on this in Section 4.2.4.

Question 4.4

If artificial fertilizers (or their residues) build up in rivers, and then run off into the sea, this could stimulate marine productivity by supplying the limiting nutrients, nitrogen and phosphorus, and so perhaps alter the natural carbon cycle in *coastal* waters.

Question 4.5

By analogy with radioactive decay, it would take one half-life to reduce the concentration to half, and two half-lives to reduce it to a quarter.

For CFC-11, $\tau = 0.69 \times 65 = 44.8\,\text{yr}$, so the answers are (a) 45 years, and (b) 90 years.

For CFC-12, the lifetime is double, giving (a) 90 years, and (b) 180 years.

Question 4.6

Hopefully the reference in the question drew your attention to the reaction which initiates the oxidation of methane (Equation 4.5): this suggests that the OH• radical is 'keen' to regain a hydrogen atom — so forming H_2O. Hence, a plausible loss mechanism for HCFC-22 would be chemical reactions within the *lower* atmosphere, triggered off by the following process:

$$CHF_2Cl + OH• \rightarrow CF_2Cl• + H_2O$$

Since the fragment is itself a free radical, it should engage in further reactions: it does. The important general point is that this, and all other non-fully halogenated hydrocarbons, are subject to chemical attack in the troposphere: that is, their removal from the atmosphere is not dependent upon slow transport up into the stratosphere. And this shortens their atmospheric lifetimes — or at least, it does as long as *other* human activities don't seriously drain the global supply of OH• radicals!

Question 5.1

From Figure 5.2c, the 'new' global-mean surface temperature $T_s = 289.8\,\text{K}$. Using the Stefan–Boltzmann Law (Equation 2.1),

$$E = \sigma T_s^4 = (5.67 \times 10^{-8}\,\text{W m}^{-2}\,\text{K}^{-4}) \times (289.8\,\text{K})^4$$
$$= 400\,\text{W m}^{-2}$$

So $G = E - F$
$$= (400 - 236)\,\text{W m}^{-2} = 164\,\text{W m}^{-2}$$

Thus the greenhouse effect has increased by $(164 - 157)\,\text{W m}^{-2} = 7\,\text{W m}^{-2}$ over the original situation in Figure 5.2a (where $G = 157\,\text{W m}^{-2}$).

Question 5.2

The crucial point here is the high albedo of surfaces (be they land or ocean) covered by snow or ice (recall Table 2.2 in Section 2.3.1). A reduction in such cover would result in less reflective surfaces, which would in turn absorb *more* solar radiation, thereby amplifying the original warming trend. One would expect this amplification to be more marked at high latitudes, where snow and ice cover is currently most extensive. (This positive feedback loop was mentioned in Section 3.3.4: in that context, it was invoked as one of the factors that could act to amplify a *cooling* trend induced by the Milankovic–Croll orbital effects.)

Question 5.3

The quoted values of $\Delta T_{2\times}$ are *all* larger than the 'zero climate feedback' response to a CO_2-doubling (i.e. 1.2 K or 1.2 °C) given in Figure 5.2. Thus the *net* effect of the feedbacks simulated by these GCMs is a *positive* one — acting to enhance the global warming, substantially at the top end of the range of climate sensitivity.

The second and third points in our list indicate that all of these models capture the effect of two feedback processes which are expected to make a positive contribution to this overall effect — enhanced atmospheric moisture (water vapour feedback) and reduced sea-ice and seasonal snow cover (snow–ice albedo feedback, Question 5.2). But there is no information about the actual, or even relative, strength of these feedbacks — and hence no basis for any conclusions about the sign or magnitude of the simulated cloud feedback.

Question 6.1

As discussed in Section 5.2, the radiative forcing is the difference between the solar flux absorbed by the Earth–atmosphere system and the longwave flux emitted to space. From parts (b) and (c) of Figure 6.8, the *magnitude* of the radiative forcing is $(69.69 - 69)$ or $(69 - 68.31) = 0.69$ units, which is equivalent to:

$$\frac{0.69}{100} \times 342\,\mathrm{W\,m^{-2}} = 2.4\,\mathrm{W\,m^{-2}}$$

The forcing is *positive* for a 1% increase in the solar constant (i.e. the Earth–atmosphere system then absorbs an energy flux $2.4\,\mathrm{W\,m^{-2}}$ greater than it emits, Figure 6.8b); it is negative when the solar constant declines (Figure 6.8c).

Question 6.2

(a) The sulphate compensation effect might help to explain why the Northern Hemisphere has not been warming as rapidly as the Southern Hemisphere. This explanation remains speculative, but it has been suggested by some researchers.

(b) Because of the limited atmospheric lifetime of sulphate aerosols, any possible effects they may have on climate (either directly or indirectly via cloud albedo) would be expected to fall off rapidly as SO_2 emissions are decreased. Thus, if some compensation for the greenhouse forcing has been occurring, it may not continue to operate as effectively in the future.

Question 8.1

(a) See the completed table below:

	low	best estimate	high	uncertainty of best estimate
thermal expansion of oceans	2	4	6	±2
glaciers/small ice-caps	1.5	4	7	±3
Greenland ice-sheet	1	2.5	4	±1.5
Antarctic ice-sheet	−5	0	5	±5
total estimated	−0.5	10.5	22	±11.5
observed	10	15	20	±5

(b) The Greenland ice-sheet has the lowest uncertainty (1.5 cm) and the Antarctic ice-sheet the highest (5 cm).

(c) The melting of glaciers and small ice-caps has a much faster response time to climatic change, and so contributes to a greater rise in sea-level over the 100-year time-scale than the Greenland ice-sheet, even though the latter is larger.

Question 8.2

Figure 8.5 gives the best estimate of sea-level rise in 100 years from 2000 as 55–60 cm.

The best estimate for the observed rise over the last 100 years is 15 cm (Table 8.1).

Question 8.3

In the 'real world', the photosynthetic rate is constrained by factors other than atmospheric CO_2 levels. These data indicate the importance of nutrients such as phosphorus in the soil; where such nutrients are already in limited supply, the CO_2 fertilization effect is unlikely to be significant.

Question 9.1

Whereas much of the destruction of the ozone layer could be traced to a few, totally human-made industrial chemicals, greenhouse gas emissions are an intrinsic part of most human activities involving energy use, forestry, agriculture and waste management.

Answers to activities

Activity 2.1

(a) From the analysis in the text, 100 units (i.e. 100%) of the globally-averaged solar flux incident on the planet is equivalent to:

$$(1\,368/4)\,W\,m^{-2} = 342\,W\,m^{-2}$$

$(100 - x)\% = (100 - 30)\%$ or 70% of this is actually absorbed, which is equivalent to:

$$\left(342 \times \frac{70}{100}\right) W\,m^{-2} = 239.4\,W\,m^{-2}, \text{ or } 239\,W\,m^{-2} \text{ (as a rounded estimate)}.$$

(b) Thus the globally-averaged outgoing terrestrial flux, $[(100 - x)$ units] in Figure 2.5, must also be $239\,W\,m^{-2}$. Equating this with the black body expression in Equation 2.1, gives:

$$\sigma T_s^4 = 239\,W\,m^{-2} \text{ (using the rounded estimate does not affect the answer)}$$

$$\text{or } T_s^4 = \frac{239\,W\,m^{-2}}{5.67 \times 10^{-8}\,W\,m^{-2}\,K^{-4}}$$

$$= 4.2152 \times 10^9\,K^4$$

$$\text{So, } T_s = (4.2152 \times 10^9)^{1/4}\,K^*$$

$$= 255\,K$$

Since $273\,K = 0\,°C$, $255\,K = (255 - 273)\,°C = -18\,°C$.

(* There are two ways to work out this value. Since $x^4 = (x^2)^2$, taking the 'square root' *twice* would be one way. More generally, you can use the button labelled y^x on your calculator, where in this case, the 'power' or 'index' $x = \frac{1}{4} = 0.25$, However, it is vital that you do not 'round' the answer at this intermediate stage in the calculation: if you did, to 4×10^9 say, your final answer would be $251\,K$.)

Activity 2.2

White light contains *all* the visible wavelengths, whereas red light is at the long wavelength end of the visible spectrum. 'White-hot' objects therefore emit light of shorter average wavelength than cooler 'red-hot' ones. Generalizing, as the temperature of an object increases, so the average wavelength of the radiation it emits will decrease — implying higher *energy* photons, on average (Equation 2.2). This ties in with the Stefan–Boltzmann law for black-body emitters (Equation 2.1), which reveals that the *total* energy flux increases with increasing temperature.

Activity 2.3

(a) $(8 + 17 + 6) = 31$ units (i.e. 31%) of the incoming solar radiation are reflected, so this *is* the globally-averaged albedo of the Earth–atmosphere system.

(b) $(9 + 40 + 20) = 69$ units of longwave radiation are ultimately emitted to space from the Earth–atmosphere system.

(c) The total radiation flux lost to space — by a combination of reflection (of incoming shortwave radiation) and emission (of outgoing longwave radiation), i.e. $(31 + 69)$ units — is equal to the total solar flux intercepted by the planet (100 units). In other words, the radiation budget for the whole Earth–atmosphere system is balanced, as it should be (recall Figure 2.9).

(d) Absorption by O_2 and O_3 in the stratosphere (the 3 units entered in Figure 2.14) effectively 'filters' out most of the shorter uv wavelengths in the incoming solar radiation *before* it penetrates deep into the troposphere. However, Figure 2.7b also records atmospheric absorption of some of the longer ('near' infrared) wavelengths on the other 'wing' of the solar spectrum. This is mostly due to water vapour — the bottom panel in Figure 2.7c — in the troposphere, but there is a small contribution from CO_2 as well.

(e) The best way to do this is to draw up a check list:

Energy fluxes absorbed by the atmosphere

Incoming shortwave radiation		23	(i.e. 20 + 3)
From the surface:	longwave radiation	106*	
	latent heat	24	
	sensible heat	7	
		160	units

*Note that 9 units of the 115 emitted by the surface are *not* absorbed by the atmosphere: this radiation (at wavelengths in the window region) escapes directly to space.

Energy fluxes emitted by the atmosphere

Longwave radiation:	to surface	100	
	to space	60	
		160	units

Thus the energy fluxes to and from the atmosphere as a whole do indeed balance.

(f) We do not, in fact, 'accumulate more than we receive' because the radiation budget is balanced (as it should be) at the *top* of the atmosphere. The 'apparent' increase in radiation involved in the greenhouse cycle occurs because longwave radiation is repeatedly absorbed, emitted, re-absorbed and re-emitted by atmospheric constituents (the greenhouse gases *and* clouds — more on which in the text). The 100 units of 'additional' radiation input to the planetary surface effectively corresponds to the *y* units shown in Figure 2.9. It is precisely because this radiation cycles *within* the atmosphere that an absorbing atmosphere leads to surface warming.

Although not asked for in the question, it is worth noting the energy balance at the Earth's surface as well, with (46 + 100) = 146 units absorbed, and (115 + 7 + 24) = 146 units lost.

(g) The calculation here repeats the one you did in Activity 2.1, only this time the energy flux emitted by the surface is equivalent to 115% of the solar input, i.e.

$$(342 \times \frac{115}{100}) \, W \, m^{-2} = 393.3 \, W \, m^{-2}$$

Thus $\sigma T_s^4 = 393.3 \, W \, m^{-2}$

or $T_s^4 = \dfrac{393.3}{5.67 \times 10^{-8}} \, K^4.$

So, $T_s = 288.6 \, K$

which is close to the global-mean surface temperature (288 K) quoted in Section 2.2.2.

Activity 2.4

Hopefully you noted the following key points:

1 The separate panels in Figure 2.7c reveal that the 'troughs' in Figure 2.15 correspond to wavelengths which are strongly absorbed by the main greenhouse gases in the atmosphere — CO_2, H_2O and O_3, as indicated in Figure 2.36.

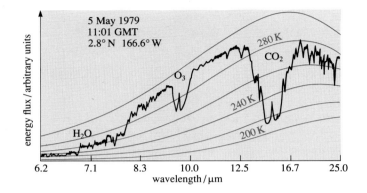

Figure 2.36 Answer to Activity 2.4. From Figure 2.7c, CO_2 absorbs strongly around $15 \, \mu m$, O_3 between $9 \, \mu m$ and $10 \, \mu m$, and H_2O at wavelengths less than about $8 \, \mu m$.

2 Using the coloured 'black-body' curves as a guide suggests that radiation at these wavelengths comes from regions of *lower temperature*, on average, than the rest of the spectrum.

In broad terms, these points support the picture developed in Section 2.2. Where the atmosphere has a *non*-absorbing window (Figure 2.7b), radiation emitted by the surface escapes directly to space — or at least, it does through a cloud-free field of view (as noted in the caption to Figure 2.15): the flux at these wavelengths represents the emission from a black body at the temperature of the surface immediately below the satellite — it looks to be about 290 K, in this case. By contrast, radiation at the wavelengths absorbed by the greenhouse gases does *not* escape directly to space. It is re-emitted to space by molecules of these gases within the atmosphere — from regions that are *cooler*, on average, than the surface, as is the upper troposphere and much of the stratosphere (Figure 2.11).

(Although we shall not pursue the matter, it is worth noting that a more detailed analysis of the CO_2 band in spectra like Figure 2.15 can — and indeed does — provide information about the temperature–altitude profile up through the atmosphere.)

Activity 2.5

(a) They do indeed! According to the global estimates in Figure 2.33, the amounts entering and leaving the atmosphere each year (all in units of $10^3 \, km^3$) are:

Entering from:		*Leaving to*:	
oceans	434	oceans	398
land	71	land	107
Totals	505		505

Were this not the case, water would either gradually accumulate in the atmosphere or it would dry up completely. We know this does not happen — not on a globally-averaged scale, that is — and so the estimates included in Figure 2.33 have been *made* to balance.

(b) No. Again in units of $10^3 \, km^3$, over the oceans there is a *net* input of water to the atmosphere of $(434 - 398) = 36$, and a *net* loss of water over the land of $(107 - 71) = 36$. The overall cycle is balanced by the transport of air-borne moisture from over the oceans to over the land $(36 \times 10^3 \, km^3 \, yr^{-1})$ by winds, and back again via 'rivers etc.' $(36 \times 10^3 \, km^3 \, yr^{-1})$.

Activity 2.6

(a) On an annual average basis, the dominant influence is *latitude*, which governs the solar input at the top of the atmosphere (Figure 2.18). The fraction of that input which reaches the surface depends mainly on the amount absorbed by the atmosphere itself, or reflected back to space — mainly by clouds. There is also the albedo of the surface itself, which governs the fraction of the incident solar flux actually absorbed. The most important contrasts here are between the oceans and land surfaces in general (the oceans have a low albedo and typically absorb a larger fraction of the incident flux), and the very high albedos of surfaces (be they land or ocean) covered by snow and ice. The change in area of snow and ice cover (predominantly at high latitudes) is important to *seasonal* variations in the surface energy budget — as is the variation in cloud cover.

One final point. Alongside the broad generalizations outlined above, it is important to recognize factors that can be crucial on a more regional scale: in particular, not all land surfaces are equivalent. For example, deserts and grassland typically have significantly higher albedos than do forested areas (Table 2.2).

(b) Assuming black-body emission (Equation 2.1), the longwave radiation emitted by the surface is governed by the surface temperature. So this is likely to be greatest at low latitudes, where surface temperatures are typically higher.

(c) This is tricky, but hopefully the hint in the question directed your thoughts to the atmospheric properties (notably, concentrations of greenhouse gases and cloudiness), which together control the longwave radiation re-emitted back down to the surface. This will be enhanced by cloudiness and a *high* moisture content in the overlying air. These criteria point to regions with high evaporation — over the tropical oceans, for example. On the other hand, you might expect the downward flux of longwave radiation to be less under clear skies where the overlying air is comparatively dry — over desert regions for example. Both of these conclusions are borne out in practice. (Do not worry if you did not think of all of this yourself.)

(d) *Latent* heat transfer, i.e. the heat lost by the surface as water evaporates, was central to the discussion in Section 2.3.4. In brief, evaporation is enhanced by a high solar input, convection (or at least, turbulence) in the overlying air, and air that is not already saturated with moisture. You also need a wet (or at least moist) surface of course! All of which points to the regions identified in Section 2.3.4 — the warm oceans at equatorial latitudes and the hot, moist areas of tropical rainforest on land (where transpiration by trees makes a significant contribution). Conversely, you might expect latent heat transfer from land to be least in cold and/or arid areas, with sparse vegetation.

Sensible heat transfer is the *direct* heating of air by the underlying surface. It too is enhanced by a high solar input and mechanisms (convection or general turbulence) that sweep the warmed air away (Section 2.2.4). This again points to low latitudes — especially to hot, *dry* regions, such as the deserts, scrubland and savanna (Figure 2.1) — as being the areas of highest sensible heat transfer.

Activity 3.1

This is an activity that is not straightforward, as it asks you to decide on the *significance* of features. There is no single correct answer, but my answer would be:

1 The Earth's climate is usually stable and over geological time has generally been warmer than that at present, but with periods of cold, called Ice Ages, which only occur during 5–10% of the time.

2 There are fluctuations from cold (glacials) to warm (interglacials) within an Ice Age.

You might have included the following features instead.

3   Glacials (or interglacials) occur about every 100 ka.

4   The warming at the end of the last glacial occurred relatively quickly; 5.5 °C in 2 000 years.

Keep these features in mind as you read the following sections and note down the explanations of the points above.

Activity 3.2

(a) Your answer should look something like our attempt in Figure 3.26. We drew in the horizontal glacial/interglacial boundary by comparison with Figure 3.3a.

(b) Both figures show four glacials in the last 400 ka.

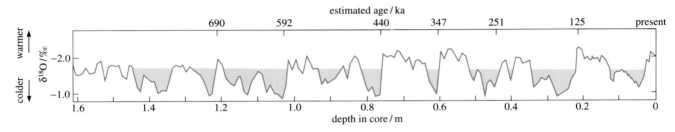

Figure 3.26   Answer to Activity 3.2. Glacial periods are shaded.

Activity 3.3

Both records show the same general pattern of warm periods about every 100 ka (interglacials) separated by colder, glacial periods. Both records seem to have major warm peaks and cold troughs at about the same time, given the limitations of the time-scales. However, the relative sizes of some peaks and troughs differ in the two records; for example, the last interglacial on Figure 3.8 (Figure 3.26 above) has a distinct single peak around 125 ka, but Figure 3.9a has two peaks, at around 95 ka and 120 ka. Both records show that the change from cold to warm conditions (such as that of 10–20 ka ago) takes place more rapidly than the change from warm to cold conditions (such as 180–200 ka ago).

These are the main points of comparison, but you may have added others.

Activity 3.4

Long time-scale (hundreds of million years):

Solar output (much lower for the early Earth)

Plate tectonics

Atmospheric composition (very different for the early Earth)

Medium time-scale (hundreds of thousand to tens of thousand years):

Orbital changes

Atmospheric composition (triggered by temperature changes)

Short time-scale:(centuries and decades)

Solar output (sunspot variation)

Volcanic activity

Activity 4.1

(a) *Downward flux of carbon*: From the figures supplied in the question, the annual exchange of water between the two boxes in our model carries down:

$$(2.0\,\text{mol m}^{-3}) \times (2 \times 10^{15}\,\text{m}^3) = 4.0 \times 10^{15}\,\text{mol of DIC.}$$

If 1 mol of DIC contains 12 g of carbon, then this is equivalent to:

$$(4.0 \times 10^{15}) \times 12\,\text{g} = 48 \times 10^{15}\,\text{gC} = 48\,\text{PgC.}$$

Upward flux of carbon: Following a similar reasoning, the upward flux is:

$$(2.2\,\text{mol m}^{-3}) \times (2 \times 10^{15}\,\text{m}^3) \times (12\,\text{g mol}^{-1}) = 52.8\,\text{PgC.}$$

So the *net* annual upward flux is just $(52.8 - 48) = 4.8$ PgC.

These are only very rough figures, but the final estimate is close to the 4 PgC for the biological pump quoted in the text.

(b) From Figure 4.7, the deep ocean reservoir contains 38 000 PgC, so the residence time based on the figures from part (a) is around (38 000/52) years, i.e. something like 750 years. This looks about right — roughly the same order of magnitude at least as the figures quoted earlier (between 200 and 1 000 years, Section 2.3.3) for the residence time of *water* in the deep ocean, as it should be, since DIC is carried around by the oceanic circulation.

Activity 4.2

(a) From the figures supplied, the atmospheric concentration of CO_2 increased by $(348 - 288) = 60$ p.p.m. between 1850 and 1986. This is equivalent to:

$$60 \times 2.12\,\text{PgC} = 127\,\text{PgC}$$

(b) Taking the central figures from the estimates quoted in Section 4.2.3, the CO_2 released to the atmosphere during this period was:

	PgC
from fossil fuel usage	195
from deforestation and changing land use	117
Total	312

As a percentage of the total input, the CO_2 accumulated in the atmosphere amounts to

$$\frac{127}{312} \times 100 = 41\%.$$

(c) The most obvious conclusion to be drawn is that something like 60% of the CO_2 that human activities have been pumping into the atmosphere has disappeared again.

But there is also a more subtle point: don't worry if you missed it. Unless the estimates of anthropogenic CO_2 emissions are wildly out (which is unlikely), this analysis suggests that some natural *sink* for atmospheric CO_2 has been operating during this period. It is thus highly unlikely that an even larger *natural* source has contributed to the observed buildup. In other words, there is further evidence here that the accumulation of atmospheric CO_2 is down to us.

Activity 4.3

The important general point is that two of the entries in Table 4.2 — the estimated emissions from deforestation and changing land use, and the modelled oceanic uptake — are highly uncertain, and hence so too is the net imbalance recorded there: it *could* be as little as $0.2\,PgC\,yr^{-1}$, for example. In other words, these figures do not provide firm evidence for the *necessary* existence of some 'missing' sink.

[You may also have noted (but don't worry if you didn't) that the box models used to estimate the 'strength' of the oceanic sink (Figure 4.15) are actually highly simplified. This issue is taken up in the text.]

Activity 4.4

(a) Hopefully, you recognized that these arrows represent the movement of carbon through the land-based carbon cycle *on a global basis*: (i) is the CO_2 taken up annually by plant photosynthesis (Equation 4.2), and (ii) that returned to the atmosphere by plant respiration; (iii) is the annual accumulation of carbon in dead organic matter, and (iv) that lost from this terrestrial reservoir through heterotrophic respiration (mainly by the decomposers in soil and detritus). (v) is the *net* CO_2 released annually via deforestation and changing land use (mainly in the tropics at present) — by cutting down trees and burning the wood, or allowing it to decay, and through the oxidation of organic matter in the soil following clearance.

(b) Similarly, these arrows represent the movement of carbon *within* the world's oceans: (vi) is the dissolved CO_2 withdrawn from surface waters by the photosynthetic phytoplankton, and (vii) that returned to the upper layer via the respiration of zooplankton and other organisms; (viii) is the fixed carbon *not* recycled within the surface ocean — the rain of particulate matter ('marine snow') down through the water column known as the biological pump. (ix) and (x) represent the dissolved inorganic carbon (DIC) carried into the depths and returned to the surface ocean, respectively, by the vertical movement of water between the upper mixed layer and the deep ocean.

(c) According to Figure 4.19, the annual net uptake of CO_2 by the surface ocean is $(92 - 90)\,PgC = 2\,PgC$, and the annual transfer into the deep ocean is $(4 + 35 - 37)\,PgC = 2\,PgC$. These figures represent current estimates of the 'efficiency' of the oceanic sink for anthropogenic CO_2: they come from modelling studies of the type outlined in Section 4.2.4. Your reservations should have focused on the deficiencies of existing models of the ocean–atmosphere carbon system — notably the fact that they do not yet incorporate any biology: neither the part played by phytoplankton (and their seasonal 'blooms' in particular, Figure 4.17) in the exchange of CO_2 across the air–sea boundary, nor the workings of the biological pump in general. Getting a better understanding of the balance between physico-chemical and biological controls over the oceanic carbon system is a central objective of JGOFS (Figure 4.18).

(d) According to the estimates collected in Figure 4.19, there is a *net* annual uptake of $2\,PgC$ [i.e. $102 - (50 + 50)$] by terrestrial ecosystems, which balances the $2\,PgC$ released annually through (tropical) deforestation: so the short answer to the question posed is 'yes'. Remember that these are *global* estimates. The net uptake noted here implicitly assumes that there *is* a land-based sink for anthropogenic CO_2 *somewhere* on the planet: several possibilities were touched on in Section 4.2.4. Your reservations here should refer back to the points raised in Activity 4.3: as yet there is no *independent* evidence for such a sink. That is one of the issues being addressed by the IGAC programme.

Activity 4.5

(a) No. Adding up the best estimates gives:

total sources	525 Tg CH_4 yr^{-1}
total sinks	−530 Tg CH_4 yr^{-1}
imbalance	−5 Tg CH_4 yr^{-1}

So according to these figures, CH_4 should be *disappearing* from the atmosphere at a rate of $5\,Tg\,yr^{-1}$: in practice, it is *increasing* at a rate of $44\,Tg\,yr^{-1}$ — the final entry in Table 4.3. This, in turn, suggests that *either* there may be a missing source of CH_4 (or identified sources may have been underestimated) *or* the sink for CH_4 has been overestimated.

(b) To answer both questions together: no. For many of the entries, the figure listed in the first column is not a simple average of the range of values quoted alongside. In each case, that range presumably encompasses various estimates that have appeared in the literature. In drawing up a set of 'best estimates', the scientists involved in the IPCC assessment will have used *value judgements* (not simple objective criteria) over the reliability of various estimates — perhaps based on the procedures different workers used, their scientific reputations, how extensive their samples were, and so on. All measurements are not equal!

Activity 4.6

(a) (i) Compare your list with mine:

Greenhouse gases and their main anthropogenic sources

Carbon dioxide (CO_2)	Burning of fossil fuels
	Burning of biomass
	Deforestation and change in land use
Methane (CH_4)	Wetland rice cultivation
	Domesticated ruminants (e.g. cattle, sheep, goats)
	Release from gas, oil or coal production, and leakage during gas transmission
	Landfill waste sites
	Burning and decay of biomass
Halocarbons (CFCs, etc.)	Release resulting from use as refrigerants, aerosol propellants, solvents, foaming agents, etc.
Nitrous oxide (N_2O)	Burning of fossil fuels
	Burning of biomass
	Agricultural activities

Note: Tropospheric ozone is *not* included in this list because it is not actually *released* to the atmosphere: rather it is generated *in situ*, see below.

(ii) There are two major groupings here. First, there are trace gases which can be involved in the generation of tropospheric ozone (in 'photochemical smog', for example) — namely partial combustion products, in the presence of elevated levels of 'reactive' nitrogen oxides (NO_x). The main anthropogenic sources are fossil fuel and biomass burning, although agricultural activities can also stimulate emissions of NO_x (Section 4.3.2).

Second, there are trace gases which influence the global abundance of $OH^\bullet$ radicals — and hence the major atmospheric sink for methane (Section 4.3.1) *and* the non-fully halogenated hydrocarbons likely to succeed the CFCs (Section 4.3.3, Question 4.6). So this draws in the 'precursors' to tropospheric ozone listed above, which (along with water vapour) are crucial for generating $OH^\bullet$ radicals, and a range of other gases (notably CO, again from fossil-fuel and biomass burning), that compete with CH_4 in destroying them again.

(b) Have your thoughts on future emissions from these sources to hand as you work through Section 4.4.

Activity 5.1

The important general point — emphasized in the closing paragraphs of Section 5.2.1 — is that radiative feedback mechanisms, triggered off by global warming, may themselves interact. There is no *a priori* reason to suppose that the *new* equilibrium state for the whole Earth–atmosphere system will necessarily be characterized by the *same* radiation balance at the top of the atmosphere as the old one. In particular, changes in snow and ice cover and/or cloudiness could alter the average planetary albedo — and hence the fraction of the incoming solar radiation actually absorbed by the Earth–atmosphere system.

Activity 5.2

(a) The important factors here were touched on in our discussion of Figures 2.18 and 2.21 in Section 2.3.1. In brief, the observed albedos recorded in Figure 5.13b contain contributions from clouds and the planetary surface (recall Figure 2.18) *averaged* around each latitude band. At near polar latitudes, the dominant contribution comes from the high albedo of snow and ice cover: elsewhere, cloud cover is the major factor (although the relative amounts of land and sea also exert an influence). The correlation referred to in the question reflects the intense hydrological cycle typical of the Intertropical Convergence Zone near the Equator. Here extensive cloud cover (and the high albedo of cumulonimbus clouds, Table 2.2) increases the local albedo, and is associated with high rainfall.

(b) The short answer is 'No'. For any given model, discrepancies between the computed and observed albedos could be due to inadequate simulation of cloud and/or snow cover and sea-ice (at higher latitudes) and/or to the way surface or cloud albedos are specified. The considerable disparity among the model results stems from the same complex set of factors.

Activity 5.3

At first sight, the results from the two high resolution models (Figures 5.14b and c) appear broadly similar: both indicate a general summer drying at northern mid-latitudes. Closer inspection, however, reveals significant differences between them on the regional scale. For example, the UKMO scenario is noticeably drier in the American heartland, parts of Europe and across central Asia than is that generated by the GFDL model.

The more obvious discrepancies, however, are between these scenarios and that produced by the NCAR model. Here, there are large regions of North America, parts of Europe and great tracts of central Asia where the simulated soil moisture either changes little or actually increases.

Activity 5.4

From the global-mean surface temperature rises recorded in Plates 5.4a and b, some $2 \cdot 3/4 = 0.58$ of the eventual equilibrium response is actually realized when the concentration of CO_2 doubles (after 70 years of the time-dependent simulation).

The required geographical regions stand out in Plate 5.4c: in the North Atlantic (especially in the region between the UK and Greenland), and in Antarctica and the

Southern Ocean around it the fractional response is only some 0–0.4. As a result, these regions do not show the *enhanced* high-latitude warming which is such a pervasive feature of this (and other) equilibrium scenarios: compare parts (a) and (b) of Plate 5.4.

Hopefully, the hint in the question reminded you that these regional 'anomalies' coincide with ocean areas where there is a strong downwelling of surface waters (Section 2.3.3) — a mechanism which might be expected to move 'excess' heat transported towards the poles by winds and surface currents into the deep ocean (much as it serves to sequester 'excess' CO_2, as discussed in Section 4.2.4). A more subtle point (and don't worry if you missed it) is that any mechanism which itself suppresses surface warming at high latitudes is also likely to reduce the strong, positive snow–ice albedo feedback that makes a significant contribution to enhanced high-latitude warming in typical equilibrium scenarios.

Activity 6.1

(a) Given the suppositions in the question, it could have been $0.5 \pm 0.2\,°C$ — i.e. as high as $0.7\,°C$ or as low as $0.3\,°C$.

(b) In general terms, it suggests that the value of $\Delta T_{2\times}$ deduced from Figure 6.5 is deceptive: higher or lower values could also be consistent with the observational record. For example, if the 'true' *greenhouse* warming was actually $0.7\,°C$, this implies that the real climate system could be *more* sensitive to the historical greenhouse forcing (Figure 6.2), i.e. $\Delta T_{2\times}$ could be higher — than the simple comparison in Figure 6.5 would suggest. And vice versa.

You were *not* asked to do this in the question, but a very rough and ready way of estimating the wider range of 'permitted' $\Delta T_{2\times}$ values is shown in Figure 6.13.

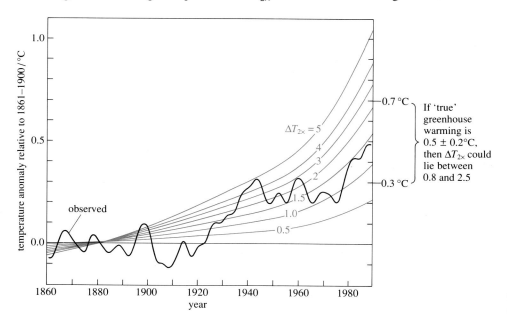

Figure 6.13 Answer to Activity 6.1.

Activity 6.2

(a) From the answer to Question 6.1, a change in solar constant by 1% gives a radiative forcing of $2.4\,W\,m^{-2}$, so a change of $\pm 0.5\%$ translates into a radiative forcing of $\pm 1.2\,W\,m^{-2}$. So the *total* radiative forcing over the past century could have been $2.5 \pm 1.2\,W\,m^{-2}$, i.e. $1.3\,W\,m^{-2}$ or $3.7\,W\,m^{-2}$.

(b) The flaw in this argument goes back to our discussion of radiative forcing itself, i.e. to the effect of an imbalance between the radiant energy flux absorbed by the Earth–atmosphere system and that emitted to space. We have reliable records that document a steady buildup of greenhouse gases in the atmosphere. It is illogical to argue that the climate system is sensitive to one type of radiative forcing (i.e. that induced by a long-term increase in the solar constant), but not to another (i.e. that induced by the observed accumulation of greenhouse gases). Beyond that, you may also have noted that there is no direct *observational* evidence to support the contention in the question.

(c) The modelling studies that produced the curves in Figure 6.5 were based on the time-evolving radiative forcing in Figure 6.2, i.e. on the forcing 'contributed' by the greenhouse gases alone. If the *total* forcing over the past century has actually been greater than this (i.e. if solar forcing has made a positive contribution), this implies that the real climate system could be *less* sensitive to radiative forcing than the comparison in Figure 6.5 would suggest, i.e. $\Delta T_{2\times}$ could be lower. Conversely, a negative contribution from solar forcing over the past century would allow a higher value of $\Delta T_{2\times}$. In short, the general conclusion you reached in Activity 6.1 again applies: both higher and lower values of $\Delta T_{2\times}$ could be consistent with the observed increase in global-mean surface temperature.

(A more detailed analysis would strictly require the modelling studies that produced the curves in Figure 6.5 to be repeated, but incorporating some hypothetical history of the solar forcing over the past century.)

Activity 6.3

The major protagonists here (Broecker and those attending the Workshop) all stress the inevitability of an enhanced greenhouse effect if greenhouse gases go on accumulating in the atmosphere. But these letters do highlight some important differences in the stance taken by various scientists. To me they can be crystallized under three heads.

o *Detection of the greenhouse signal.* This was undoubtedly the central issue in the debate sparked off by Hansen's testimony! As Risbey points out, establishing cause-and-effect is always a tricky business. In this case, the difficulties that frustrate detailed interpretation of the observed global warming this century were well rehearsed in Section 6.3. On purely objective grounds, that warming cannot, as yet, be confidently attributed to the accumulation of greenhouse gases. The Workshop press release emphasizes this lack of 'objective' evidence, whereas Hansen's 'high confidence' statement is more of a subjective value judgement (drawing on a whole body of circumstantial evidence, as Risbey points out).

o *The scientific case for action* (i.e. policy making) now, stressed by Broecker (despite all the remaining model uncertainties) — as opposed to an emphasis on further research to narrow those uncertainties (implicit in the Workshop press release).

o *Communication* (an issue raised explicitly by Risbey, but implicit in the other contributions, e.g. the Workshop did put together a press release). In attempting to communicate their underlying concern about the continuing buildup of greenhouse gases, one scientist's clear simplification of the problem, or judgement concerning the evidence to hand, could well be another's irresponsible *over*-simplification or misleading assessment. This sets the scene for disputes, which are picked up and often magnified and/or distorted by the media.

These issues — and other related points — are explored further in Section 6.4. Have your own notes to hand as you work through that material.

Activity 6.4

In my own judgement, the important parallels can be summed up as follows. *In both cases*:

o the 'threat' was first identified by scientists — based on observations of atmospheric change (i.e. the buildup of CFCs and of CO_2 and the other greenhouse gases) and theoretical arguments, and elaborated through computer simulations;

o the system being simulated is highly complex, far from completely understood, and the model forecasts are subject to large uncertainties;

o identification of the 'threat' generated a major research effort, aimed at both increasing the level of confidence in model forecasts, and at monitoring the behaviour of the real system;

o natural variability (and other factors) nevertheless make *early* detection, and hence validation, of the predicted changes highly problematic;

o the consequences (although uncertain) could be serious, not only for humankind, but also for other life forms;

o the 'threat' is long-term — recall that, like the CFCs, CO_2 (Section 4.4) and N_2O also have long atmospheric lifetimes — which means that the choices *we* make have implications for future generations as well;

o the problem is a global one. It has major international policy implications — for a group of industries in the case of the CFCs, but for a wide range of basic human activities when it comes to the other greenhouse gases. And this draws into the debate, not only the views of opposing advocate groups within any individual country, but also the complex political and economic forces at work on the international stage;

o key international agencies (UNEP and WMO) have been deeply involved in the process of building a broad scientific consensus that the problem is a 'legitimate cause for concern'.

The second question in the activity is taken up in Section 6.4.3: other points are explored further in the remaining chapters of this book.

Activity 7.1

In thinking about this question, I organized my 'life-style' under two headings: 'home' and 'travel'.

Home: Here the obvious areas of energy consumption have to do with heating (space and water), lighting — and all of the other myriad ways of using electricity (cooker, washing machine, fridge/freezer, kettle, and so on). So the sort of questions to ask yourself are: How well insulated/draught-proofed is your home (roofspace, walls, doors, windows, etc.)? How energy-efficient is the heating system (be it electric, gas or solid fuel, especially if burnt on an open fire)? What about regulating the temperature? What about energy-efficient lighting? Or switching off unnecessary lights? How energy-efficient are the other electrical applicancies? What about using them (for cooking, heating water, etc.) in an energy-efficient way? And so on.

Travel: What proportion of the travelling you do is by public transport, private car (or equivalent), motorbike, bicycle, on foot — and why? If you have a car, how fuel-efficient is it — and did you buy it, and do you drive it, with this in mind? Are you part of a car pool for regular journeys (to work, taking children to school, etc.)? And so on.

Many of the questions above (and this is just a sample of the ones you may have thought about) contain implicit hints to ways of saving energy. But they also touch on some of the barriers to doing so in practice: these are spelt out in general terms in the text that follows this activity.

More telling perhaps — and worth reflecting on if you have time — are questions that probe a little deeper. Is energy conservation something to which you do (or feel you should!) accord a high priority? If so, is your chief motivation the need to keep fuel and electricity costs in check? Or has media coverage of global warming (and/or your study of this book) played a part? What about the influence of *other* environmental issues related to energy use in modern societies — traffic congestion and *local* air pollution, for example? Do you feel you have — or know how/where to get — objective information about the best, and most cost-effective, ways of saving energy (as regards home insulation, alternative heating systems, choosing more energy-efficient electrical appliances, etc.)? How resistant are you to making changes in the way you use energy — especially ones that trespass on your sense of personal freedom (witness, use of 'the car' for many of us!)? And what would it take to erode that resistance?

One final point. The questions above focus on *direct* energy consumption in the home and for 'personal' travel. It is important to bear in mind that *all* the manufactured goods in your home also have an 'energy-cost': at present this is often very different from their 'economic' cost.

Activity 7.2

(a) As, usual, the first step here is to write down the substances involved (remembering that atmospheric oxygen is O_2):

$$C_2H_5OH + O_2 \rightarrow CO_2 + H_2O$$

Next, note that the formula of ethanol tells you how many C and H atoms there must be in the products — a balance achieved by multiplying CO_2 and H_2O by 2 and 3, respectively, as:

$$C_2H_5OH + O_2 \rightarrow 2CO_2 + 3H_2O$$

Finally, it is a simple matter to balance the O atoms — a 3 in front of O_2 does the job in this case. So the equation you should have come up with is just:

$$C_2H_5OH + 3O_2 = 2CO_2 + 3H_2O$$

(b) Burning ethanol (or methanol) derived from biomass still releases CO_2, but it does not unlock further amounts of *fossil* carbon. Rather, it effectively recycles the carbon 'fixed' in the plant material during its lifetime — the proportion actually returned to the atmosphere as CO_2 being dependent on the details of the fermentation or chemical process ('losses' to other possible products, 'undigested' vegetable matter, etc. would come in here) and subsequent combustion of the alcohol in a vehicle engine (likely, in practice, to be more complex than an idealized 'complete combustion' equation, like the one above, would suggest).

(c) In thinking about the scope for — and impact of — this type of fuel switching, I came up with the following set of questions. You may well have included others.

o   How important is the *type* of plant material? What land area would be needed to support a given level of fuel supply? What about competition with alternative uses for the same land, in terms of both human exploitation and the pressure on natural ecosystems?

o   What kind of resources (intellectual, financial, etc.) are needed to overcome existing technical constraints (as regards the conversion process, engine and vehicle design, and so on)? What about the time-scale for such research and development — and the economic viability of this particular option?

o What would be the overall effect on the *total* atmospheric burden of greenhouse gases, or their precursors? For example, would 'biomass plantations' need heavy applications of fertilizer — possibly enhancing emissions of nitrogen oxides? How would emissions of NO_x and CO compare with those from a 'conventional' engine? And so on.

o What other (non-fossil fuel-based) — and possibly more attractive — options exist for the transport sector?

Activity 7.3

(a) A release of 6 PgC per year for 110 years comes to 660 PgC (more than three times that released to date!). The reasons why this is likely to be a serious under-estimate were embedded in Section 7.1.1.

In brief, CO_2 emissions from the energy sector are determined by two factors:

o global energy demand; and

o the proportion of that demand met by burning a particular mix of fossil fuels, coal being the most carbon-intensive.

Two key determinants of energy demand are the population and the level of economic development of different countries. With stable (or even falling) populations, energy-saving measures (new technologies and designs, improved insulation of buildings, etc., coupled with structural changes in the transport sector, for example, or in patterns of work) could significantly reduce energy demand in OECD countries — even allowing for continued economic growth. However, rapid progress in this direction is unlikely without active government support.

That message holds with even greater force elsewhere, in the countries of the Soviet bloc (the former USSR and eastern Europe) and throughout the developing world. In the latter case, the push for economic development is bound to produce some increase in per capita energy use — even given the kind of concerted *international* action (to tackle the Third World debt crisis, for example) needed to give these countries access to more energy-efficient technologies. Coupled with rapid population growth (Figure 7.3), this can only fuel a continuing rise in global energy consumption. And if existing technical, economic or other constraints (as regards the nuclear and biomass options, for example) continue to limit the role played by non-fossil fuel energy sources, that will translate into *increasing* CO_2 emissions from the energy sector — not the constant release rates assumed above. In which context, it is worth noting that some developing countries (China, for example) are rich in coal.

(b) (i) At 15×10^6 hectares per year, 110 years would see the loss of $110 \times (15 \times 10^6) = 1.65 \times 10^9$ hectares of tropical forest. Given the limited information in the question, an estimate of the associated CO_2 emissions has to be based on the following assumptions:

o that *all* the carbon stored in plant biomass on the cleared land is released as CO_2 during this time period — either by burning or decay;

o that subsequent use (or recolonization) of the cleared land does not result in any *net* uptake of atmospheric CO_2 by plants; and

o that clearance and subsequent land use has no net effect on *soil* carbon.

With these assumptions the CO_2 added to the atmosphere would represent:

$$(1.65 \times 10^9\,\text{ha}) \times (150 \times 10^6\,\text{gC ha}^{-1}) = 2.48 \times 10^{17}\,\text{gC}$$

$$= 248 \times 10^{15}\,\text{gC}$$

$$= 248\,\text{PgC}$$

(It is worth noting — and perhaps you did — that this estimate is based on somewhat crude assumptions. A better figure would need to incorporate information on the *rate* at which carbon is either released or stored during and after the clearance of tropical forest — matters touched on in Section 4.2.3.)

(ii) Of the existing 2 billion (= 2×10^9) hectares of tropical forest, this scenario would see the loss of:

$$\frac{1.65 \times 10^9}{2 \times 10^9} = 0.825, \text{ or around } 83\%.$$

(c) (i) Averaged over a 100-year period, the forest would need to accumulate carbon at the *same* rate as the fossil carbon emissions, i.e. at 1.4×10^{15} gC per year.

$$\text{So the area required} = \frac{1.4 \times 10^{15}\,\text{gC yr}^{-1}}{2.7 \times 10^6\,\text{gC ha}^{-1}\,\text{yr}^{-1}}$$

$$= 5.185 \times 10^8 \text{ hectares}$$

This represents $(5.19/8) = 0.65$ (65%) of the continental USA — a pretty unrealistic scenario, quite apart from the logistics of actually planting such a vast area!

(ii) The short answer to this question is 'No'. The figure quoted represents the *average* rate of carbon accumulation over a 100-year period. Early on, the net uptake of atmospheric CO_2 would be much greater, falling off to zero as the forest matures (recall Section 4.2.3 again). Furthermore, there are problems associated with harvesting the 'crop' once the trees are mature: *the wood could not be burnt or otherwise allowed to decay!*

(d) My own thoughts on the matter went as follows. Given that the value in part (a) is likely to be a serious underestimate (without concerted international action, that is), whereas that in part (b) is probably an overestimate (in view of the assumptions made), continued use of fossil fuels looks set to be the major driving force behind the accumulation of atmospheric CO_2 in the future. Furthermore, the calculation in part (c) points to the limited impact afforestation programmes on a *realistic* scale could have. Such schemes would make some contribution to *slowing* the buildup of CO_2, as would efforts to slow, halt or even reverse tropical deforestation, but by themselves, they cannot provide a sufficient (nor indeed, permanent) 'solution'. That can only come through agreement to curb energy-related emissions — the central thrust of the quote from the São Paulo workshop.

One final point about this quote: hopefully you recognized that the message behind it is really a political one (captured in the accompanying cartoon). At present, *developing* countries are under considerable pressure over tropical deforestation. That is indeed a serious cause for concern — but more because of its *other* consequences (loss of biodiversity, soil erosion, flooding, damage to indigenous peoples, etc.). As far as the enhanced greenhouse effect is concerned, the emphasis on fossil fuels underscores the responsibility of the *developed* world — both directly (by curbing its own CO_2 emissions) and indirectly (through the financial, technical, etc. assistance needed to ensure that economic development in the Third World does not necessarily follow a 'traditional' carbon-intensive path).

Activity 7.4

(a) The key starting point here is the correlation in Figure 4.21 which points to a strong link between the global population level and anthropogenic emissions of methane. In a BaU scenario, feeding an expanding population (Figure 7.3) is likely to generate enhanced agricultural activity, thus increasing the methane emissions linked to rice production (a staple food in many of the developing countries predicted to see the greatest population growth, Figure 4.20) and rearing livestock. Unchecked forest clearance would also increase the release of methane as biomass is burnt (Table 4.3). Turning to the energy sector, increased methane emissions (linked to the extraction of *all* fossil fuels — not just natural gas usage *per se*) would be driven by the assumptions about global energy demand and supply embedded in the BaU scenario for CO_2. Finally, if past trends continue, more people in increasingly industrialized societies will generate more waste — so landfill sources of methane could rise as well.

(b) Chiefly, those related to the energy sector: greater energy efficiency (scenario B), especially if coupled with a gradual (C) or more rapid (D) move to alternative (i.e. non-fossil fuel) energy sources, should act to curb the release of methane as well. On the other hand, greater reliance on natural gas (in the short to medium term at least, as assumed in scenario B for CO_2) could have an undesirable side-effect — unless steps are taken to reduce the leakage from gas pipelines, and eliminate the common practice of venting methane at oil and gas production sites (remember that CH_4 is a more potent greenhouse gas than CO_2, Table 4.4 in Section 4.3.3). Slowing the rate of deforestation would also curb the CH_4 released through biomass burning.

(c) This comes down to the agricultural and landfill sources of methane. Depending on your background, you may well have come up with some ingenious ideas under the first heading, but basically, there is no way of actually preventing methane emissions from livestock(!), or from rice paddies (although ongoing research is suggesting ways in which they could be reduced somewhat). A more drastic strategy would be universal vegetarianism, or at least to rely on crops for a higher proportion of world food supplies, thus reducing the overall numbers of ruminants. Under the second heading would come strategies to reduce the waste generated by modern society (more recycling, or indeed, less consumption, etc.). One point you might not have thought of is the scope for recovering the methane released, for use as a fuel. The latter would, of course, produce CO_2 but, as noted above, this is a less potent greenhouse gas than CH_4.

(One final point: your 'immediate' thoughts may well have included the question of population control, with its inevitable focus on the countries of the developing world. Indeed, the fact that the IPCC's policy scenarios effectively side-stepped this complex and deeply contentious issue may have struck you earlier. Suffice it to say that this was undoubtedly a deliberate strategy, especially in the run up to the Second World Climate Conference. It helped to ensure that debate about the *scientific* case for or against a 'need for action' was not hopelessly entangled with arguments about this particular source of conflict, as between the developed and developing worlds.)

Activity 7.5

(a) There are three main deficiencies:

o The simple models still widely used (as in Figure 4.15) do not contain an explicit description of ocean dynamics, and hence of the physical processes that move 'dissolved' carbon (DIC) around the globe, and govern its exchange between surface and deep waters. Having studied Chapter 5, you should now appreciate that even existing OGCMs are deficient in this respect.

o The models do not incorporate *any* biological factors — neither the role played by phytoplankton in the exchange of CO_2 across the air–sea boundary, nor the workings of the biological pump.

o The models do not include the terrestrial carbon cycle, and so cannot simulate its response to changing levels of atmospheric CO_2.

(b) Projecting the time-evolving atmospheric burden of methane requires information about its rates of emission *and loss* (recall Equation 4.1, Section 4.1), through reaction with the OH• radical (Equation 4.5). As outlined in Box 4.3, the global abundance of OH• radicals is determined through complex networks of chemical and photochemical reactions involving a whole range of chemical species. But key ingredients include water vapour and tropospheric O_3 — crucial for generating OH• radicals — and certain other gases (notably CO) that effectively 'compete' with CH_4 in destroying them again. So, along with the mathematical description of atmospheric chemistry built into the model, the calculations behind Figure 7.15b must have included *assumptions* about future levels — or emissions — of water vapour, CO and key precursors of tropospheric O_3 (notably NO_x), as well as CH_4.

(Note: Points raised in parts (a) and (b) are taken up in the text, and again in Section 7.3.2.)

(c) Since the values recorded in Figure 7.15c take the 'pre-industrial' atmosphere as a base-line, the simplest approach is to draw a horizontal line across the diagram corresponding to the value 4 W m^{-2}, and then just estimate the date at which the *total* forcing (the top blue line), and that due to CO_2 alone (the bottom black line), reaches this value. I make it around 2018 and 2050, respectively. So, according to this BaU scenario, the 'other' greenhouse gases could shorten the time-scale for an equivalent CO_2-doubling by roughly 30 years.

(d) Three main candidates were identified in Section 6.3.2:

o *Solar forcing*   Without the necessary data (which long-term monitoring of the solar constant should eventually provide), the problems of assessing the sign and size of any possible solar forcing over the past century apply equally well to the next one.

o *Major volcanic eruptions*   Such events have a short-term cooling effect on the surface climate, but reliable forecasts of their frequency and global distribution cannot be made.

o *The 'sulphate effect'*   Again, both the size and sign of any future forcing are uncertain — the latter depending on what happens to the tropospheric burden of sulphate aerosols. If efforts to reduce sulphur emissions are successful and the aerosol load falls off, then so too should the negative forcing associated with the *present* situation (whatever that may be) — a possibility touched on in Question 6.2. The change to a smaller negative value (take -1.0 W m^{-2} to -0.5 W m^{-2} as a concrete example if this helps) would then amount to a *positive* forcing of the climate system, thus enhancing the projected greenhouse forcing. On the other hand, the latter could be partially offset by a continuing increase in sulphate aerosols — as it may have been in the past (the 'compensation effect').

Another potentially important positive contribution to Figure 7.15c would come from a long-term, truly global increase in *tropospheric* ozone. The reasons for excluding it from the IPCC assessment were mentioned in Section 4.3.2.

(e) This question refers back to points raised in the wake of Activity 6.4. For all the reasons explored in Section 6.3, it is impossible to define a set of objective criteria whereby all — or some part — of the observed global warming over the past century might be reliably attributed to the enhanced greenhouse effect: the situation was neatly summarized in the closing paragraph of Section 6.3.3. By the same token, a simple comparison between the observational temperature record and the model-predicted signal of greenhouse warming cannot, as yet, provide an *objectively* quantified measure of the climate sensitivity (ΔT_{2x}) of the *real* planetary system, as discussed in Section 6.4.3.

Given this situation, the figure endorsed by the IPCC necessarily contains a subjective element — based on the 'collective' judgement of the scientists involved that the climate sensitivity probably lies toward the lower end of the range (1.5–4.5 °C) produced by equilibrium simulations with existing GCMs. Hence the term 'best estimate'. Doubtless, there were dissenting voices in the discussions that produced this consensus!

(f) From the 'best estimate' line in Figure 7.15d, I estimated the model-predicted temperature increase over the period 2000–2100 to be:

$(4.2 - 1.2)\,°C = 3.0\,°C.$

From the discussion in Chapter 3:

(i) the recurrent cool periods during the Holocene seem to have been characterized by a drop in global-mean surface temperature of some 0.4–0.6 °C.

(ii) the average temperature change between glacials and interglacials is around 5 °C.

(g) From the answer to part (f), under a BaU scenario the 'best estimate' of the average rate of global warming during the next century is about 0.3 °C per decade. From Figure 7.15d, I estimated the *range* of model-predicted warming over the period 2000–2100 to be:

high estimate: $(6.2 - 1.7)\,°C = 4.5\,°C,$

low estimate: $(3.0 - 1.0)\,°C = 2.0\,°C.$

Thus, the average rate of warming over the next century is predicted to be around 0.3 °C per decade (best estimate) — with an uncertainty range of 0.2–0.45 °C.

Assuming a century time-scale for the onset/end of 'Little Ice Age' type events, the average rate of cooling/warming would be 0.04–0.06 °C per decade — slower than the *bottom* end of the model-predicted range. The last glacial/interglacial transition took place over several thousand years (Section 3.1), so the *average* rate of warming during this transition was slower still. (The emphasis on the word 'average' is important, for reasons that are taken up in Section 7.3.3.)

(h) Given the discussion in Section 6.3, the reminder about other (presently unquantifiable) forcing factors in part (d) above, and not forgetting the influence of internally-generated natural variability (on annual, decadal, and quite possibly century time-scales), I trust your answer to this question was a resounding 'No'! (At the time of writing, one specific example was the 'expected' cooling effect of the eruption of Mount Pinatubo in the Philippines in 1991, and the influence that might have on global temperature trends during the early 1990s.) Compare your notes with the text following this activity.

Activity 7.6

(a) The main point here is the considerable uncertainty about the likely geographical distribution of changes in the important climate parameters — surface temperature and, especially, soil moisture. Discrepancies between existing model forecasts of the latter for northern midlatitudes were the subject of Activity 5.3. Another look at Figure 5.14 reveals similar discrepancies at the latitudes of most existing wetland sources of methane. This unresolved question only underlines the need for more reliable regional forecasts — that is, for climate models with better spatial resolution in general, and more sophisticated treatments of surface processes, in particular.

According to Table 4.3, the other major natural sources of methane are non-domestic ruminants and termites. Here the uncertainties outlined above are compounded by the further layers of modelling studies needed to assess the impact of climatic change on wild populations of animals and insects — a problem we return to in Chapter 8.

(b) By contrast, the equilibrium scenarios generated by existing GCMs all predict enhanced warming at high northern latitudes, especially during the winter. Further, the temperature rises recorded in Plate 5.2 could well be sufficient to cause significant thawing of permafrost, thus releasing the methane trapped therein.

However, the time-scale over which this potentially important positive feedback might take effect is much less clear. Remember that Plate 5.2 records the *equilibrium* warming for an equivalent CO_2-doubling. On a BaU basis, the latter might occur early in the next century (at around 2018, from Activity 7.5c), but the *realized* warming at that time would be significantly less. Further, early experiments with coupled AGCM/OGCMs (Section 5.6) suggest that enhanced warming at high latitudes may well be supressed during the time-evolving phase of climatic change. Finally, the time taken for surface warming to actually melt the permafrost (metres below the surface in some places) would be another critical factor.

Activity 8.1

(a) It is better to use the 5-year mean solid curve, as this has removed much of the interannual variation. To get the best estimate of rate of rise, draw a best-fit straight line through the solid curve (the blue line on Figure 8.17). This represents a change of sea-level of about 10 cm in 100 years, which is 1.0 mm yr^{-1}. Estimation of the uncertainty is more difficult, involving drawing the lines of minimum and maximum gradient. I chose a minimum between the points A and B, and a maximum between C and D. This gives values of 7 and 12 cm, which gives rates of 0.7 and 1.2 mm yr^{-1}. The rate, with its uncertainty, is therefore (1.0 ± 0.3) mm yr^{-1}.

Don't worry if your method or values were different to mine; the point of this activity was to make you aware of the problems of calculating an average sea-level rise from existing records.

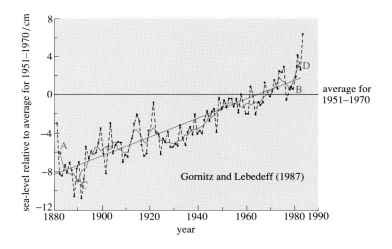

Figure 8.17 Best-fit line to the 5-year mean solid curve of Figure 8.2a. A–B = minimum gradient, C–D = maximum gradient.

(b) A line cannot be drawn through the whole time period on Barnett's record; the values fall slightly until about 1907, then rise. Instead, you might calculate the rate between about 1907 and 1986.

Activity 8.2

The major errors (including gross over-statements) are:

o   All plants would not 'make more food in a CO_2-rich world'. Section 8.3.1 explains that the CO_2-fertilization effect is often short-lived and not all plants display it — remember the runner bean.

o   Extrapolating readily from orange trees grown in glasshouse conditions to field conditions is problematic. In a CO_2-rich world, enhanced growth may not be sustained and wide-ranging.

o   *Nuclear* power stations are not major sources of CO_2 release.

o   As Section 8.3.2 explained, higher temperatures may not always lead to more growth (see Figure 8.10), and no such conclusion could be properly drawn from the events of spring.

o   Plants are indeed often better able to conserve water in a CO_2-rich environment, but they do so via control of their stomata (not their 'cuticle' cells). Some limited loss of water is inevitable.

The author has much too simplistic a view on a topic you now know to be very complex! In particular, (i) the effects of raised CO_2 are not as clear-cut as implied, and (ii) the deleterious effects of reduced soil moisture are not considered. It is the net effect of the interaction of a range of possible climatic factors (i.e. temperature, CO_2, soil moisture, precipitation) that is important.

Activity 8.3

(a) Answers will vary but these strike me as the most important impacts:

1   CO_2-fertilization effect (especially C3 plants);

2   temperature shifts from optimum for growth;

3   higher temperatures affect plant development;

4   longer growing season for crops;

5   high temperatures restrict crop maturation;

6   'desynchrony' of plant/animal interactions;

7   increased influence of pests;

8   more efficient use of water in plants;

9   regional reduction in soil moisture;

10 increased soil leaching/erosion;

11 relocation of the geographical distribution of plants/animals;

12 altered composition of communities;

13 threatened loss of rare species;

14 migration rates too slow to avoid losses;

15 novel crops grown in temperate climates;

16 increased crop productivity;

17 diminished crop yields in existing dry areas;

18 increased requirement for irrigation;

19 reduced food security;

20 food shortages.

(b) In my list, the minority of effects could be classified as 'beneficial' — numbers 1, 4, 8, 11, 15 and 16; it is likely that you found the same pattern with your list. This activity should remind you that global warming is very much a mixed blessing, but the preponderance of adverse effects shows that the risks it presents are very substantial indeed.

Activity 9.1

Compare your notes with the list in the following table.

Sector	Measures to limit greenhouse gas emissions
Energy production and use:	Improve energy efficiency and conservation. Switch fossil fuels (from coal → oil → gas). Switch to non-fossil energy sources. Structural changes in energy use. Reduce gas leaks.
Industrial production:	Halt CFC production and incinerate or re-cycle existing CFC stocks.
Forestry:	Limit deforestation. Encourage afforestation. Store and recycle wood/biomass.
Agricultural practices:	Reduce wet-rice production and ruminant herds. Prevent excessive fertilizer use.
Waste management:	Use methane emissions from landfills as fuel. Limit methane emissions from oil extraction and coal mining.

Activity 9.2

The characteristics that pose the greatest monitoring problems are italicized.

Power stations are a large source of greenhouse gases, but they are relatively few, are stationary, and represent a point source. Monitoring would be difficult but technically feasible. Selective forest clearances represent a source that is *intermittent, emits only small amounts of gas*, and exists in *large numbers*; these features, also true for domestic energy sources, would make this source of emissions extremely difficult to monitor. Note too that sites of forest clearance change with time, i.e. they are *mobile* (as are for example, transport energy sources (cars, aircraft, and ruminants), which also makes direct measurement difficult. Finally, note that selective forest clearing is spread over a wide area, i.e. it is *diffuse*, as are the sources from, for example, paddy fields and ruminants.

All these highlighted features would mean monitoring would be complex, present substantial technical challenges, and therefore be very expensive.

Acknowledgements

The Course Team would like to acknowledge the help and advice of Dr Mick Kelly, and of the external assessor for this book, Dr John Harvey. The contributions of Owen Greene, Shelagh Ross and Paul Smith to *Global Environmental Issues* (Book 4 of U206, *Environment*) were also of considerable value in the preparation of this book.

Grateful acknowledgement is also made to the following sources for permission to reproduce material in this book:

Text

Extract 6.1 Letters page from *Science*, 4 August 1989, pp. 451–452, © American Association for the Advancement of Science; Broecker, W. S. (1989), 'Hansen and the greenhouse effect', *Science*, 4 August 1989, © W. S. Broecker; Schlesinger, M. E. (1989), letter to *Science*, 4 August 1989, © M. E.Schlesinger; Risbey, J. (1989), letter to *Science*, 4 August 1989, © J. Risbey; Kerr, R. A. (1989), letter to *Science*, 4 August 1989, © R. A.Kerr.

Figures

Figure 1.2 (1) Kerr, R. A. (1988), 'Report urges greenhouse action now', *Science*, 1 July 1988, © 1988 by the American Association for the Advancement of Science; *Figure 1.2* (3) Clover, C. (1990), 'The climate heats up for the diplomacy of pollution', *Daily Telegraph*, 7 November 1990, © The Daily Telegraph plc 1990; *Figure 1.2* (4) Reprinted with permission from *Nature*, **349**, 17 January 1991, © Copyright 1991 Macmillan Magazines Ltd; *Figure 2.1* Cox, B., Moore, P. D. and Whitfield, P. (1989), *The Atlas of the Living World*, Marshall Editions Ltd; *Figures 2.7a, b, 2.14* Mitchell, J. F. B. (1989), 'The greenhouse effect and climate change', *Reviews of Geophysics*, **27**(1), American Geophysical Union; *Figure 2.7c* Fleagle, R. G. and Businger, J. A. (1963), *An Introduction To Atmospheric Physics*, Academic Press Inc.; *Figures 2.10, 2.11* Wayne, R. P. (1991), *Chemistry Of Atmospheres*, Oxford University Press; *Figure 2.12* adapted from United Kingdom Stratospheric Ozone Review Group (1987), *Stratospheric Ozone*, reproduced with the permission of the Controller of Her Majesty's Stationery Office; *Figure 2.15* adapted from Dickinson, R. E. (1982), in Clark, W. C. (ed.), *Carbon Dioxide Review*, Oxford University Press; *Figure 2.16* adapted from Barry, R. G. and Chorley, R. J. (1987), *Atmosphere, Weather and Climate*, Methuen and Co; *Figure 2.17b* Strahler, A. N. (1965), *Introduction To Physical Geography*, John Wiley and Sons Inc., © A. N.Strahler; *Figure 2.18* adapted from Sellers, W. D. (1965), *Physical Climatology*, University of Chicago Press; *Figure 2.19* adapted from Strahler, A. N. (1963), *The Earth Sciences*, HarperCollins, © A. N. Strahler; *Figures 2.20a, b* Frank Lane Picture Agency; *Figure 2.20c* Heather Angel, Biofotos; *Figure 2.21* adapted from Vonder Haar, T. and Suomi, V. (1971), *Journal of Atmospheric Science*, **28**, pp. 305–314, American Meteorological Society; *Figure 2.22* Reprinted with permission from *Nature*, **314**, © Copyright 1985 Macmillan Magazines Ltd; *Figure 2.24* From *Understanding Our Atmospheric Environment* by M. Neiburger, J. G. Edinger and W. D. Bonner. Copyright © 1973 by W. H. Freeman and Co. Reprinted by permission; *Figure 2.25* Perry, A. H. and Walker, J. M. (1977), *The Ocean–Atmosphere System*, Longman Group UK Ltd; *Figure 2.27* Anikonchine/ Sternberg, *The World Ocean*, © 1981, p. 176. Adapted by permission of Prentice-Hall, Inc., Englewood Cliffs, NJ; *Figure 2.30* Meadows, P. S. and Campbell, J. I. (1988), *An Introduction To Marine Science*, Blackie Academic & Professional (an imprint of

Scott Polar Research Institute; *bottom right*, James Clark Ross — Chris Gilbert, British Antarctic Survey; *Figure 6.1* Anderson, I. (1988), 'Greenhouse warming grips American corn belt', *New Scientist*, 30 June 1988, IPC Magazines Ltd; *Figure 6.4* From Jones, P. D. and Wigley, T. L. (1990), 'Global warming trends', *Scientific American*, August 1990, p. 70, Copyright © 1990 by Scientific American, Inc. All rights reserved; *Figures 6.5, 6.13* Based on Figure 2 in an early draft of Wigley, T. M. L. and Raper, S. C. B. *'Detection of the enhanced greenhouse effect on climate'* — a paper presented to the Second World Climate Conference. An updated version of this figure appeared in the published Conference Porceedings, published as Jäger, J. and Ferguon, H. L. (eds, 1991), *Climate Change: Science, Impacts and Policy*, Cambridge University Press; *Figure 6.12* John Storey/World Medicine; *Figures 7.3, 7.12* IPCC (1990), *Formulation of Strategies IPCC Working Group III Report*, June 1990, International Panel for Climate Change; *Figure 7.9* (*top left*) Lord Marshall (1990), 'The Marshall nuclear plan', *The Independent*, 3 July 1990; *Figure 7.9* (*top right*) Courtesy of British Nuclear Fuels plc; *Figure 7.11* © Third World Network Features and Consumers Association of Penan; *Figure 7.17* reproduced with permission of the Department of the Environment; *Figure 7.19* Reprinted with permission from *Nature*, **328**, p. 124, 9 July 1987, Copyright 1987 Macmillan Magazines Ltd; *Figure 7.20* Heather Angel, Biofotos; *Figure 8.9* adapted from Akita, S. and Moss, P. N. (1973), 'Photosynthetic responses to CO_2 and light by maize and wheat leaves adjusted for constant stomatal apertures', *Crop Science*, **13**, pp. 234–237, American Society of Agronomy; *Figure 8.10* Fitter, A. H. and Hay, R. K. M. (1981), *Environmental Physiology of Plants*, Academic Press Ltd; *Figure 8.12* Watt, A. D., Ward, L. K. and Eversham, B. C. (1990), 'Invertebrates', in *The Greenhouse Effect and Terrestrial Ecosystems of the UK*, Institute of Terrestrial Ecology Research Publication No 4, reproduced with the permission of the Controller of Her Majesty's Stationery Office; *Figure 8.13a* adapted from Graham, R. W. and Grimm, E. C. (1990), 'Effects of global climate change on the patterns of terrestrial biological communities', *TREE*, Elsevier Trends Publications, **5**(9), September 1990; *Figures 8.13 b, c* Adapted with permission from *Toward An Understanding of Global Change*, National Academy Press, Washington, D.C., 1988; *Figure 8.14* Parry, M. L., Carter, T. R. and Porter, J. H. (1989), 'The greenhouse effect and the future of UK agriculture', *Journal of Royal Agricultural Society of England*, November 1989, Royal Agricultural Society of England; *Figure 8.15* Yoshino, M. *et al.* (1988), 'The effects of climatic variations on agriculture in Japan', in Parry, M. L., Carter, T. R. and Konijn, N. T. (eds), *The Impact of Climatic Variations on Agriculture, Volume 1, Assessments in Cool Temperate and Cold Regions*, Kluwer Academic Publishers; *Figure 8.16* Downing, T. E. (1991), 'Vulnerability to hunger in Africa', *Global Environment Change*, Butterworth–Heinemann Ltd.

Tables

Table 3.1 Reproduced, with permission, from the *Annual Review of Earth and Planetary Sciences*, **16**, © 1988, by Annual Reviews Inc.; *Tables 8.1, 8.2* Houghton, J. T., Jenkins, G. J. and Ephraums, J. J. (1990), *Climate Change The IPCC Scientific Assessment*, Cambridge University Press, © IPCC; *Table 8.3* Nikonov, A. A. *et al.* (1988), 'The effects of climatic variations on agriculture in the semi-arid zone of European USSR. A. The Stavropol territory', in Parry, M. L., Carter, T. R. and Konijn, N. T. (eds), *The Impact of Climatic Variations on Agriculture, Volume 2, Assessments in Semi-Arid Regions*, Kluwer Academic Publishers; *Table 8.4* Parry, M. L. and Swaminathan, M. S. (1992), 'Effects of climate change on food production', in Mintzer, I. M. (ed.), *Confronting Climate Change*, Cambridge University Press.

Cartoon

p.173 Scott Willis/*San José Mercury News*, © Scott Willis/Copley News Service.

Colour Plates

Plate 1.1 Kunsthistorisches Museum, Vienna; *Plate 2.1* NASA Goddard Space Flight Center; *Plate 2.2* Science Photo Library/National Remote Sensing Centre; *Plate 4.1* Environmental Picture Library; *Plate 4.2* GEOPIC, Earth Satellite Corporation; *Plate 4.3* NASA/Science Photo Library; *Plate 4.4* R. Lampitt, IOS Deacon Laboratories; *Plate 4.5* South Coast Air Quality Management District, Los Angeles; *Plate 5.1* Drs A. Raval and V. Ramanathan, Scripps Institution of Oceanography, University of California, San Diego; *Plates 5.2, 5.3, 5.4* Houghton, J. T., Jenkins, G. J. and Ephraums, J. J. (eds) (1990) *Climate Change, The IPCC Scientific Assessment,* Cambridge University Press © IPCC; *Plate 6.1* From P. D. Jones and T. M. L. Wigley, 'Global warming trends' *Scientific American,* August 1990, pp. 66–67 Copyright © 1990 by Scientific American, Inc. All rights reserved; *Plate 6.2* NASA Goddard Space Flight Center.

Index

Note: Entries in **bold** are key terms. Page numbers in *italics* refer to figures and tables. Colour plate numbers are prefixed by '*Pl.*'.

ablation from ice-sheet, **195**–6

accumulation of snow onto ice-sheet, **195**–6

adaptive strategies for climatic change, 225–6

aerosols, *see* sulphate aerosols; tropospheric aerosols

AGCMs, *see* general circulation models

agriculture
    adaptation to climatic change, 225–6
    effects of sea-level rise, 200
    impacts on, of future climatic change, 202–7, 209–10, 216–20
    source of methane, 94–6, *234*, 235
    source of nitrous oxide, 103, *234*

albedo, **12**, 42
    clouds, 24, 27, 28–30, 43, *113*, *120*, 148
    effect of aerosols, 68, 147
        in the stratosphere, 67–71, 147
        in the troposphere, 147–8
    geographical variations
        modelled, *123*
        observed, *28*, *31*, 123–4
    planetary, 12, 24, 28, *31*, 68, *120*, 123, 147, 250
    surfaces
        land, *28*, 30, *120*
        sea, 30, 39
        snow/ice, 30, 39
        vegetation, 30, *120*
    see also feedback mechanisms; radiation balance

Antarctic Bottom Water, **39**

Antarctic circumpolar current, *see* West wind drift

Antarctic Divergence, **38**, 83

Antarctic region, 37, 38, 39, 44, *Pl. 2.1*
    ice-sheet, 197–8, *199*
    see also ozone 'hole'; ozone layer

anthropogenic sources of greenhouse gases, 78, 89, *234*
    see also carbon cycle; entries under names of individual gases; fossil fuels; greenhouse effect

anticyclones, **33**, 37, 122

Arctic region, 37, 38–9, *Pl. 2.1*

atmosphere
    composition, 17, 76–9, 94–103
        future, 104–6, *177*
        past, 71–4
    general circulation, 32–5, 44–5
    models, *see* general circulation models
    radiation trapping by, 15–19
    vertical structure, 19–22
    see also climate system; radiation balance

atmospheric lifetimes, **97**
    carbon dioxide, *100*, 105, 107, 160, 238
    halocarbons, 99–103, 158, 180
    methane, 97, 100
    nitrous oxide, 100, 103

atmospheric window, 16, **17**, 19, *24*, 77

BaU, *see* 'Business as Usual' scenario

Benedick, R. E., 5, 159

biogeochemical carbon cycle, **72** *see also* carbon cycle

biological pump, **85**, 88, 91, 182

biomass, *41*, **80**, 81, *83*, 85, 87, *94*, 95, *96*

biomes, **10**, *11*, 45, 119

black body, **12**, *13*
    radiation, 15–16, 24, *25*
    see also Stefan–Boltzmann law

boundary fluxes, **116**, 117
    see also energy flux; hydrological cycle

Broecker, W. S., 150–51, *152*, 154, 180, 185–7, 188

'Business as Usual' (BaU) scenario, developed by IPCC, **173**, 176–9, 188, 191, 198, *199*, 200
    carbon dioxide emissions, 173–4
    changes in sea-level, 198–200
    methane emissions, 175
    model-simulated climatic change, 176–9, 189, 191

CCC, *see* climate modelling groups

C3 plants, 204, 205

C4 plants, 204

carbon
    ^{14}C anomalies, **65**–7
    dissolved inorganic (DIC), **84**, 85–6, 92
    dissolved organic (DOC), 91–2

carbon cycle,
    global, 79–94
        on land, 80–81, 90, 183
        ocean–atmosphere, 82–6, 90–93, 182
    human activities, effects of, 86–7, *94*, 169, 172
    models of, 88–90, 105, 162, 176, 178, 182–3
    see also biological pump; carbon dioxide; deforestation; greenhouse gas feedbacks; Joint Global Ocean Flux Study; International Global Atmospheric Chemistry Programme

carbon cycle models, **105**–6

carbon dioxide (CO_2)
    absorption of radiation, 16, 17, 25, 109–11

atmospheric concentration, 17, 19–20, 78, 99
    correlation with global-mean surface temperature, 63, 73–4, 181–2
    effect of doubling on climate, 109–14
        see also climate sensitivity; equilibrium climatic change scenarios
    measurement in ice-cores, 73, 77–8
    monitoring, 76
    projected, 104–6 *177*
    response of plants to, 203–5, 209
atmospheric lifetime, *100*, 105–6, 238
'dissolving' (in oceans), 84
emission scenarios, 105–6, 174
emissions
    characteristics of anthropogenic sources, 233–5
    monitoring, 233–4, 235
emissions from fossil fuel burning
    factors affecting, 104, 163–9, 172, 178–9
    past and present, 9, 78–9, 86, 87, 89, 94, *164*, 233–4
    strategies for reducing, 164–9, *174*, 236–8
emissions from deforestation and changing land use
    past and present, 9, 86–7, *89*, 94, 233–4, 238
    tropical, 169–73
fixation, 203
    see also photosynthesis
formed from methane, 96
removal from emissions, 224–5
sinks, 77, 86, 87–94
see also carbon cycle; deforestation; energy; Framework Convention on Climatic Change; greenhouse gas feedbacks

carbon dioxide fertilization effect, 90, 204

carbon monoxide (CO), 96, 97, 98, 106, 178

carbon tetrachloride (CCl$_4$), 99, 101

carbonate sediments/rocks, 72, *81*, *82*, *94*

causes of climatic change
    forcing factors, 149
        see also greenhouse forcing; radiative forcing; solar forcing; sulphate aerosols
    internally-generated natural variability, 142–4, 178
    lithospheric plate movements, 51–2
    orbital effects, *see* Milankovic–Croll effects
    volcanic eruptions, 67–71, 147

CFCs, *see* chlorofluorocarbons

'chemistry' models, 105–6, 157, 159, 176, 183

chlorofluorocarbons (CFCs), 5, 77, 99–103, 156–9
    atmospheric concentrations, 78, *100*
    controls over emissions, 158–9, 228
        see also Framework Convention on Climate Change; Montreal Protocol; Vienna Convention for the Protection of the Ozone Layer
    emission scenarios, 174
    zero net radiative effect, 180–81

climate
    defined, 10
    geographical and seasonal variations in, 10, *26*, 27–43, *122*, *123*

model simulations of future changes in, *see* 'Business as Usual' scenario; equilibrium climatic change scenarios; pace of climatic change; realized warming; etc.
    natural variability of 142–4
    past changes in, 5, 47–51
        glacial/interglacial cycles, *50*, 54–63
        Holocene, *50*, 65–7, 145
        recent past, *50*, 67–71, 138–41

climate modelling groups
    Canadian Climate Center (CCC), *122, 123, Pl. 5.2a and d, Pl. 5.3a and d*
    Geophysical Fluid Dynamics Laboratory (GFDL), 116, *122, 123, 127*, 130–32, 143–4, 187, *Pl. 5.2b and e, Pl. 5.3b and e, Pl. 5.4*
    Goddard Institute for Space Studies (GISS), 8, 116, *122, 123*, 136, *150*, 217
    National Center for Atmospheric Research (NCAR), *109, 122, 123, 127*, 128
    United Kingdom Meteorological Office (UKMO), 8, 116, *122, 123, 127, Pl. 5.2c and f, Pl. 5.3c and f*

climate sensitivity (ΔT_{2x}), 124–6, 128, 131, 132, 133, 142, 160–61, 178

climate sensitivity parameter (λ), **111**, 112, 124

climate system, 10, *45*, *115*
    interconnectedness of, 43–5, 114–15
    models of, *see* general circulation models

climatological averages, 121

cloud condensation nuclei (CCN), 28, 147–8

cloud feedback, 113–14, 118, 125–6, 178

clouds, 23, 24, 35, 43, 77, 110, *Pl. 2.2*
    albedo, 24, 27, 28–30, *113, 120*, 148
    models, parameterization schemes, 118
    radiation trapping by, 25, 110
    types of, 28–30, *113*
        cirrus, 28, 29, 30, *113, Pl. 2.2*
        cumulonimbus, 28, 29, 30, 43, *113, Pl. 2.2*
        stratocumulus, 28, 29, 30, 43, *113*

coal, reserves of, 166 *167*
    see also carbon dioxide emissions; fossil fuels

conduction, *see* sensible heat

consequences of greenhouse gas-induced climatic change
    for agriculture, 216–20
        cereals, 206–7, 209–10, 216–17, 218, 220
        changes in growing seasons, 206, 217
        food security, 219–20
        pests, 207
        spatial shifts, 217
    from changing sea-level, 200–201
    economic and political, 221–3
    for natural ecosystems, 212–16
    for plants and animals, 205–11

control simulations, 121–4, *143*

convection, 22–3, 32–3, 43

Coriolis force, 32
    atmospheric circulation, *32*, *34*
    oceanic circulation, 36, *38*

cryosphere, **44**, *45*, 115

cyclones, 32, **33**, *34*, 37, 122, 192
    tropical, **35**, 153, 218

deforestation, 86–7, 89, 104, *Pl. 4.1*, *Pl. 4.2*
    limitation, 238
    monitoring, 235
    tropical, 86, 169–73, 174
    see also carbon dioxide; carbon cycle; Framework Convention on Climate Change; United Nations Conference on Environment and Development

dendrochronology, 66

detection issue, 136, **137**–61, 188

deuterium temperature record, 57–8, 61

developed world, 164, 222, 226
    emissions limitation, 236, 237
    energy demand, *164*, 165
    reforestation, 172, 238
    role in FCCC, 228, 229

developing world, 164, 222, 226
    CO_2 emissions, 164
    deforestation, 169–72, 238
    emissions limitation, 236, 237
    energy demand, 164, *165*, 166, 173
    impact of climatic change, 219–20, 222, 226
    population, *163*
    role in FCCC, 228, 237

development
    use of term, 164

DIC, *see* dissolved inorganic carbon

dimethylsulphide (DMS), 147

dissolved inorganic carbon (DIC), **84**, 85–6, 92

dissolved organic carbon (DOC), 91, 92

DMS, *see* dimethylsulphide

DOC, *see* dissolved organic carbon

downward transport in oceans and carbon cycle, **83**, 86, 88, *91*

downwelling, **38**, *39*, 44, 83, 130, 132, 187

Earth
    eccentricity of orbit, 53, 59, 60
    orbital variations, 52–63
        see also Milankovic–Croll effect
    precession of axis, 53–4, 59, 60
    tilt of axis, 27, 53, 59, 60
    see also radiation balance

Earth Radiation Budget Experiment (ERBE), *113*, 148

Earth Summit, *see* United Nations Conference on Environment and Development

eccentricity, *see* Earth, eccentricity of orbit

ecosystems, effect of climatic change, 212–16
    and carbon cycle, 80, 81, 90
    distribution of, *120*
    see also consequences of climatic change

effective radiating temperature of Earth, **15**, 16, 18, 25

electromagnetic spectrum, **15**

emission quotas, 236–9

emission scenarios, **105**–6, 162–79, 187, 188, 198, 199
    see also 'Business as Usual' scenario; entries under names of greenhouse gases

energy
    demand, 163–6, 173–4
    efficiency and conservation, 164–6, *174*, *179*, 236–7
    statistics, 234
    supply, 166–9, *174*

energy efficiency and conservation, **164**–6, *179*, 236–7

energy flux, **12**
    from black body, **12**
    latent heat, 23, *24*, 42, 43, *120*
    longwave, emitted to space, *13*, *14*, *19*, *24*, 25, 110, *146*
        variation with latitude, *31*, *123*
    longwave, emitted by surface, *14*, *19*, *24*, 43, *110*
    sensible heat, 23, *24*, 43, *120*
    solar, 12–14, 145–6
        variation with latitude, 27–31

energy intensity (of different economies), **164**

Epochs (geological time), **47**, *49*

equilibrium climatic change scenarios, *110*, 111, 124, **125**–8, 153 191, 212
    precipitation, 125, 126, *Pl. 5.3*
    soil moisture, *127*, 128, 210
    temperature changes, 125, 128, *Pl. 5.2*, *Pl. 5.4*
    see also climate sensitivity

Eras (geological time), **47**, *48*, *49*

ERBE, *see* Earth Radiation Budget Experiment

evaporation, 42, *45*
    and marine salinity, 44, 185–6
    see also hydrological cycle; latent heat

evapotranspiration, **42**, 120, 207–9

external factors in greenhouse effect, **142**, 145–8

extreme events, 153, 218

faculae, **64**

faint Sun paradox, 64, 72

FCCC, *see* Framework Convention on Climate Change

feedback mechanisms (processes), 62
    greenhouse gas, 181–4
    positive or negative, definition, 62
    radiative
        cloud, 113–14, 125–6, 178
        snow–ice albedo, 62, 112, 114, 125, 126
        water vapour, 62, 112, 125

fingerprinting technique for detection, 149, 152

foraminifera, 55, 56, *185*

forcing factors, **149**, 178
    see also radiative forcing

fossil fuels, *81*, 82, *94*
    carbon dioxide release from, *see* carbon dioxide emissions
    carbon dioxide removal from emissions, 224–5
    carbon 'intensity' of, 166

methane release from, *see* methane emissions
nitrogen oxides release from, *see* nitrogen oxides
reserves, *167*
projected usage, *174*
see also coal; energy; FCCC; natural gas; oil
Framework Convention on Climate Change (FCCC), **226**–30, 236–7, 239
  review process, 229, 231–2
  verification of commitments, 232–6
'framework' convention, 227–8
free radicals, 96
  see also hydroxyl radicals
Freon, *101*
  see also chlorofluorocarbons
frequency spectrum, 59–61

GCTE, *see* Global Change and Terrestrial Ecosystems
general circulation models (GCMs), 115, **116**–21
  AGCMs, 119, 129, 143
  coupled AGCMs/OGCMs, 129, 130–32, 141, 143–4, 149, 187, 191
  deficiencies in, 118–21
  OGCMs, 119, 129
  validation of, 120, 121–4
  see also equilibrium climatic change scenarios; realized warming; *etc.*
geological time, 47, *48*
GFDL, *see* climate modelling groups
GISS, *see* climate modelling groups
glacial, 49–50, 55, 58–9, 61, 63, 74, 178, 181–2, 184, 185, 214
glacier, 41, 44, 45, *115*
  advance and retreat, *8*, 65, 140, 196–7, 198–9
Global Change and Terrestrial Ecosystems project (GCTE), **107**
global-mean sea-level, 192
  see also sea-level
global-mean surface temperature, 8, **10**, 18, 25
  calculation of, for black-body planet, 14
  natural variability, *138*, 140–41, 142–4, *Pl. 6.1*
  projected increase over next century, *see* global warming
  past variations in, 48–51, 65, 72, 138–41, 202–3
global warming, 5–9. 10, 109
  over past century
    interpretation of, 142–54
    modelled, *141*
    observed, 8, 138–141
  projected for next century by IPCC, 177–179
  see also climate sensitivity; equilibrium climatic change scenarios; pace of climatic change; realized warming
global warming scenarios, 109
greenhouse effect, 18
  enhanced/anthropogenic, 19, 137, 148–50
    see also radiative forcing
  'natural', 12, 15–19, 24, 49
  on Venus, 72–3
greenhouse forcing, 112, *133*, 187

greenhouse gases, 5–7, 10, **18**–19, 76–8, 94–103
  feedbacks, 181–4
  measure of effectiveness, 99
  monitoring anthropogenic sources, 233–5
  see also entries under names of individual gases; emission scenarios; FCCC; Montreal Protocol
greenhouse signal, 137, 144, 178
  detection of, *see* detection issue
Greenland, ice-sheet, 196, 197, 198, 199
gross photosynthesis, 203, 205, 206
gyres (in oceans), **36**, 52

Hadley cell, 32, *33*
half-life (τ) of halocarbons, 102
halocarbons, 99–103
  atmospheric concentrations, **76**–7, 78, 99
  atmospheric lifetimes, 99, 100, 102
  emission scenarios, 174, 175
  see also chlorofluorocarbons (CFCs) *etc.*
Hansen, James, *136*, 150–52, 153–4, 230
HCFCs, *see* hydrochlorofluorocarbons
HFCs, *see* hydrofluorocarbons
Holocene epoch, **50**, 66
  climatic changes during, *50*, 65–7, 145
hurricanes, 35, 153
hydrochlorofluorocarbons (HCFCs), 102, 103
  HCFC-22, 99, 102, 174
hydrofluorocarbons (HFCs), 102, 103
hydrological cycle, 35, 40, **41**–3, 114, 115, 125
  land surface hydrology, 119–20
    parameterization schemes for, *121*
  role of vegetation in, 41, *42*, *120*
hydroxyl radicals, 96–8, 105–6, 176, 183

Ice Ages, *8*, **49**, 51–2, 64, 214
  see also Little Ice Age
ice-cores
  analysis of trapped air, 73, 77–8, 181, *184*
  detection of volcanic eruptions, 69–70
  isotope studies, 54, 55, 56–8, 61, 185
  sulphate in, 69–70
ice-sheets, *45*, 49, 55, 62–3, 65, 185
  effects of temperature, 54, 195–8
ICSU, *see* International Council of Scientific Unions
IGAC, *see* International Global Atmospheric Chemistry Programme
IGBP, *see* International Geosphere–Biosphere Programme
index of food security, 219
infrared (ir) radiation, *15*, *17*
  absorbing greenhouse gases, 76, 130
  emitted to space, 25
  emitted by surface, *120*
  see also longwave radiation
interglacial, 49–50, 55, 58–9, 61, 63, 74, 181–2, 186

Intergovernmental Panel on Climate Change (IPCC), 1990 report, **7**, *8*, 93, 155, 230
  assessment of
    anthropogenic emissions of carbon dioxide, 86, 87
    climate sensitivity, 126, 160, 176
    GCMs, 122–4, 125, 126
    global warming trends, 138, 140
    sources and sinks of methane, 95
    sulphate aerosol effects, 148
    trends in tropospheric ozone, 98
  role in policy making, 7, 155–6, 230–32
  scenarios for next century
    atmospheric concentrations of greenhouse gases, *177*
    changes in soil moisture availability, 210
    emissions of greenhouse gases, 173–6
    pace of climatic change, *177*, 178, 191, 203
    radiative forcing, *177*
    sea-level rise, 198–200
  Tropical Forest Workshop, 170, 173
  working groups, 156, 173, 231
internally-generated natural variability, 142–4, 178
International Council of Scientific Unions (ICSU), 79, 105, 231
International Geosphere–Biosphere Programme (IGBP), 79, 92, 93, 107
  see also International Global Atmospheric Chemistry Programme; Joint Global Ocean Flux Study
International Global Atmospheric Chemistry Programme (IGAC), 93, 107
International Satellite Cloud Climatology Project (ISCCP), *113*
Intertropical Convergence Zone (ITCZ), 33, *34*, 122, *Pl. 2.2*
IPCC, *see* Intergovernmental Panel on Climate Change
ISCCP, *see* International Satellite Cloud Climatology Project
ITCZ, *see* Intertropical Convergence Zone

JGOFS, *see* Joint Global Ocean Flux Study
Joint Global Ocean Flux Study (JGOFS), 92, 107, 182

kelvin temperature scale, 12

land-ice
  melting, 195–8
  see also glaciers; ice-cores; ice-sheets
land surface hydrology, 119, *120*, *121*
latent heat of vaporization, **23**, *24*, 25, 39, 41, *42*, 43, 77, *120*
leaf, structure, 208–9
limiting factors, 91
  in photosynthesis, **208**
Little Ice Age, 5, 50–51, 65, 71, 145, 181, 196, 203, *Pl. 1.1*
longwave (ir) radiation, 17
  absorption and re-emission by greenhouse gases, 17–19, 77
  emitted to space, *13*, *14*, *19*, *24*, *25*, *45*, 110, *146*
    spectrum, *25*
    variation with latitude, 30, *31*, *123*
  emitted by surface, *14*, *19*, 22, *24*, 43, *110*

Ma (millions of years geological time), **47**
marine sediments, 54–6, *58*, 182
  carbonate, 72, *81*, 82, *94*
  micropalaeontological studies, 54, 56, 185
  oxygen isotope studies, 54–5, *58*, 60–61
marine snow (fluff), 85–6, *Pl. 4.4*
Mauna Loa observatory, Hawaii, records, 76, 78
Maunder Minimum (sunspot numbers), 67
media, role in climate debate, *6*, *8–9*, 86, *136*, 153, 154–5, *168*
Medieval Climatic Optimum, 50–51, 202
mesoscale eddies, 37, 44, 129
methane
  absorption of longwave radiation, *16*, *17*, 19
  atmospheric chemistry, 94–8
    models of, 105, 176, 183
  atmospheric concentration, 17, 76, 78, 94, *95*, 100
    correlation with global-mean surface temperature, *184*
    projected by IPCC, *177*
  atmospheric lifetime, 97, 100
  emissions
    monitoring, 234, 235
    rates of, 104, 105
    scenarios, 175, 178
  sinks, 95, 96–8
  sources, 77, 94–6
    anthropogenic, characteristics of, 234
    natural, effects of climatic change on, 183–4
methyl chloroform, 100, 103
micropalaeontology, 54, 56, *185*
Milankovic–Croll effects (orbital changes), **53**–4, 59–63
  amplification of, 62–3, 74, 182
mixed layer (ocean), **37**, 82, *89*, 119, 126
'mixed-layer ocean' model, 118–19, 124, 130
models, *see* carbon cycle; 'chemistry' models; general circulation model; 'mixed-layer ocean' model
molecular vibrations, 17–18
monsoon, 35, 122
'Montreal Protocol on Substances that Deplete the Ozone Layer', 101, 102, 156, 159, 175–6, 228

natural gas, 166, 234
  reserves, *167*
  see also carbon dioxide emissions; fossil fuels; methane
NCAR, *see* climate modelling groups
negative feedback, *see* feedback mechanisms
net photosynthesis, 203–4, 205
  response to temperature change, 205–6
net primary production (NPP), 80, 81, 86
  response to carbon dioxide levels, 203
Newton's first law of motion (atmospheric circulation), **32**
nitric oxide (NO), 98
  see also nitrogen oxides
nitrogen, 17, 66, 98
nitrogen dioxide (NO_2), 98
  see also nitrogen oxides

nitrogen oxides (NO$_x$),. 98
    nitric oxide (NO), 98
    nitrogen dioxide (NO$_2$), 98
    precursors of tropospheric ozone, 98–9, 103,
      176, 178
    sources, 90, 98, 183, 234
    see also nitrous oxide
nitrous oxide (N$_2$O), 103
    absorption of longwave radiation, *16*, 17, 19
    atmospheric concentration, 17, 76, 78
    atmospheric lifetime, 99
    emissions
        monitoring, 233, 234
        scenarios, 174
    sink, 103
    sources, 103, 183, 234
NMHC, *see* non-methane hydrocarbons
non-methane hydrocarbons (NMHC), 98
North Atlantic Deep Water, 39
North Atlantic drift, *36*, 37, 39, 52
northeast trade winds, 32
NO$_x$, **98**, *see also* nitrogen oxides
NPP, *see* net primary production
nuclear power, 166–7, *168*

ocean–atmosphere system, *see* climate system
oceans
    albedo, 30
    in carbon cycle, 72, 81–6, 90–93, 182, 187
    circulation, 31, 36–40, 44, *45*, *115*, 182
        past variations, 52, 63, 185–7
        and phytoplankton blooms, 91, *92*
    DIC in, 84, 85–6
    heat transport in, 31
    influence on climate, 43–4, 132
        see also climate system
    influence on pace of climatic change, 128–33, 187
    layered structure, 37
    models, 82, 88–9 118–19, 129, 133
    salinity, 39–40, 44, 185–6
    sink, for anthropogenic carbon dioxide, 88–9, *94*
    temperature, 26, 37
    thermal expansion, 195, 198, 199
    thermal inertia, 142
    volume of basins, 192
    see also climate system; downwelling; general
    circulation models; mixed-layer ocean models;
    phytoplankton; sea-surface temperature; thermohaline
    circulation; upwelling; World Ocean Circulation
    Experiment
OECD countries, **164**
OGCMs, *see* general circulation models
oil, 166
    reserves, *167*
    see also carbon dioxide emissions; fossil fuels
Organization of Economic Co-operation and Development,
see OECD countries

oxygen
    absorption of radiation, *16*, 17
    atmospheric concentration, 17
    $\delta^{18}O$, **55**, *57*, *58*
    isotopes, climatic record, 54–5, 56–8, 185
ozone
    absorption of longwave (ir) radiation, *16*, 17, 19, 25
    absorption of shortwave (uv) radiation, *16*, 21–2, 156, 181
    stratospheric, *see* ozone layer
    tropospheric, 20, 25, 76, 77, 97, 98–9, 104, 178, *Pl. 4.5*
ozone layer, 20–22, 25
    depletion, 7, 77, 101–2, 156–9
        cooling effect of, 180–81
        ozone 'hole', 101, 156, 157, 159, 183, 188, *Pl. 6.2*
    protection, *see* Framework Convention on Climate Change;
    Montreal Protocol; Vienna Convention for the Protection of
    the Ozone Layer

pace of climatic change
    effect on living organisms, 214, 216
    future, projected by IPCC, 177–8
    model simulations of, 128–33
    past, 177–8, 184–7, 203
palaeomagnetic techniques, sediment dating, **55**
parameterization (in climate models), **118**–21, 124, 126, 130, 132
period of curve, **59**
    see also time series
Period (geological time), **47**, *48*, *49*
photic zone, 83, 85
photochemical processes, **21**, 25, 98, *99*, 100, 103
'photochemical smog', *Pl. 4.5*
photolysis, 21
    CFCs, 100–101
    nitrogen dioxide, 99
    ozone, 21, 97–8
photosynthesis, 80, 203–4, 208–9
    see also carbon cycle; plants
phytoplankton, 83, 84, 85, 91–2, 182, *Pl. 4.3*, *Pl. 4.4*
plants
    effect on climate, 45, 114–15, *120*
    effect on hydrological cycle, 42, *120*
    effects of climatic change, 205–11, 212–13, 214–16
    response to carbon dioxide levels, 203–5, 209
        see also carbon dioxide fertilization effect
    see also biomes; transpiration
plate tectonics, 47, **51**–2, 192–3
Pleistocene epoch, *49*, **50**
polar easterlies (winds), **33**
policy-making, role of scientists, 7, *8–9*, 230–31
'policy' scenarios developed by IPCC, 173–6
    see also 'Business as Usual (BaU)' scenario; emission
    scenarios
'polluter pays' principle, 237
population, world, *95*, 163
positive feedback, 62
    see also feedback mechanisms

precautionary principle, **157**, 228

precession, *see* Earth, precession of axis

precipitation, 10, *41*, 42
    modelling studies, 122, 125, 126, 210, 219–20, *Pl. 5.3*
    variation with latitude, 122
    see also climate system; consequences of climatic change;
    hydrological cycle

preventive strategies for climatic change, 224, 226–30
    see also Framework Convention on Climate Change

proxy data, **48**, *49*, 58–9, 69, 185
    sources, *see* ice cores; marine sediments; *etc.*

Quaternary Period, *48*
    Ice Age, 49–50, 59

radiation balance, 12–**14**
    of Earth–atmosphere system, 17, 19, 24–5, *31*, 43,
    109–10, *123*, 145–6

radiation trapping (by atmospheric constituents), 15–19, 25,
77, 100, 110
    see also greenhouse effect

radiative forcing, 109–**111**, 130, 132, 137, 142, 145–6,
147–8, 176–7
    simulating response to, 111, 130–32
        see also climate sensitivity; realized warming
    see also greenhouse forcing; solar forcing

radicals, **96**
    see also hydroxyl radicals

radioactive dating, sediments, **55**

radiocarbon, **65**, 66

realized warming, **130**–33, 141, 178, 191, *Pl. 5.4a*

renewable energy sources, 166–7

reservoirs
    carbon cycle, 81–2, 86, 93–4
    hydrological cycle, **41**, 42

residence time, **42**, 82, 105

respiration (plant), **80**, 203
    response to temperature rise, 205–6

response strategies to climatic change, 224–6

response times (ice melting), **195**

rice paddies, methane sources, 94–6, 175, 234, 235

ruminants, methane source, 94–5, 234, 235

salinity of seawater, 39–40, 44, 185–6
    see also thermohaline circulation

Schlesinger, Michael, 150, 151, 152, 154, 160

Schneider, Stephen, 109, 136–7, 150, 154, 155

science, role in policy-making, 7, *8*–9, 230–31

sea-ice, 38–9, 44, *Pl. 2.1*
    albedo, 30
    models, 116, 118, 119, 124, 126
    see also climate system; snow–ice albedo feedback

sea-level, change in, *8*, 140, 192–201
    causes, 192–3, 195–8
    consequences, 200–201, 220
    projected by IPCC, 198–200

    response to, 225

sea-surface temperatures (SSTs), *26*, 44, **112**, 140, 185, *Pl. 5.1*
    and cyclone formation, 153
    methods of measurement, *139*
    modelling studies, 116, 118–19, 122, 124

seasons, 27, 35, 54

Second World Climate Conference (Geneva, 1990), 6, *8*,
155–6, 224

sensible heat, **23**, *24*, 25, *39*, 43, *120*

shortwave radiation, 17, *19*, *24*
    see also ultraviolet radiation

sinks, **77**
    for carbon dioxide, 77, 86, 88–93, 182, 187
    for methane, 77, 96, 97
    for nitrous oxide, 77, 103

snow–ice albedo feedback, **112**
    see also feedback mechanisms

soil moisture, *42*, **119**, *120*, *121*
    effect on plant growth, 205, 208, 209–10, 216, 217
    modelling studies, *121*, 122, *123*, 126–8, 210, 219
    variation with latitude, *122*
    see also hydrological cycle

solar constant (solar irradiance), **12**–14
    variations in, 63–7, 145–6

solar flux (solar energy flux), **12**–14, 22, *24*, 25, 145–6
    variation with latitude, 27–31

solar forcing, **146**–7

solar irradiance, **12**
    see also solar flux

sources, **77**
    for carbon dioxide, 77, 87, 89, *94*, 234
    for methane, 77, 94, 95, 96, 183–4

southeast trade winds, **32**, *33*

spatial shifts, **217**

spectral analysis, **59**, 60, 61, 73

SSTs, *see* sea-surface temperatures

steady state, **21**
    of carbon cycle, 80, 81
    of hydrological cycle, 42
    of ozone concentration in stratosphere, 21–2

Stefan–Boltzmann constant, 12

Stefan–Boltzmann Law, **12**, 110

stomata, **208**–9

storm surges, **201**

stratosphere, **20**, 25
    vertical transport in, 22
    see also halocarbons; ozone layer; radiation balance;
    sulphate aerosols

sulphate aerosols
    in stratosphere, **68**–71, 147
    in troposphere, 147–8

sulphate compensation effect, **148**
    future, 148, 176
    past, 148

sulphur dioxide, 68, 69, 97, 147, 148

sunspot minima, **66**–7, 145

sunspot numbers, *8*, **64**–5

surface temperature (surface–air temperature), *14*
  geographical and seasonal variations, 26, 27, 122
  see also global-mean surface temperature

sustainable development, 228

technical fixes, **224**–5

thermocline, 37

thermohaline circulation, **40**, 44, 182, 185
  shutdown, 186–7

thermosphere, 20

Third World, *see* developing world

tilt, *see* Earth, tilt of axis

time-dependent simulation, **130**–31, 141, 143–4, 147

time series, **59**, 139
  see also spectral analysis

Toronto Conference (1988), 153, 156

trade winds, **32**

transpiration, **41**, 42, *120*, 208, 209
  see also evapotranspiration

1,1,1-trichloroethane, *see* methyl chloroform

tropical cyclones, **35**

tropopause, **20**, 22–3

troposphere, **20**, *29*, 32, 183
  see also halocarbons; ozone; radiation balance; sulphate
  aerosols

tropospheric aerosols, **147**–9

tundra zone, *11*
  source of methane, 184
  threat to, 216

typhoons 35, 153

UKMO, *see* climate modelling groups

ultraviolet (uv) radiation, *15*, *16*, **17**
  absorption by stratospheric ozone, 21–2, 156
  damage to biological material, 22
  see also shortwave radiation

'umbrella' conventions, **227**–8

UNCED, *see* United Nations Conference on Environment and
Development

uncertainty in climatic change studies
  and climate debate, 5, 150–55, 159, 160–61, 211, 220
    see also FCCC
  emission scenarios, 103–4, 162, 173–6, 179
  impact assessments, 191, 198–200, 212, 216, 221–3
  modelling studies
    climate sensitivity, 109, 125–6, 160
    model deficiencies, 90–93, 105–6, 117–21, 122, 128–9,
    132, 176–8, 180–87

pace of change, 132, 178
  spatial pattern of change, 109, 126–8, 132, 191, 210, 212

UNEP, *see* United Nations Environment Programme

United Nations Conference on Environment and Development
(Rio de Janeiro, 1992), 6, 7, *9*, 226, 238

United Nations Environment Programme (UNEP), 105, 156,
158

United States National Academy of Sciences (NAS), 126

unprecedented change approach, **149**

upward transport in oceans
  and carbon cycle, **83**, 86, 88
  see also upwelling

upwelling, **37**–8, 44, 83, *91*, 130

urban heat island effect, 139, 140

'Vienna Convention for the Protection of the Ozone Layer'
(1985), 158–9, 228

volcanic eruptions, 67–71, 147
  effect on carbon cycle, 68, 72, *81*

Vostock ice-core, *57*
  composition of trapped air in, 73, 77, 181–2, *184*
  deuterium record, *57*, *58*, 61, 73
  oxygen isotope record, *57*

water
  availability to plants, 207–11
  distribution systems, 225, 226
  heat capacity, 35
  latent heat of vaporization, 23, *24*, 41, 43
  stress, 208–9
  see also hydrological cycle; soil moisture

water stress in plants, **208**–9

water vapour
  absorption of radiation, *16*, 17
  atmospheric concentration, 17, 77
  molecular vibrations, 18
  see also energy flux; feedback mechanisms

West wind drift, 36, 37, 38, 52

westerlies (winds), **33**

winds, 32–5, 39, 44
  transport of heat and moisture, 31, 43, *45*, *115*, 117

WMO, *see* World Meteorological Organization

WOCE, *see* World Ocean Circulation Experiment

World Meteorological Organization (WMO), 105, 156, 158

World Ocean Circulation Experiment (WOCE), **129**–30,
182, 188, 195

Younger Dryas, 184, **185**–7

zooplankton, 85

Plate 1.1 'Hunters in the snow'—an imaginary landscape painted by Pieter Bruegel the Elder in February 1565, during the first of the great winters of the next 200 years. This seems to have been the most severe period of the 'Little Ice Age', which stretched from around 1400 to 1850, at various times and to differing degrees in various parts of the world.

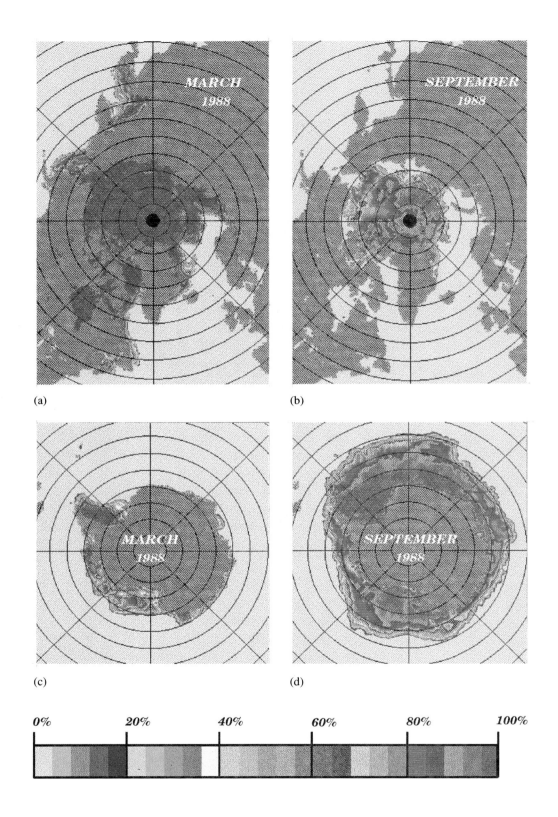

Plate 2.1 Sea-ice cover in the polar regions, from satellite measurements. Images (a) and (b) are centred on the North Pole, (c) and (d) on the South Pole. The scale gives the percentage of the ocean covered by sea-ice: pink is 100% coverage and blue 20% or less. (a) End of Arctic winter (March 1988, near-maximum ice-cover). (b) End of Arctic summer (September 1988). (c) End of Antarctic summer (March 1988). (d) End of Antarctic winter (September 1988).

Plate 2.2 A composite, false-colour image from a weather satellite (from above the Equator at the intersection with 0° longitude) showing the partly cloud-covered Africa–Atlantic Ocean side of the Earth. The dense clouds (white) around the Equator are cumulonimbus, associated with the ITCZ. There is a mid-latitude cyclone, rotating anticlockwise, in the North Atlantic Ocean. The polar regions have a thinner cloud cover (pink) of mainly cirrus and stratus clouds. The Sahara desert (yellow) is clearly visible, but much of the African rainforest (green) is covered by clouds.

Plate 4.1 The giant forest fires (*queimadas*) that accompany the clearing of tropical forest in Amazonia.

(a)

Plate 4.2 The on-going march of deforestation in Amazonia revealed by Landsat (Land Remote Sensing Satellite) images of a 185-km square area of Rondonia (western Brazil) in (a) June 1976, and (b) September 1981. Such images are based on the spectral characteristics of the radiation reflected back up from the surface. Following computer processing, dense leafy vegetation (interpreted as 'undisturbed' primary forest) appears red. The diagonal line across both of these images marks the course of Highway BR-364. The pattern of fine blue lines and rectangles closely associated with the road reveals farmland and pasture, created by 'slash and burn' clearing: the pink colour may be growing crops or scrub. This large-scale, systematic forest disturbance is a government-planned colonization project. Immigrants to Rondonia are sold 100-ha plots of forest to use for agriculture or pasture. Plant diseases, decreasing soil fertility and the prohibitively high cost of artificial fertilizers limit economical crop production on a given plot to some 1–4 years. This land obsolescence is compensated for by clearing more of the primary forest.

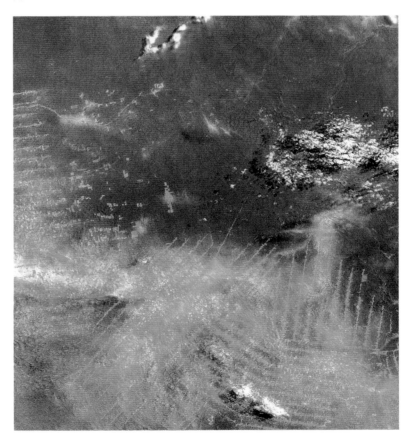

(b)

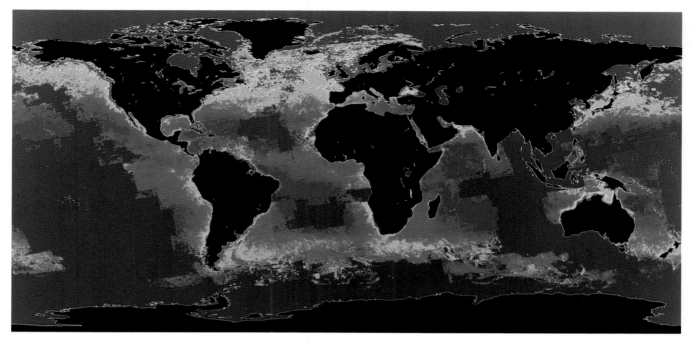

(a)

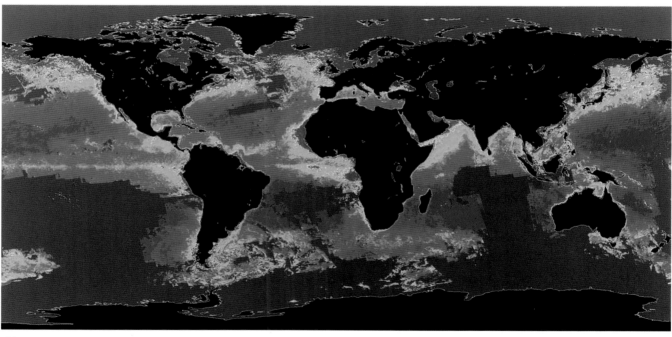

(b)

Plate 4.3 False-colour satellite images of the world's oceans, showing the distribution of phytoplankton in the surface water (from data collected by NASA's Nimbus 7 satellite). The colours represent varying phytoplankton densities, from red (most dense) through to yellow, green and blue to violet (least dense). Grey indicates areas with insufficient data for the image. (a) Average of distributions for April–June 1979, showing the blooming of phytoplankton throughout the North Atlantic during the northern spring. (b) Average of distributions for October–December 1979, showing the seasonal build up along the equator, especially in regions of localized upwelling off the western coasts of Africa and South America.

(a)

(a)

(b)

Plate 4.4 Photographs of the sea-bed at 4 000 m depth in the north-east Atlantic were taken with a time-lapse camera in 1983. Between 1 May and 15 June (a), there was little change (the mound in the foreground was made by an animal). During the next few weeks, heavy falls of marine snow (called 'fluff' by the scientists who took the pictures) all but obliterated the sea-bed, and by 14 July (b), only the top of the mound was still visible. The origin of the fluff was a phytoplankton bloom during May and early June.

(b)

Plate 4.5 Photographs of Los Angeles in clear air (a) and after formation of 'photochemical smog' (b)—a noxious brew of chemicals (including O_3) and particles that can be a serious health hazard. Such episodes result from the action of sunlight on the mix of gaseous pollutants (NO_x and hydrocarbons) released by burning fossil fuels (and biomass): in urban areas, vehicle exhausts are a major contributing cause. The problem is particularly severe where the local topography often results in a 'temperature inversion' (i.e. warm air overlying colder air) near the ground, as it does in the Los Angeles Basin, thus 'trapping' pollutants and preventing their rapid dispersal.

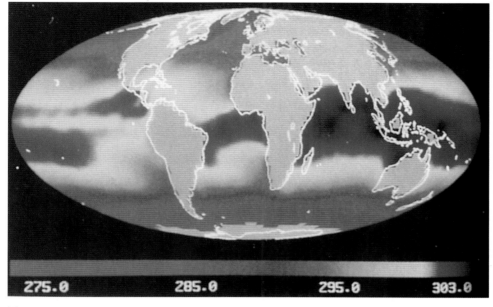

(a)

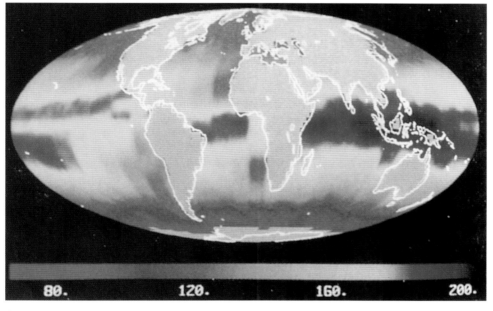

(b)

Plate 5.1 (a) Monthly-mean map of observed SSTs (in kelvin) for April 1985. (b) Monthly-mean map of the green-house effect (*G*) of the atmosphere under clear skies (in W m^{-2}). This comparison suggests a strong correlation between *G* and the SST. For example, *G* is a maximum over the relatively warm western equatorial Pacific Ocean (around Indonesia), but low over cold regions of oceanic upwelling, like those in the central and eastern equatorial Pacific, and off the west coasts of Africa and South America.

Plate 5.2 (*overleaf* ➔) Equilibrium scenarios for changes in surface-air temperature resulting from a doubling of the atmospheric concentration of CO$_2$ as simulated by three high resolution GCMs. (a)–(c) Averages for December, January and February (DJF), and (d)–(f) averages for June, July and August (JJA). Acronyms as in Figure 5.10. Averaged over the year *and over the globe*, the climate sensitivities (i.e. values of $\Delta T_{2\times}$) were 3.5 °C for the CCC and UKMO models, and 4 °C for that developed at the GFDL.

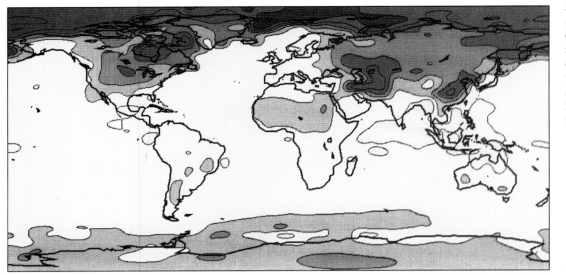

(a) CCC: Canadian Climate Centre

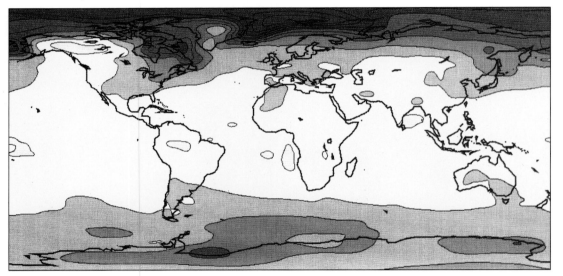

(b) GFDL: Geophysical Fluid Dynamics Laboratory

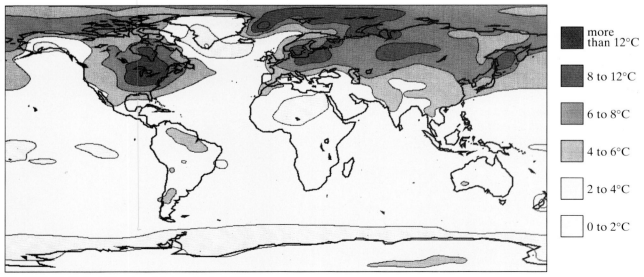

(c) UKMO: United Kingdom Meteorological Office

Plate 5.2 Computer simulations of the equilibrium temperature response to a CO_2-doubling, for (a)–(c) winter, and (d)–(f) summer, in the Northern Hemisphere (see p. 7 for full caption).

more than 12°C

8 to 12°C

6 to 8°C

4 to 6°C

2 to 4°C

0 to 2°C

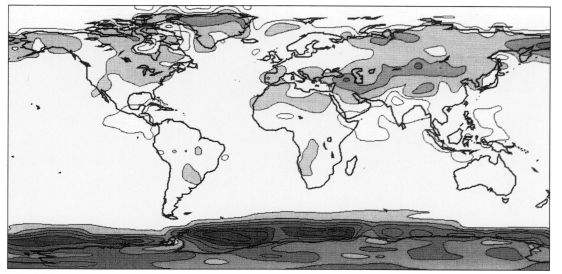

(d) CCC

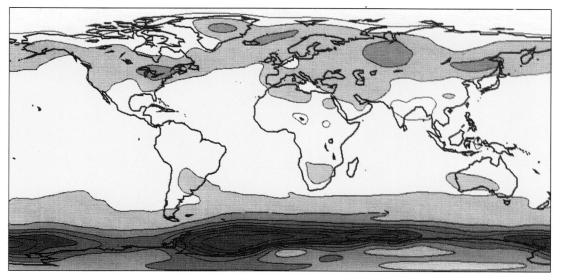

(e) GFDL

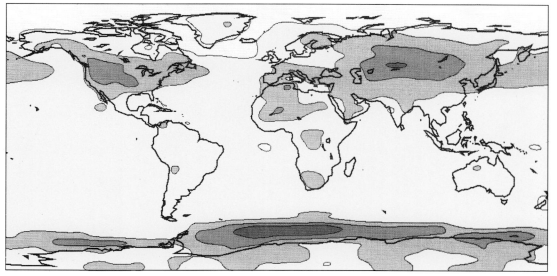

(f) UKMO

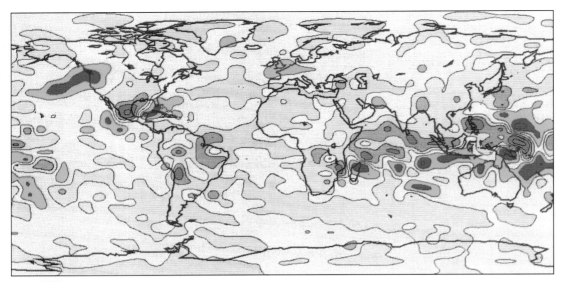

(a) CCC

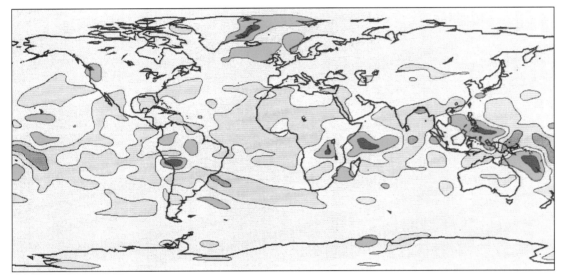

(b) GFDL

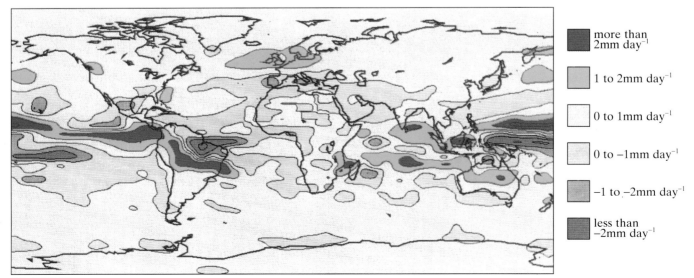

(c) UKMO

Plate 5.3 Changes in daily precipitation resulting from a doubling of the atmospheric concentration of CO_2, as simulated by the three high resolution models in Plate 5.2. (a)–(c) DJF averages, and (d)–(f) JJA averages.

more than 2mm day^{-1}

1 to 2mm day^{-1}

0 to 1mm day^{-1}

0 to −1mm day^{-1}

−1 to −2mm day^{-1}

less than −2mm day^{-1}

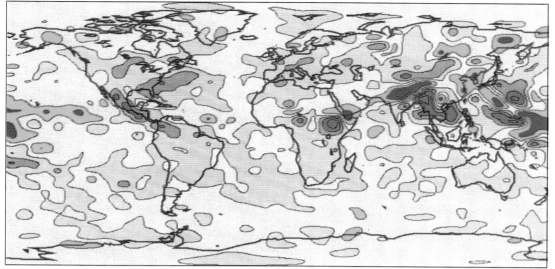

(d) CCC

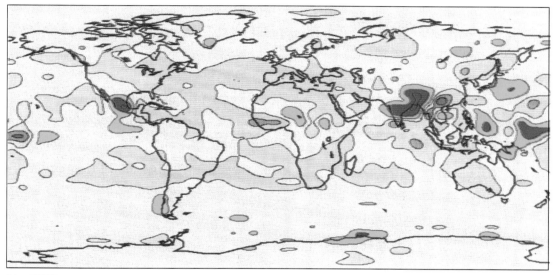

(e) GFDL

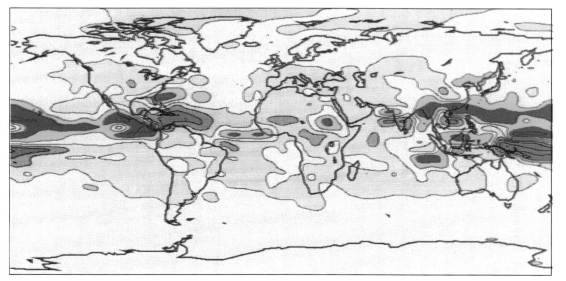

(f) UKMO

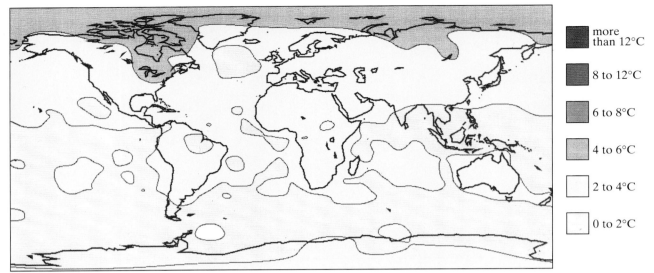

(a) Realized global-mean warming: 2.3 °C

(b) Equilibrium global-mean warming: $\Delta T_{2\times} = 4$ °C

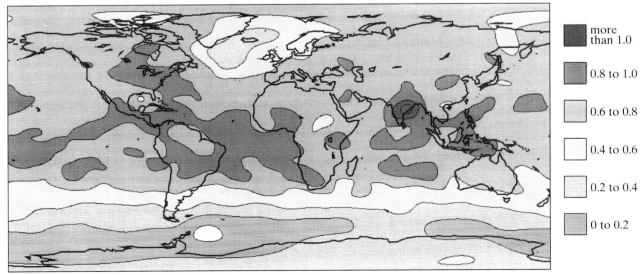

(c)

Plate 5.4 (a) The realized warming after 70 years (when the atmospheric concentration of CO_2 doubles) as simulated by the coupled AGCM/OGCM developed at the GFDL. (b) The equilibrium warming scenario due to a CO_2-doubling, as simulated by the same AGCM coupled to a mixed-layer ocean model. (c) The ratio of the realized warming in (a) to the equilibrium warming in (b).

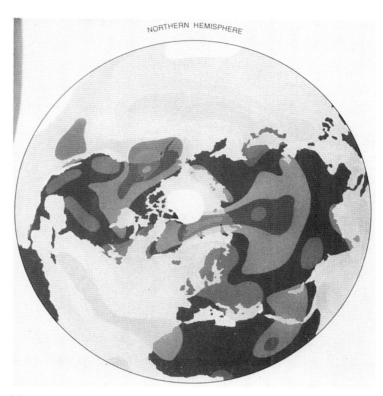

(a)

(b)

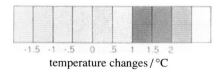

temperature changes / °C

Plate 6.1 The geographical distribution of observed changes in annual-mean temperature between 1967 and 1986 for (a) the Northern, and (b) the Southern Hemisphere (white areas represent regions with insufficient data to define a trend). Over this period, most regions (in both hemispheres) experienced a warming trend, but a few—notably the northern Pacific and Atlantic—cooled somewhat.

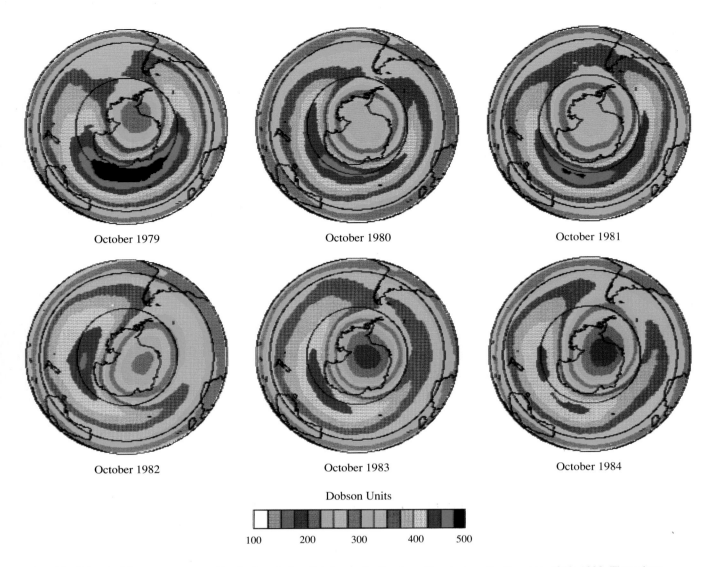

October 1979

October 1980

October 1981

October 1982

October 1983

October 1984

Dobson Units

100   200   300   400   500

Plate 6.2 'Maps' of the average ozone distribution during October in the Southern Hemisphere for the years 1979–1992. The values recorded here are based on data collected by the Total Ozone Mapping Spectrometer (TOMS) on board NASA's Nimbus 7 satellite. They are a measure of the total 'ozone column', i.e. the total number of molecules of ozone in a column (stretching up to the top of the atmosphere) above each 1 cm^2 of the Earth's surface, a 'Dobson Unit' (DU) being equivalent to 2.7×10^{16} molecules cm^{-2}. The picture for 1979 is typical of the situation that used to prevail over Antarctica, with column ozone values roughly constant (at around 300–350 DU) throughout most of the winter and spring. The recent situation is very different. Now ozone amounts over Antarctica (and beyond) fall rapidly with the return of sunlight in spring (September/October)—usually to 150 DU or less (purple and pink)—before recovering again during the summer. Through to the late 1980s, there seemed to be a roughly biennial cycle in the severity of the ozone hole (possibly linked to natural variations in the dynamics of the stratosphere): that pattern has since been broken—with four consecutive 'bad' years, 1989–1992. The bleak prognosis for Antarctic ozone—and quite possibly for Arctic ozone as well—is the driving force behind efforts to further tighten the provisions of the Montreal Protocol.

October 1985   October 1986   October 1987

October 1988   October 1989   October 1990

October 1991   October 1992